LEADING THE WAY

Leading the Way

A History of Lancashire's Roads

edited by

A. G. CROSBY

Lancashire County Books, 1998

Leading the Way, A History of Lancashire's Roads

edited by Dr A. G. Crosby

First edition published 1998 by
Lancashire County Books, 143 Corporation Street, Preston

Copyright © Lancashire County Books, 1998

Text copyright © contributors, 1998

Designed and typeset in Monotype Bembo by
Carnegie Publishing, Chatsworth Road, Lancaster
Printed in the UK by Alden Press, Oxford

British Library Cataloguing-in-Publication Data
A catalogue record for this book is available from the British Library

ISBN 1-871236-33-9

Contents

Acknowledgments

In writing a book of this length and complexity the contributors have inevitably drawn upon the knowledge and experience of others, and we have all been given invaluable help and advice from friends and colleagues. We should like to express our warmest thanks to all of them, and we hope that the book meets with their approval. As editor I should like to record my particular gratitude to John Greenhalgh and John Priestley, who have spent a great deal of time in discussing the later parts of the book, pointing to examples and providing additional information, and to Eric Waterhouse for checking factual material. My personal thanks go to Zoë Lawson, who provided all the essential administrative support during the planning and preparation of the book, and gave so much help with picture and map research, and to Anita Addiman, who took over from Zoë towards the end of the project. The advice and interest of the County Librarian, Michael Dolan, was invaluable.

A special debt is owed to Michael Callery, the former County Surveyor and Bridgemaster of Lancashire, who originally conceived the idea of writing and publishing this book and who has been an enthusiastic supporter and promoter of the project from its beginning. The very generous sponsorship of this work which has been provided by AMEC plc and Sir Alfred McAlpine plc has been fundamental to the entire project: without their support it would not have been possible to research, write and produce the volume, and our sincere thanks go to both companies for this help.

Alan Crosby (Editor)

List of Abbreviations

C.B.	County Borough
C.N.W.R.S.	Centre for North West Regional Studies (Lancaster University)
C.R.O.	Cheshire Record Office
C.S.	Chetham Society
E.P.N.S.	English Place-Names Society
L.P.R.S.	Lancashire Parish Register Society
L.R.O.	Lancashire Record Office
L.S.L.	Local Studies Library
M.B.(C.)	Municipal Borough (Council)
M.o.T.	Ministry of Transport
NS	New series
OE	Old English
ON	Old Norse
OS	Old series, also Ordnance Survey
P.R.O.	Public Record Office
R.D.(C.)	Rural District (Council)
R.S.L.C.	Record Society of Lancashire and Cheshire
T.C.W.A.A.S.	Transactions of the Cumberland and Westmorland Antiquarian and Archaeological Society
T.H.S.L.C.	Transactions of the Historic Society of Lancashire and Cheshire
T.L.C.A.S.	Transactions of the Lancashire and Cheshire Antiquarian Society
U.D.(C.)	Urban District (Council)
Y.A.S.R.S.	Yorkshire Archaeological Society Record Series

About the contributors

Ben Edwards was educated at Colchester Royal Grammar School and the University of Durham (1953–1956). He was commissioned in the Royal Army Signals Corp and in 1963 was appointed as County Archaeologist for Lancashire – he was not only the first incumbent of that post but also the first county archaeologist in the country. In 1968 he was elected as a Fellow of the Society of Antiquaries of London. He has published very widely on most periods of British archaeology, from the Mesolithic elk skeleton discovered at Poulton-le-Fylde, through Bronze Age artifacts and Roman inscriptions, to medieval pottery and more recent 'antiquarian' studies, and was also a pioneer in the field of the use of archives in archaeological research. He retired from the post of County Archaeologist in 1995.

Alan Crosby was born in Surrey of exiled Lancastrian parents. He read geography at St Edmund Hall, Oxford, and in 1982 obtained his doctorate there. Since then he has been a freelance local historian, involved in writing, researching, teaching and lecturing throughout the north west. For over ten years he has been a part-time tutor in local history for the continuing education departments at Lancaster and Liverpool universities. He holds honorary research fellowships at the University of Liverpool and at the Centre for North West Regional Studies, Lancaster University, and is the editor of the *Lancashire Local Historian*, General Editor for the British Association for Local History, and Secretary of the Chetham Society.

Mary Higham is a retired geography teacher, born in Rossendale and now living in Clitheroe. For many years she has been an active researcher and writer on the local history and historical geography of the north west, specialising in the medieval period. In 1992 she was awarded a PhD from Lancaster University for her thesis on the effects of the Norman Conquest on the landscape and history of north Lancashire. She has written numerous articles and is now well-known as an extra-mural lecturer for the universities of Liverpool, Lancaster and Manchester.

John Whiteley was born in 1921 and educated in Surrey. He obtained his degree from the University of London in 1942 and, after serving in the Royal Engineers until 1947, joined Surrey County Council's

Surveyors Department. He moved to Lancashire in 1949 as an engineer with the former county council, engaged on the design and supervision of a wide variety of road schemes. After reorganisation in 1974 he became deeply involved in implementing the new council's public transport policies, and eventually retired from the post of Deputy County Surveyor in 1984. Apart from his professional association with roads he has had a lifelong interest in maps, archaeology, industrial archaeology and the history of railways. Research on the matters included in this book began in the 1950s!

Diana Winterbotham was born at Swinton, and educated at Eccles Grammar School. She became a librarian with the Salford Library Service, and during the late 1950s began to specialise in local history there and, from 1960, at Eccles Public Library. In 1971 she was appointed County Local Studies Librarian with the Lancashire County Library in Preston, a post which she held until her retirement in 1993, and under her auspices the county library created one of the finest local studies collections in northern England. She has also been a very active researcher, writer and teacher on the local history of the county, and her ceaseless efforts to promote the subject are one of the main factors behind its present strength throughout Lancashire. She is a former vice-chairman of the British Association for Local History, Chairman of the Friends of Lancashire Archives, and a council member of several other county and regional local history societies. In 1993 she was awarded the M.B.E. in recognition of her services to librarianship.

Harry Yeadon was born in Accrington and, after graduating from Manchester University in 1942, was commissioned in the Royal Engineers and served in Italy. He joined the staff of the County Surveyor and Bridgemaster of Lancashire in 1948 as an assistant engineer concerned with the improvement and maintenance of the road network. Later he was closely involved in the motorway programme, supervising bridgeworks on the Preston bypass scheme and working as resident engineer on the Preston-Lancaster section of the M6. On the formation of the North West Road Construction Unit in 1967 he was seconded to its headquarters as Superintendent Engineer (Construction) with responsibilities for major contracts throughout the region. In 1969 he rejoined the staff of Lancashire County Council as a deputy county surveyor, and in 1974 was appointed County Surveyor and Bridgemaster, a post which he held until his retirement in 1985. He is former vice-president of the Institution of Civil Engineers and is a Fellow of the Royal Academy of Engineering. He was joint author, with James Drake, of the book *Motorways*.

Preface

THE INVENTION of the wheel thousands of years ago created the need for paved surfaces. Rude tracks, later to become surfaced roads, reflect man's progress from his earliest hunter days right up to his present complex lifestyle, with its accompanying massive reliance on wheeled locomotion. Over the centuries ancient tracks, ridgeways and holloways have merged into the more recent road system, developing and changing into the comprehensive network which serves our present economic, social and leisure needs.

Transport is fundamental to our civilisation, a cornerstone of the economic prosperity we now expect. The freedom of movement enjoyed (and perhaps taken for granted) by an increasing proportion of the community is largely based on road–borne transport and, in the case of personal transport, predominantly on the motor car.

The arrival of the motor car more than one hundred years ago elicited strong reactions, just as its widespread use does today. In 1895 *The Surveyor* (a technical journal for civil engineers), said in an editorial outburst against cars being preceded by a man with a red flag, that 'the mechanically propelled road carriage has come to stay and Parliament should encourage it, rather than leave it to be stifled by restrictions which were only meant to apply to traction engines.' Shortly afterwards, in 1896, when the Locomotives on Highways Act made the man with the flag redundant and allowed speeds of up to 14 m.p.h., a Mrs Bridget Driscoll had, at Crystal Palace, the unfortunate distinction of becoming the first person to be killed by a motor car. Following the inquest, the coroner was recorded as saying that he hoped no such thing would ever occur again.

Nearer to home, Lancashire can boast a proud record in the development of the total transport infrastructure. Examples of 'firsts' include the Bridgewater Canal in 1761, the opening of the Liverpool and Manchester railway in 1830, pioneering the operation of passenger trains running to a timetable, the Manchester Ship Canal in 1894 and, more recently, the opening in 1958 of the first section of motorway in the United Kingdom, the M6 Preston bypass.

Motorway critics often point to the M25 as an example of how motorways fill up with traffic as soon as they are opened. That is certainly true of the M25, the only survivor of a series of orbital routes planned for the Greater London area in the early 60s. The criticism is not valid for the bulk of the motorway network in the UK. The M6 Preston bypass has carried its increasing load of traffic for more than thirty years and now, following its widening to four lanes in each direction, it continues to provide a high level of service for up to 100,000 vehicles a day.

The Preston bypass was just one element of the 1949 *Road plan for Lancashire* produced by my illustrious predecessor, Sir James Drake, and his staff of civil engineers. This was a visionary initiative which has led to our inheritance of a comprehensive network of high-standard and comparatively safe roads in the north-west of England. The relatively low level of objection encountered in promoting the earlier motorways in Lancashire bears witness to the generally supportive attitudes pre-vailing at that time, as well as the skill of those locally involved in promoting the 1949 plan.

The recent apparent unpopularity of new additions to the motorway network, pointed up by the media, together with the associated catch-phrase 'motorway madness,' have their parallels in the earlier days of the turnpikes. Sir William Addison's book *The Old Roads of England* referred to the contemporary journalistic use of the term 'turnpike madness' and the reaction to toll roads at that time was summed up in the succinct phrase 'Lancashire men fought long and hard against their (the turnpikes') introduction'.

The reaction of Lancastrians to change was not confined to new initiatives in the transport field. As Harry Yeadon points out in chapter seven, Lancashire was subjected to substantial overall reorganisation. The old county of Lancashire had its boundaries radically redrawn in 1974 although by that time most of the 1949 *Road plan* was already in place. This suggested an appropriate time to draw to a close the account of the history of Lancashire's roads which is dealt with in this book. Developments since 1974 can be more readily assessed when the recent great debate on transport hopefully produces a wider consensus on the way to deal with the increasing use of the motor car and the related congestion on our roads.

The link between good quality roads and economic prosperity has been a common theme in the policies of successive governments over the last half-century. As recently as 1989 a government white paper *Roads for prosperity* expanded the trunk road programme expenditure by 90% following a national study, *The Review of highway investment needs*, which concluded that investment levels would need to be doubled to meet demand. An associated thrust, which has gained momentum in the last ten years, was directed at reversing the worrying trend in road accidents, the target being to reduce the accident level by one third by the end of the century. This contributed to widespread use of traffic calming techniques in residential areas as well as the introduction of mini-roundabouts at junctions.

The aspirations of *Roads for prosperity* fell far short of realisation – the roads programme was, as in the past, used as an easy route to control public expenditure. The centralisation of administrative and financial structures, the demise of the Road Construction Units in the early 1980s and changes in the agency arrangements with the Minister of Transport removed the direct influence of the county councils in developing the trunk road networks. In addition, the substantial input of resources for the construction of high quality roads in new towns contrasted with the lag in standards used for all-purpose trunk and principal county roads. A limited source of compensatory funding arose for special categories of roads, mainly in urban areas, from the European Development Fund and this has assisted the increased emphasis on inner relief roads, helping the process of ridding town centres of unwanted traffic and facilitating the introduction of pedestrianised precincts and dedicated bus lanes.

Whilst the early construction of the inter-urban road network in Lancashire had a fair wind in terms of public support, it is worth reflecting on the changing thinking about the environment which began in the early 1970s. Although there was continued recognition that the quality of life and associated economic prosperity of the majority of the population relied on efficient access to goods, services, people and places, the increasing dependence on motor vehicles and the associated demand for more road space led to conflict between the strong desire for personal mobility and the consequential concerns about the effect of vehicle emissions on health. Alongside this, there were worries about environmental damage (global and local), noise and the growing cost and frustration associated with congestion. Conflicting views began to emerge on the relationship between new road provision and economic regeneration. The proposed extension of the M62 into Liverpool city was one hotly contested example. There was also an issue at the public inquiry into the M65 extension from the east of Blackburn to the M6. Nevertheless, the substantial body of evidence put forward by the supporters of this scheme, drawing on the contribution the earlier sections of the M65 had made to the regeration of the north-east Lancashire towns (the so-called 'string of pearls' of brand new industrial developments close to the line of the motorway), provided a telling contribution to the eventual decision to proceed with the construction of the new road.

If there is one specific time and event which marked the beginning of the changing perception of road building, I venture to suggest it might be associated with the oil crisis of 1973, when worries about escalating petrol prices coupled with an increasing realisation that the world's reserves of oil were finite, brought home to people the vulnerability of our reliance on the internal combustion engine.

Local government reorganisation in 1974 and the subsequent abolition of the Road Construction Units presented opportunities for restructuring with a more specific focus on public transport provision. Many county councils adopted new titles such as 'Director of Highways and Transportation', to point up a broader approach. Lancashire's 'County Surveyor and Bridgemaster' was considered too precious a title to forego for the sake of a new image; neverthless, the new county council vigorously pursued a policy of co-ordinating and subsidising bus transport by means of agency agreements with bus operating companies, as well as taking a leading role in supporting the improvement of the local rail infrastructure and services. A strong political and professional enthusiasm remained, however, for maintaining Lancashire's record of high quality roads.

The new *Transport policy and programme (TPP)*, which county councils were required to submit annually to the Department of Transport as part of the bidding process for capital funds for transport infrastructure, supported what was essentially a grass-roots movement towards formulating more objective and balanced transport policies against the background of the longer-term, broader-based county *Structure Plan*. The *TPPs* became the vehicle for putting forward bids for packages of measures aimed at reducing the extent of car usage, particularly by commuters into the larger Lancashire towns such as Preston, Blackpool and Blackburn, and ameliorating the intense congestion and related environmental problems in the historic city of Lancaster.

The Transport Act 1985, which deregulated bus services, created enormous difficulties for county councils who wished to pursue policies to co-ordinate services. In Lancashire, it is a tribute to the county council at the time and to the skill of its officers who worked closely with the new bus companies, that the disaster which was feared did not materialise. Neverthleless, the initial view of the county council persists – that a process of inviting competitive franchising for bus networks in discrete areas of the county would have been a preferable option to total deregulation, greatly simplifying the process of co-ordination.

The doubt which began to take root in the 1970s intensified in the early 1990s with an increasing questioning of the dominance of private transport, the ubiquitous motor car, with its demand for more space, as opposed to more environmentally-friendly modes, such as bus, train and cycling, or walking. Increasing objection to major road schemes, particularly motorways, has forced the government to review its transport policies and to take refuge in the so-called great debate on transport issues.

Major road schemes, because of their linear nature, have almost always attracted some degree of objection from those directly affected. In many instances, objections of this type were withdrawn as a result of negotiations or changes to the proposals either before, during or after an inquiry. In addition, strong objections from particular interest groups, opposing the proposal in general or the effect of a specific route, have featured in the promotion of road proposals and related inquiries since the early days. More recently, however, it has become a feature at some road schemes for minority groups to ignore the Secretary of State (after the statutory procedures have been completed) by attempting to prevent the commencement of construction. This has been demonstrated in the recent fashion of tree-dwelling, the first Lancashire instances of which occurred on the route of the M65 extension to the M6 in Cuerden Valley Park and at Stanworth.

A succession of recent market research surveys and polls has demonstrated an apparent ambivalence even in motorists' attitudes – on the one hand a degree of support, at least in principle, for the protesters whilst at the same time their confirmation that traffic congestion is a major problem! These conflicts in attitude, coupled with reducing resources and increasing congestion, have presented politicians and local planners with the extremely difficult task of trying to pursue a coherent range of transport policies. The promotion, however, of balanced 'packages' of measures which favour restraint, coupled with park and ride and public transport solutions, do seem to offer a way forward in the larger urban areas of Lancashire, such as Preston.

During the past few years, on behalf of the North West Regional Association of Local Authorities and the North West Business Leadership Team (now combined with wider regional interests, public and private, in the North West Partnership) I have had the privilege of chairing a group of transport professionals charged with producing the *Regional transport strategy for North West England*. This is an attempt to reflect changing perceptions and the growing wish to see roads, rail and other modes of transport considered as part of a co-ordinated and balanced whole, serving the economic, social and recreational needs of the region. The vision of creating a high quality regional rail network into the next century is a major plank of the *Strategy* and there is strong support from all elements of the Partnership for a comprehensive study to achieve this goal. In some respects the study now contemplated in the 90s echoes the road network study of the 40s in Lancashire. The widespread support for the current balanced transport strategy, with its much greater emphasis on public transport-related solutions, is indicative of the sea-change in thinking that has occurred since Sir James Drake produced the *Road Plan* in 1949. It is important to recognise that public opinion was increasingly geared to road transport at that time and indeed that it remained largely supportive throughout Lancashire's 'motorway era'.

We are now on the threshold of a period of renewed vigour in promoting our public transport infrastructure. The Manchester Metro, combining part of the conventional rail system with on-street trams is a very successful example of the right horse for the right course. We must not lose sight of the fact that for many years we will continue to rely to a huge extent on road transport, both for passenger and freight movements. Our lifestyle, the pattern of land use development we have created in the last half-century coupled with our appetite for an immense range of commodities neatly packaged in plastic wrappers, increasingly delivered to and purchased from out-of-town shopping centres, are not likely to change radically in the short term.

The traditional solution of attempting to solve road congestion solely by expanding the road network is, however, no longer socially acceptable. As we move rapidly into the 'Information Age' the challenge for politicians and transport planners alike is to develop a balanced transport system which is innovative and efficient, safe amd environmentally sustainable and which supports the economic performance of the United Kingdom. That is the goal of the *Regional transport strategy,* one building block in the process of developing a socially acceptable national transport system.

This book is concerned with how the roads of Lancashire have developed over the centuries, how construction methods have changed to keep pace with rapidly accelerating demands and how the road network is now woven firmly into almost every aspect of our modern life. Lancashire can be justly proud of its achievements in transport innovation. Past colleagues from the county surveyors and bridgemasters department and experts in the field of road transport have pooled their knowledge to contribute to this history of Lancashire's roads, an important step in recording those achievements.

As well as thanking them for their unstinting efforts, I would also like to express my profound gratitude for the enthusiastic sponsorship of Michael Dolan, County Librarian of Lancashire, Sir Alan Cockshaw, chairman of AMEC plc and Bobby McAlpine, until recently chairman of Alfred McAlpine plc.

Editor's Introduction

This book has been written to provide a comprehensive account of the character, extent and development of the road network of Lancashire (and, by no means unimportant, of the traffic which used it) from prehistoric times until the late twentieth century, setting roads firmly within their context – social, political, economic – so that the reasons for their existence and their significance are clearly explained. The writers – some of them historians and others who have been professionally involved in the design and building of roads – are conscious throughout of the historical perspective. Roads did not just 'happen' by accident – they were built, or developed gradually, for very good practical reasons of engineering and traffic needs, whether in the Neolithic period or the 1960s. Their routes were chosen with care, with an eye for topography, ground conditions, and the origin and destination of traffic flows, two thousand years ago just as twenty years ago. We have tried to indicate the continuities and the comparisons with the experience of the present day, as well as the ways in which roads and their traffic have changed and adapted over the centuries.

In the first chapter Ben Edwards, the former County Archaeologist of Lancashire, reviews evidence for the existence of tracks and 'proto-roads' in pre-Roman Lancashire. That the prehistoric inhabitants of our county – as of other parts of England – did construct trackways in difficult areas (notably across mosses and boggy ground) has long been known, but only with modern archaeological investigation is the scale and sophistication of their enterprise becoming clear. In the next few years, as surveying of the wetland areas of the Lancashire lowlands progresses, more information about this fascinating element in the prehistoric landscape and society of the county is likely to become available.

In contrast, the road-building activities of the Romans have never been forgotten and are known about in great detail, though there is still much to learn. The existence of the Roman road network is one of the 'facts' of history which is known to almost everybody and the dramatically straight alignments of the major roads remain an important landscape feature. The network which the Romans established has had a lasting impact upon the pattern of roads across the country as a whole.

In Lancashire, as Ben Edwards shows, there is plenty of detailed evidence to explain the precise alignments which the Roman surveyors, working in difficult and hostile country, picked out and then constructed. The network of roads is known in essence, but gaps and other possibilities remain to be filled or investigated – recently there have been growing indications that south-west Lancashire, long thought to be lacking in Roman sites, may have been settled and that routes such as that followed by the A59 could have had Roman origins.

Many road histories have an embarrassingly scanty chapter covering the period of more than a thousand years between the departure of the Romans and the beginning of the turnpikes. There is a very powerful impression that not much happened in all that time and many misconceptions about the lack of use of roads in general have been perpetuated. But as Mary Higham makes clear in chapter two, the medieval road network was in reality complex and well-used, by wheeled vehicles as well as by horses and other beasts, and there were serious and often reasonably effective attempts to regulate and improve travelling and roads. The building of new bridges was a feature of many river-crossings, while the designation of certain roads as 'king's highways' shows an appreciation of the different uses and status of individual routes. Much of the minor road network of Lancashire is unquestionably at least medieval in origin (and probably much older) – when we use the country lanes of the Lune or Ribble valleys, and when we use the older roads in urban areas, we are almost certainly following the routes of our medieval ancestors.

Mary Higham shows how the roads were an essential element in the medieval economic system, as the expansion of national and inter-national trade produced increasing volumes of freight traffic and as the growth of administration and the integration of the English state led to business and social use of the roads. The religious houses, the multi-national corporations of the medieval period, were actively en-gaged in providing and maintaining roads, which were essential to their commercial enterprises. The medieval road network was portrayed on maps, such as the famous Gough Map of the early fourteenth century, and in the thirteenth century occurred the first attempts by the state to define the responsibility for the financing and upkeep of roads. Seven hundred years later the matter is still the subject of debate and uncer-tainty!

It is often said that wheeled vehicles came very late to Lancashire and statements to that effect frequently appear in print: 'Even Man-chester and Liverpool were linked to each other only by packhorse routes until 1760', says Hindle in his *Roads, Tracks and Their Interpretation* (1993). Yet there is plenty of documentary evidence to support an opposite view. Many writers have relied over-heavily on the prejudiced or ill-informed reports of outsiders and travellers who came to the region (as, indeed, to other parts of Britain more distant from London) and were disparaging in their views. There is also a tendency on the part of human beings, which has certainly not disappeared today, to complain incessantly about the state of the roads. Local documentary sources reveal a different picture, with numerous examples of the regular and indeed heavy use of wheeled vehicles from the sixteenth century.

My own account, chapter three, shows how from the 1630s onwards there were frequent complaints from townships across south Lancashire about the damage to roads and highways, and particularly to bridges, which resulted from the intensive industrial traffic. Many of these documents refer specifically to carts, carriages and wheeled vehicles. Maps give comparable evidence for the use of roads by carts as early as the 1590s – for example, a plan of Penwortham in 1590 shows the 'wain [wagon] way' and the 'horse way' to Preston, suggesting that segregation of different types of traffic was practised as early as Elizabeth's reign! My chapter also considers the administration and financing of roads, a subject for which copious quantities of information are available after 1600, and about which there was much contemporary debate. Questions such as these, together with a general growth in traffic and hence in the need for road repair and improvement, eventually led to the introduction of turnpikes. Here the principle of 'user pays' replaced, in whole or in part, that of 'community pays'.

The day-to-day use of roads is a subject of great interest. Who were the travellers and why were they travelling? What did they encounter when on the road, how were their basic needs provided for – food, accommodation, fuel and stabling for the horses? How did the road network cope with unusual traffic and how did the needs of commerce and trade prompt the development of the system? In the fourth chapter Diana Winterbotham looks at the way in which the road network served the community and considers the experiences of the people who made use of the roads over the centuries. Many of these experiences were alarming and reflected badly upon the roads – and upon other road-users – but we should always bear in mind that 'good news is no news' and that safe, uninterrupted and uneventful journeys did not make good copy, in letters or diaries or in published sources.

In chapter five John Whiteley discusses the growth of the great turnpike network in Lancashire, highlighting its geographical spread and tracing its piecemeal and uncoordinated evolution. He also shows how eventually much of the county was covered in a dense web of roads. Changing fashions are revealed. In the early days existing roads were turnpiked with no alteration in alignment. In the middle period, from the 1760s to the 1790s, significant diversions and alterations were made to improve routes, while after 1790 the remarkable and still-impressive achievements of the highway engineers in creating networks of completely new roads in the difficult Pennine areas of the county made an enduring legacy. The often tangled financial and administrative aspects of the turnpikes are described, as are the problems which the trusts encountered as the railway network grew from the 1830s onwards.

Chapter six, also by John Whiteley, deals with the far-reaching changes which were introduced from the end of the nineteenth century as the impact of the internal combustion engine began to be felt. The collapse of the turnpike system – or at least of its finances – in the face of railway competition was clear, though in Lancashire the volume of road traffic remained high and few roads fell into semi-disuse. Competition with the railway freight charges meant that tolls were drastically reduced, and income slumped, but the traffic levels were surprisingly resilient. This chapter shows how the local authorities responded to the administrative needs of the system by taking over and 'maining' roads, and then began to undertake increasingly ambitious works to improve the roads to cope with the new traffic and to meet the challenge of, for example, tramway construction.

By the 1920s new roads were being planned and constructed and Lancashire emerged as a pioneer and innovator in that field, a position it has retained ever since. Such work as Liverpool's development of reserved-track tramways on central reservations, the construction of the East Lancashire Road (Britain's first inter-urban trunk route designed for motor vehicles), and the preparation of routes for what would eventually become motorways all reveal the effective way in which the highway authorities within the county looked to the future. The 1920s also saw the beginning of an often uneasy relationship between central and local government in the area of road-building, road-funding and road-planning. The involvement of central government, both as a financing agent and as the instigator of a myriad of controls on the use and design of highways of all types has continued to grow ever since.

In chapter seven Harry Yeadon, who for many years worked at the very heart of the post-war road programme in the county, traces the development of the motorway network in which Lancashire led England. In 1958 the Preston bypass, Britain's first motorway, was opened, the first tangible fruit of the ambitious and visionary plan for roads in Lancashire which had been drawn up in 1949. Its author was the county surveyor, James Drake, one of the outstanding highway engineers of the century. Under his guidance the county's motorway network grew apace, building upon and developing pre-war plans which Lancashire had pioneered.

Drake and his team introduced many ideas which later became universal but for which there was no precedent, not only in design but also in the collection and analysis of background information on, for example, safety and traffic flows. The result of their efforts, and of their colleagues in other Lancashire highway authorities, is a road network which is second to none in Britain and which is marked by towering achievements of engineering and design – the first Thelwall viaduct, the Lune bridge, the Barton bridge, the Mancunian Way (Britain's first true urban motorway), the second Mersey tunnel, the Runcorn-Widnes bridge, the superb alignment of the M62 across the Pennines, the curving complexities of the Worsley interchange. These men changed the face of Lancashire, helping to mould and shape its economy, its society, its geography, its landscape. Their achievement was an outstanding and remarkable one, in which they led the rest of the country. Their work will endure for many generations. This book will record for posterity the achievement of the road-builders who helped to make Lancashire what it is today.

Alan Crosby

I

The Romans and Before

A$_\text{S SOME}$ of the most impressive physical manifestations of the Roman occupation, a period of great importance in British history and one which has captured the imagination of antiquarians, historians and the general public for centuries, Roman roads have for over three hundred years been a subject of enduring interest. The straightness and directness of the major roads, striking out boldly across the countryside, have been their characteristic hallmarks in the popular mind, while the grand strategy which lay behind their construction has been seen as typical of the power and might of the Roman empire and its administrators and soldiers. Despite this, much remains to be discovered about the Roman road network and its construction, and there are many unexplained gaps and puzzles.

In Lancashire, current archaeological, documentary and field research is helping to resolve some of these difficulties (although others will always remain) and attention is once again beginning to turn to a formerly neglected aspect of the early history of our roads – the nature and purpose of the routes which were already there when the Romans came. Investigation of the present and former peat mosses of the county, a process which is now being seriously tackled as part of the North West Wetlands Survey, may well provide some clues to the latter, especially in the light of dramatic discoveries in comparable areas such as the Somerset Levels. This chapter reviews the present knowledge about the Roman and pre-Roman roads within Lancashire. First, though, it is necessary to consider just what is meant by the term 'road' in the context of two thousand and more years ago.

The Ordnance Survey maps of England and Wales, and to a lesser extent those of Scotland, have always been scattered with the annotation ROMAN ROAD. Fortunately for those with an interest in the past the Survey's staff had, from the beginning, a great interest in the visible traces of antiquity. Much more rarely the words *Prehistoric Trackway* appear, and it is interesting to note the difference in the noun used. To the modern generation a road is a clearly defined phenomenon, a route with a hard – usually tarred – surface. Anything other than this is regarded as a track or bridleway, and is considered to be less than a road. However, we have to remind ourselves that what the present day thinks of as a road is in fact a feature only of this century. For many centuries before the motor age a road more closely resembled what we would call a track, or a modern farm road. Not for nothing did the pioneers of motoring, in their open cars, wrap themselves in greatcoats, gloves and goggles to protect themselves from mud, dust, rain and snow.

The road in this more ancient sense was, in this country, effectively an invention of the Romans. While people and goods undoubtedly moved across the country in prehistoric times – a mobility the true scale of which is only now becoming apparent – we can seldom identify with certainty the precise course of a pre-Roman road. The evidence of unsurfaced 'roads' in undeveloped countries shows us why this is the case. Travellers on such roads, rarely encumbered by vehicles, chose their precise line in response to local conditions. They skirted puddles and other wet places, they avoided obstructions such as fallen trees, and they varied their route in detail according to the season. As a result the road changed its course from time to time, shifting across what was often quite a wide band of country. In Britain the evidence for this process having happened in the past can most easily be seen where a road has not acquired a modern surface (and so has not been fixed) and is negotiating a hill, a situation in which a fan or web of different tracks may have developed. Even where a modern surface has been applied, and a road has become stabilised, traces of parallel ways can sometimes be seen on either side.

There are two main phases in the development of a road. The first is the selection of the route itself, and the second is the engineering or improvement of the carriageway. In most cases the prehistoric road was the result of the first phase alone. The route would largely be determined by the nature of the traffic which was to travel on the road, its origin and its destination, and the ease with which it might travel. In the 'Lowland Zone' of Britain – roughly the area south and east of a line from the Bristol Channel to the Wash – this frequently involved the use of a ridgeway-type route. The finger-like ridges of Jurassic and Cretaceous rocks which radiate from the general area of Salisbury Plain provided such routes. It is comparatively difficult to get lost on a ridgeway, and travel was often easier there because the vegetation was less luxuriant than on the lowlands. Such routeways stand out in geographical and geological terms, and frequently their use in prehistoric times can be demonstrated by distribution maps of the find-spots of certain classes of artifact.

In the 'Highland Zone' of Britain, in contrast, it was often the routes *through* the higher areas – notably the river valleys and the passes – which were used, and which can be defined in the same way by the discovery of artifacts. Here, however, the nature of the routeway is likely to bear less resemblance to a 'proper' road. Ridgeway routes naturally tended to keep to the top of the ridge, and as far as possible they lay within narrow limits. Valley routes were less much closely confined, and they were more susceptible to local deviations and diversions.

There are two main routeways through the county of Lancaster which can be shown, in the most general sense, to have been in use in prehistoric times. The earlier of these is that by which stone axe blades, quarried and processed in Langdale, were carried towards the south and west of England in the Neolithic period (*c.*3500–2000 BC). The exact route taken by such traffic is quite unclear, and in reality there were probably many local routes producing a diffuse network, but since such axe blades did unquestionably travel from their place of manufacture to distant find-spots they must have passed through the county. Much the same generalisation applies to the movement of bronze and gold artifacts from Ireland to eastern England in the later Bronze Age (second millennium BC). The lowland gap between the Ribble and Aire valleys is likely to have been a favoured route in this case, although the route along the Mersey and Irwell valleys may also have been employed.

One of the few types of prehistoric road which was the result not only of route selection but also of deliberate construction work is the wooden trackway, examples of which have been recovered from several areas of peat growth in different parts of England. By far the best known and studied are those from the Somerset Levels, where considerable lengths of well-constructed timber tracks have been excavated and closely analysed. Such structures, or something like them, were apparently uncovered and observed in parts of the Lancashire peatlands in the nineteenth and early twentieth centuries.

Kate's Pad is the name now given to the best-documented of these. It was first recorded in 1851, and was then said to consist of longitudinal timbers and cross-members (like rails and sleepers, except that the 'sleepers' rested on top of the 'rails'). At that date it was called Danes Pad, which is properly the name of a probable Roman road south of the Wyre, while Kate's Pad was in Pilling Moss, north of the river. Doubts have been cast on the authenticity of the nineteenth century finds because twentieth-century excavators have failed to discover structures as complex as those described a century and a half ago. Attention should, however, be drawn to the fact that the trackways in the Somerset Levels, although first recorded a little earlier than those of Lancashire, were not widely known in the nineteenth century. In other words, if the description of Kate's Pad given by the Rev. William Thornber in 1851 was fabricated, it is quite remarkable that he should have invented structures which we now recognise as entirely probable and plausible.

This pre-Roman 'trackway' was the subject of archaeological exploration after the Second World War. However, difficulties of interpretation then arose. What was found in 1949, and in various further examinations down to 1967, was a simpler but more enigmatic structure than that described in the 1850s. It consisted of riven tree-trunks laid end-to-end. At the ends of some of the timbers, but not all, there were vertical holes. No attempt had apparently been made to lay the timbers with a flat surface at the top. The full armoury of archaeological techniques then available was brought to bear on the problem, by the importing of an archaeologist from Cambridge, where two fairly new, but extremely important, analytical processes were being developed. The more radical, radiocarbon dating, had been invented only in 1947, and the Cambridge laboratory was one of the pioneers of the method. The radiocarbon date obtained from one of the timbers (2760 ± 120 years BP [Before Present]) indicated a 2:1 probability that the date of the trackway lay within the first half of the last millennium BC.

At the same time, pollen analysis of the deposits was carried out. As was the case with radiocarbon dating, pollen analysis in this country virtually began in Cambridge – in this instance with the work of Professor Harry Godwin. This was not the first Lancashire archaeological site on which the method had been employed, for Godwin had reported on samples from the excavations at the Bleasdale timber circles in 1935. The 1949 pollen analysis at Kate's Pad appeared broadly to support the radiocarbon dating. This date, however, began to seem increasingly improbable as more trackways were examined elsewhere in the country, and in the last few years a determined effort has been made to relocate the track. Unfortunately this has so far failed, and there may be indeed be none of the track now left in the ground. However, the characteristic stratigraphy of the peat in which it was found earlier has been located: this means that although the track itself cannot at present be located, the deposits within which it is known to have existed have been identified. Radiocarbon dating, using more accurate modern techniques, has shown that the date of the trackway is much more likely to be in the Neolithic period (3500–2000 BC), and thus compatible with the evidence from the Somerset Levels.

To return to the structure itself: it has been called 'the trackway' for convenience, but it seems unlikely that this is an accurate description of it. It would have been very difficult to walk on a single line of tree-trunks, whether or not anything was driven through the holes. It is of course possible that the timbers had been re-used, and that the holes related to their first use rather than the trackway. Another possibility is that the timbers marked the line of a drier passage through the bog, and that vertical saplings were driven through the holes. These, analogous to withies used to mark a channel, would have been tall enough to show above the vegetation. To counter this argument, one might ask why anyone should go to the trouble of cutting holes when the sapling could simply have been driven into the bog alongside the wood. The answer might be that the sapling had the additional purpose of keeping the 'trackway' in place. The Somerset tracks are certainly pegged in position, but the 1949 excavators of Kate's Pad looked for and failed to find pegs.

Although only a small section of Kate's Pad has been examined in this century, it was said in the nineteenth century to run from Hales Hall to Pilling Hall, a distance of about four miles, and a second track was reported running south-eastward in the same area. Although no other trackway has yet been recorded in Lancashire – which is not to say that they did not exist – it is worth noting that comparable tracks were seen in section in the early years of the century in Foulshaw and Stakes Mosses, which lie in the Gilpin valley of south Westmorland, only just beyond the old county boundary.

Whether or not any of the timber trackways discussed here survived in use into the first century AD, tracks of some sort must have done. The Romans will have found these when they arrived in the area, and the native inhabitants continued to use such routes together with the more familiar Roman roads. To the man in the street, the best known characteristic of the Roman roads is their straightness. This is so much the case that it is quite common for a straight stretch of road of later date to be known as a Roman road. In essence, of course, the observation is true but, like many such 'well-known facts', it does less than justice to a complex situation.

The prehistoric 'roads' so far discussed were, with the exception of the timber trackways, neither engineered nor maintained. The opportunity to undertake engineering and systematic maintenance on anything more than a purely local scale only arose with the development of something approaching a national or supra-national political consciousness and control, combined with the military capacity to enforce this. The Romans had all of these, and roads – specifically the main roads – were an integral part of their political and military structure. Many of the details of how the gradual – and ultimately incomplete – conquest of Britain was achieved, or of the precise part which was played by roads and road-building, remain unclear but the demonstrable use of a system of military posts linked by fast direct routes implies that it was a crucial element in the strategy.

If in our mind's eye we picture the first Roman troops advancing northward, through what was later to be Lancashire, during the last quarter of the first century AD, we must imagine men who were very conscious that they were on the edge of the known world. They had come from Continental Europe, and they had marched to the Channel coast through France along proper roads. After crossing the sea to England they had travelled north and west through country which had been, more or less firmly, in Roman hands for over thirty years and which also had good roads – newer scars on the landscape than those on the continent, admittedly, but certainly good and fast routes. Now, in the north-west, they had moved into country where no such roads existed, and where progress was slower and more hazardous.

They were not moving blindly into the unknown, however. The operational commander would have had intelligence services, gathering information about the area ahead. Some commercial intercourse must already have taken place; there may have been spies and quislings; and there would certainly have been prisoners – we may imagine that the Romans were not too gentle in extracting information from them. The Roman commander in the field knew, therefore, that he would be advancing along a lowland between the hills and the sea, and that his line of march would be constrained by the lowest point at which he could cross three large rivers, each of which had an estuary reaching far inland. He will also have known that much of the country was rough and difficult terrain, where a few hostile men could tie down a sizeable force for a lengthy and indeterminate time – an area which was therefore to be avoided during the vital initial phase of the occupation.

The commander will have sent back reports on his situation and progress, and these are likely to have included a recommendation that a road should be built to link the lowest crossing points of the rivers known to us as the Mersey, the Ribble and the Lune. We can be reasonably confident on strategic grounds that this road was the first to be built by the Romans in our county, and archaeological evidence from Roman sites located near these crossing points is beginning to confirm this hypothesis.

It is, however, interesting to note that, as far as we know, only one of the three sites was eventually occupied by a military post or fort. This was Lancaster, and the explanation in that case must surely lie in the effectiveness of the viewpoint from the top of the hill on which the fort lay – a factor which also guided the siting of the great castle which, a thousand years later, occupied the same hill top. Lancaster was accessible from the north either along the line of what became the A6 or down the Lune valley, but the perceived threat from across the bay – and from the sea – must always have been greater. The ability to view the whole of that bay (weather permitting) must have been a crucial aspect of the siting of the Roman fort.

In contrast to the crossing of the Lune at Lancaster, the Mersey and the Ribble crossings were marked by Roman settlements which were not the permanent home of a garrison with the task of keeping the

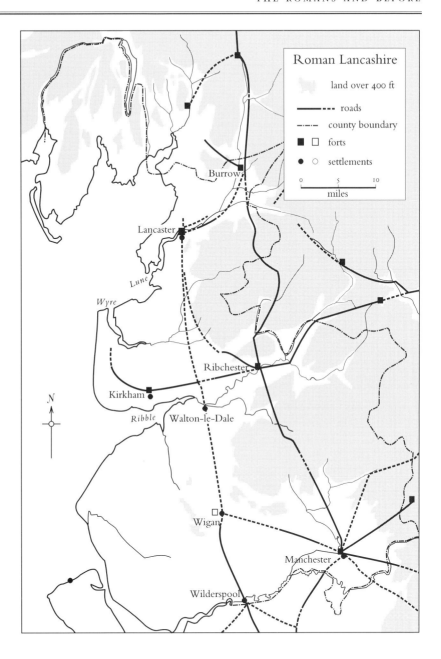

Roman Lancashire

land over 400 ft

---··· roads

---·-··- county boundary

■ □ forts

● ○ settlements

0   5   10

miles

Burrow

Lancaster

Lune

Wyre

Ribchester

Kirkham

Ribble   Walton-le-Dale

N

Wigan

Manchester

Wilderspool

Roman roads in
Lancashire.

local population under control. At Wilderspool (Warrington) and
Walton-le-Dale there developed manufacturing and trading posts,
which had an important military role – their main market was the
Roman army, and the army may have been involved in their administration – but they were not fortified settlements. That they could exist
at all was the result of the creation, very soon after the laying-out of

the 'river crossings' road, of another route, roughly parallel to it and further east, crossing the hill country.

This second route, sometimes considered to be a military road, linked a series of forts and was clearly instrumental in the process of conquering and controlling the difficult hill country along the western edge of the Pennines. It linked the same three valleys, the Mersey, the Ribble and the Lune, en route from Manchester towards Carlisle, but its settlements were military posts from the beginning and remained so throughout their existence. The three forts on the Lancashire stretch were Manchester, Ribchester, and Burrow-in-Lonsdale or Over Burrow (two miles south of Kirkby Lonsdale). To link them the road had to cross several intervening ranges of hills, and the evidence for the selection of its route is of particular interest.

Anyone who needs confirmation as to the general method of Roman route selection, which resulted in the familiar overall straightness of the roads, should go to the top of Jeffrey Hill at the western end of Longridge Fell on a clear day. On the skyline, almost due east, will be seen a prominent flat-topped hill peeping over the top of the intervening ridge: this is Pen-y-Ghent. Across the valley in the foreground, exactly aligned on the top of Pen-y-Ghent, the line of a Roman road is clearly visible, first as a series of hedgerows and then as a double line of trees flanking a modern road which lies on its alignment. This demonstrates the method used for route selection in conditions where there were no topographical difficulties. A distant sighting point was selected, and a line towards it was followed as far as was convenient. When the original sighting line was no longer feasible the road took up a new alignment. Each section of the alignment was straight if possible, but the route also reflected such factors as geology and topography, the location of river crossings, gradients, security considerations and the geographical position of the eventual destination. All of these points are demonstrated perfectly by the road we have been discussing.

Whatever the route taken by the modern observer to the top of Jeffrey Hill, his Roman predecessor travelling north will have reached it from Ribchester, in the Ribble valley some three miles to the south: the Roman road climbed straight up the side of Longridge Fell. The

The line of the Roman road from Ribchester to Burrow, seen from the top of Jeffrey Hill near Longridge. The modern road in the foreground is approximately on the line of its Roman predecessor, and this and the stretch in the middle distance marked out by a line of trees are carefully aligned on the summit of Pen-y-Ghent which can be seen above the ridge on the skyline (author).

reader might ask what sighting point it was heading for, but the answer is probably 'none' – the alignment north of the Ribble is exactly that which had been followed by the road from Manchester south of the river. The implication is that the sighting point was selected from the south, and lay on the southern rim of the valley – perhaps on the ridge at Ramsgreave. The line was then projected straight across the Ribble to pass near (but not through) Ribchester, and then up the side of Longridge Fell. There is no evidence as to how or where the road crossed the Ribble, because we do not know where in the valley the river itself ran in Roman times – rapid erosion means that its meanders have progressed downstream during the past two thousand years, and removed about one third of the fort site at Ribchester.

From Jeffrey Hill, if the aim had merely been to progress northwards, it would have been possible to swing westwards between the hills and the sea. However, this route, though it was probably used for a side road later in the Roman period, had several disadvantages. First, it would take the traveller a considerable distance to the west – a long detour, and one which in military and strategic terms was undesirable. Second, it had to avoid the prominent and steep outlier of Beacon Fell. Third, it had to cross a number of tributaries of the Wyre which are very deeply incised – notably the Brock and the Calder.

With the western route rejected at least on military grounds, it was necessary to swing eastwards up the Hodder valley, because directly ahead lay the very steep slopes above Chipping and Leagram, and the high, wet plateau of south-western Bowland. Since the ultimate destination of the road lay to the north, it must have been tempting to use the Trough of Bowland route, ascending the Langden valley and descending the Marshaw Wyre. This, however, had the disadvantage that the hills to the north of the Tarnbrook Wyre, rising to over 1800 feet at Ward's Stone, again force this route west towards the general vicinity of Lancaster.

This left little option but to cross the hills further east. Here one still has to negotiate a high traverse, but the altitude is rather less and several convenient valleys offer possible routes. It would have been feasible to ascend the Dunsop and Whitendale valleys and descend Roeburndale towards Hornby. Porter[1] suggests that this route was used in the medieval period and Crump[2] includes it as a salt route. Nevertheless, it has the significant disadvantage that valley floors in general are not the best places for roads, particularly where, as with the Dunsop and the Roeburn, the rivers are liable to rise and flood very rapidly.

It would also have been possible to use the Slaidburn–Cross of Greet–Bentham route, as Rauthmell suggested as long ago as 1746.[3] Here the modern road clings rather precariously to the valley side at the headwaters of the Hodder, rises to 1400 feet, and has to cross several

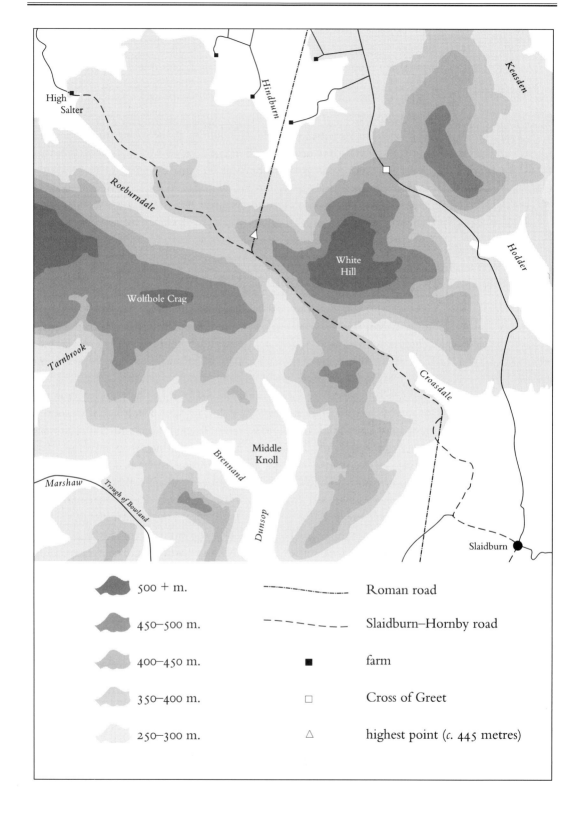

500 + m.	·—·—·—·— Roman road
450–500 m.	— — — — Slaidburn–Hornby road
400–450 m.	■ farm
350–400 m.	☐ Cross of Greet
250–300 m.	△ highest point (c. 445 metres)

tributaries of the Hindburn on its descent towards Bentham. It is also too far east in relation to the destination of the Roman road – the Lune gorge from Sedbergh to Tebay. Rauthmell's postulated route, by taking in 'Tatham Chapel' (Tatham Fells Church) in fact does regain the actual route further north. He refers to Bentham as a destination: the author of Appendix II to the 1824 edition of his book, presumed to be the publisher Arthur Foster, clearly thought that this meant Lower Bentham, but it is actually no more than Bentham parish, which is briefly crossed by the Roman road to the north of Robert Hall in Tatham.

Ruling out the Dunsop Bridge and the Cross of Greet routes on geographical and topographical grounds left the route which was actually chosen. This has the apparent disadvantage of taking the road somewhat higher – to about 1460 feet – but it has other, subtle, advantages which are apparent only as a result of knowing the country or, for us but not for the Romans, of examining a contour map. The choice of a route on the right (west) bank of Croasdale and on the left (east) bank of Whitendale made it possible to make a relatively gentle ascent and, more important, to keep the road high on the valley sides away from the danger of flooding. Whether or not, as Just suggests,[4] the possibility of avoiding ambush also entered the minds of the Roman surveyors we cannot know.

The line of the road remains at around 1350 feet above sea level for about 1½ miles. At the northern end of that stretch is the old border between Lancashire and Yorkshire, and from this point the apparently later 'modern' track continues down Roeburndale to Hornby. That route formed the usual medieval and post-medieval way between Slaidburn and Hornby, and it is perfectly possible that this, too, was used by the Romans, but this is not capable of proof. There are hints of Roman occupation in the vicinity of Hornby Castle, noted by Whitaker in the eighteenth century and mentioned by Birley in 1946,[5] and a recent field survey of the Roman and medieval routes found that the most 'Roman'-looking section of paving was in fact on the Hornby section rather than on the known Roman road.

On the watershed, at the old county boundary, the known Roman route swings sharply eastwards and climbs about 100 feet in a quarter of a mile. After this point the route descended a spur between the upper reaches of the Roeburn and Hindburn valleys, towards Lowgill. Thereafter the road crossed the headwaters of the Hindburn, the Wenning and the Greta and headed for the fort at Burrow – but it did not actually go to the fort, a point to which we will return shortly.

What emerges from consideration of this road, and its detailed alignment, is that the route was chosen with great care and skill and depended on sophisticated assessment of the inter-relationship between landforms, ground quality, and strategic and military requirements. It

The route of the Roman road from Ribchester to Burrow, passing through the Forest of Bowland using the Croasdale and Whitendale valleys to cross the watershed between the Ribble and Lune catchments (author).

The Roman road, with the modern track approximately on its alignment, looking south towards Slaidburn with Croasdale on the left. The bleak terrain and the need to choose a careful alignment avoiding difficult stream crossings are clear from this photograph *(author)*.

The road from Ribchester to Burrow looking north as it approaches the Ribble/Lune watershed, with Whitendale on the left. By keeping the road above the level of the valley floor the Roman engineers not only avoided the danger of flooding but also secured a comparatively gentle ascent to the summit *(author)*.

was clearly designed to head as directly north and south as possible, and it took into account the existence of forts. Where the nature of the country was difficult, however, the alignment of the road was related to the terrain with great skill. In those stretches where the topography was less troublesome, distant landmarks were used as sighting points and long straight alignments were possible. The result was something very close to the 'best' route which could be achieved.

It is obviously the case that the route of the road took account of the existence of forts, but it was not dictated by them. Rather surprisingly to the casual observer, neither Ribchester nor Burrow lay on the line of the main road. At Ribchester the road passed about five hundred yards east of the fort, assuming it did not deviate from the straight line in order to cross the river – as noted above, the ground evidence for this has been destroyed by the migration of meanders since Roman times. At Burrow the discrepancy was greater: the road passes almost a mile east of the fort. In other words, the Roman army saw no good reason why the precise siting of a fort or a road should be subservient to, or should dictate, the other. Service roads, linking forts to arterial roads, could and did solve this potential problem.

In the case of the road now under consideration, a difficulty is raised by the distance between the forts at Ribchester and Burrow – almost twenty-eight modern miles (29½ Roman miles). Distances as great as this rarely occur in the British section of the *Antonine Itinerary*, the great 'road book' of the later Roman period, and where they do they are usually in gentle and easy lowland country. Nevertheless the figure for the stage from Galacum [?Burrow] to Bremetonaci [Ribchester] is given in the *Itinerary* as XXVII miles. Even allowing for slight error, the gap seems unusually large. However, attempts to locate an intermediate wayside station have been doomed to failure. Even Birley[6] suggested that while there must have been 'at least in the Flavian period, a fort on the main north road' perhaps 'somewhere close to the Wenning . . . that would still make a long day's march over the hills from Ribchester, something like twenty-two miles from the Wenning'. The absence of any evidence for a Roman military site between Ribchester and Burrow implies that the Roman soldiers did indeed march this long and arduous stretch in a single day. We may beg leave to doubt whether many of them appreciated the subtleties evident in the planning of its route!

There are further points of interest about this road. For example, the alignment from Jeffrey Hill towards the sighting point on Pen-y-Ghent can be followed for at least 4½ miles, and possibly five. It was apparently unaffected by the need to cross the River Hodder, deep in a steep-sided valley near Doeford Bridge. Beyond the three farms called 'Lees', in one of which Richard Rauthmell, historian of Burrow-in-Lonsdale, was born in 1691, the modern road leaves the Roman line for almost half a mile, rejoining it near Cow Ark at the vicarage which Robert Towneley Parker built for the antiquarian clergyman Rauthmell when he held the living of Whitewell – the position of the vicarage, precisely on the Roman road, can hardly be coincidence.

The Roman road line is then followed by the modern road, with a minor deviation near Browsholme Heights. On the top of this hill at just over 950 feet above sea level, the Roman road – according to

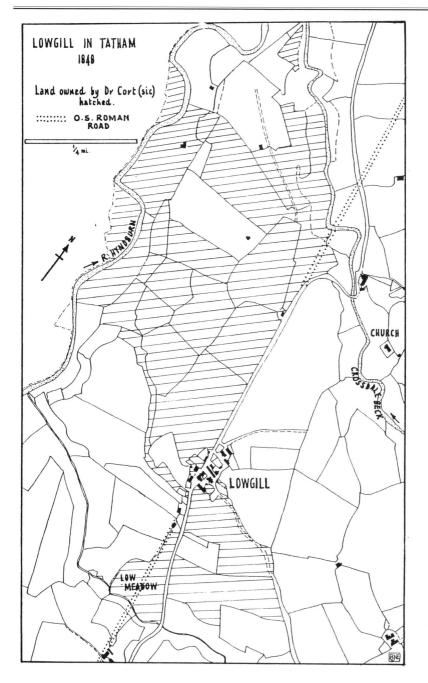

LOWGILL IN TATHAM
1848

Land owned by Dr Cort (sic)
hatched.
::::::::: O.S. ROMAN
ROAD

¼ mi.

Lowgill in Tatham: detail of the alignment of the Roman road. Before 1824 Dr Court, the landowner, found in this area a stone which was almost certainly a Roman milestone, while he was 'draining a moist meadow'. The plan shows the line of the road and the areas of land owned by Dr Court in 1848. The Low Meadow is the only point at which the land ownership, Roman road and existence of meadowland can all be recognised, and it was therefore probably here that the milestone – which is now lost – was discovered.

most authorities and the Ordnance Survey – swings some 20° westward.[7] It is then en route to cross the Hodder for a second time, near Knowlmere. The point at which this crossing took place is fairly closely defined by the alignment on the far bank, which is known with certainty, but the course between the point on Browsholme Heights,

Roman roads often survive as green lanes and footpaths; here the line of the road is marked by a modern track which runs along the boundary between the townships of Leck and Burrow-with-Burrow in the Lune valley – parish boundaries frequently follow the line of Roman roads *(author)*.

where the direction changes, and the Hodder is debatable. The alleged alignment would take the road down the valley of the Birkett Brook, a tributary of the Hodder, and involve crossings of its two right-bank tributaries, one unnamed, the other Riddle Clough.

This alignment and its crossings were first published by Percival Ross in 1916. The first part of the line was claimed to be a cropmark, allegedly bracken among heather, near a farm called Crimpton. This was said to be on a ridge, presumably the agger or raised bank of the road. The second observation was a crossing point of the unnamed tributary of the Birkett Brook. This was described by Ross as a series of rock-cut terraces. It is difficult to imagine a Roman road with ascending and descending features of this type, and the crossing which has been identified with this, and which is still in existence, cannot properly be so described. It consists of a track descending the side of the stream, which is there very deeply incised, at an oblique angle heading up stream. In other words, the plan of the crossing is similar to the behaviour of a contour when crossing such a stream. Parts of the side of this track are rock-faced, but it is clear that weathering of this rock takes place every winter, and it seems very unlikely that it is anything like two thousand years old.

The cropmark referred to earlier is certainly not bracken, and the ridge claimed to be that of the agger seems much more likely to be an abandoned enclosure boundary. This does not, in itself, disqualify it as a Roman road, but to this writer the clinching factor is that there is absolutely no need for any of these engineering works. From the top of Browsholme Heights the modern road descends the hill in a gentle curve. This curve is continued for a little further to the next summit at Marl Hill Farm. If the Roman road had run straight across the chord of this curve for just over half a mile it would have rejoined the line taken by the modern road and have continued on the same Pen-y-Ghent alignment for another ¾ mile. By swinging westwards at this point, near Ing Barn, it could have descended the spur between the Birkett Brook and Foulscales Brook and reached the Hodder at the required point in about ¾ mile without the need to cross deeply-incised streams.

The point to be made here is that details of the routes even of well-known roads are often unclear, and that there is still much scope for accurate and careful local investigation. Furthermore, many of the alignments which have long been widely accepted are based not on precise observation but on guesswork and supposition – sometimes with an element of wishful thinking in the observation of 'humps and bumps'. The exact routes of many of Lancashire's Roman roads are still to be determined, and only field observation and archaeological research can supply reliable answers. In the extreme north of the county, for example, there are a couple of observations worth making about this same road. First, in the parish of Burrow-with-Burrow we encounter one of about half a dozen Roman milestones which are known from the county.

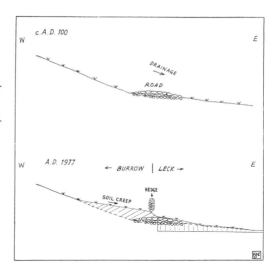

This one is not absolutely certain since it is just a stump, later incised with the letters 'BP' (Burrow parish) and 'LP' (Leck parish) because it is situated on the parish boundary. Second, within Leck itself a small excavation a few years ago established that at a point where the road is running across a slight southward slope, and is allegedly marked by a hedge line which is also the parish boundary, the road is quite literally under the hedge, soil creep having buried it. The excavation showed that the road extended only a few feet south into the field and disappeared northwards under the hedge.

An excavation in 1977 at Leck showed in detail how the precise line of a Roman road can be concealed. The general alignment is marked by a parish boundary and by a hedge, but a section across the road shows that the uphill half has been concealed beneath soil creep.

For reasons of convenience this look at the Roman roads of the county began at Ribchester, and the pivotal nature of that site in the Roman road system means that it is sensible to continue from there. On a small-scale map the road south from Longridge Fell seems to run on a single alignment to the fort at Manchester, over thirty miles away. In fact there are two alignments, but they change by only a few degrees. The key sighting point must have been on or near Rushton's Height in Darwen. This gives a single alignment of about 12½ miles from Jeffrey Hill, and the new line thence towards Manchester, which has been tested by excavation on several occasions, takes another 17½ miles. Although this seems a long distance for a single alignment, it may in fact have been somewhat longer. It is unlikely that there would have been a sighting point down in the Irwell valley, where the fort at Manchester was situated, because almost by definition a sighting point had to be prominent in the view: this implies that an even more distant point was chosen.

The earliest section of the road south from Manchester towards the Roman spa at Buxton is uncertain, but one suggestion is that it may have followed the same line towards a point on the flanks of the

Pennines such as Black Hill or Sponds Hill between New Mills and Bollington. Provided such points were technically intervisible (i.e. there was not intervening high ground) problems of actual visibility could easily have been solved by such devices as smoke columns. In the past such suggestions were less likely to have been made by antiquarians and historians, because the idea of being able to see right across the Manchester basin was quite implausible – the near-permanent pall of smoke made it a physical impossibility. However, industrial decline, the Clean Air Acts and the change to cleaner power supplies for the industries which remain, now make a clear view of the Derbyshire hills from mid-Lancashire a commonplace – we now see the view which the Romans saw, and we can appreciate that a sighting line extending from the hills above Darwen to the moors behind Maccles-field would have been perfectly realistic.

Ribchester lay on an important north–south road, which here was crossed by another road running approximately east–west. This road ran up the Ribble valley into Yorkshire, over to the valleys of the Aire and the Wharfe, its eventual destination being the great legionary fortress at York. It was one of the few cross-Pennine routes used by the Romans. South of the Tyne Gap there were only the Stainmore route (now represented by the A66), the high-level road from Ingleton to Bainbridge, the road we are now considering and the more or less direct route between York and Chester via Manchester.

Half-section of the Roman road from Ribchester to Ilkley, excavated at Fence Gate Farm near Dinckley, east of Rib-chester. This gives a good impression of the construction of an important secondary road.

East of Ribchester the general course of the road has no particularly distinctive features within Lancashire, but one location did produce some especially interesting evidence about the late Roman and post-Roman use of Roman roads. This discovery came about as a result of the construction of the Whalley–Clitheroe bypass. North-east of Clitheroe, where parish boundaries follow its line for some three miles, a stretch of the Roman road was to be destroyed by the new bypass. A small excavation revealed that the Roman road was represented here

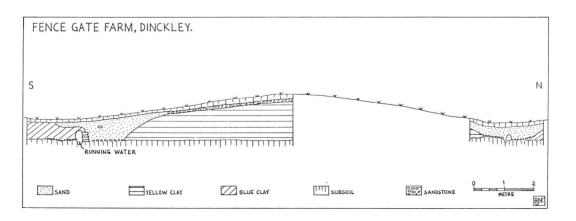

FENCE GATE FARM, DINCKLEY.

S

N

RUNNING WATER

SAND   YELLOW CLAY   BLUE CLAY   SUBSOIL   SANDSTONE   0 1 2 METRE only by a linear hollow in the natural limestone. In other words, the road had continued in use long after all maintenance of the road surface had ended – to the extent that the post-Roman traffic had worn away the Roman surface and eroded down into the limestone itself. Although the Carboniferous limestone in the vicinity of Clitheroe is not a particularly hard rock, erosion of this kind must imply either heavy use or long-continued use, the latter being much more probable. It is worth noting that neither the topography nor the geology make this section of the route one where detours, such as those discussed at the beginning of the chapter, were likely – therefore the traffic would have been markedly concentrated within the width of the road.

There is no great difficulty in defining most of the line of the road through the Ribble valley towards Yorkshire, but the mile and a half into Ribchester itself does present a problem. Briefly, we can follow the road from the vicinity of Whalley across the Calder and through Billington and Dinckley into Salesbury. Here, where a modern road descends the slope to the floodplain of the Ribble, is Marles Wood, adjacent to which is a recently constructed car park. Part of the Roman road was seen in investigations prior to the building of this car park, but its course further west is unclear.

It is unlikely to have continued precisely on the line it follows through Dinckley, because this would have taken it by a route along the front of the meander bluffs of the Ribble. Even allowing for erosion and alterations in the river course over the last two thousand years this alignment is improbable. It must, therefore, have deviated from that line, but how and where is as yet unknown. The Ordnance Survey takes the line across the fields to cross the Ribble near Ribchester Bridge and enter the village along the line of the modern road, but this alignment seems to be no more than speculation or guesswork.

The road out from Ribchester to the west presents more considerable problems. It has been generally accepted, at least since the making of the first Ordnance Survey maps in the 1840s, that Ribchester was connected directly by road to a site, presumably a fort, at Kirkham: parts of this route have been reliably plotted. However, the alignment usually mapped is – for a significant Roman road – somewhat peculiar since, from a point south of Grimsargh right through to Kirkham, it follows a gentle southward curve. Nevertheless, there seems to be plenty of evidence for it. Roman Road Farm is found near Red Scar on the banks of the Ribble, and in this area the early OS maps mark several parts of the route with the 'double dotted line' symbol which presumably indicated some trace on the ground at the time of the survey. The real problem, then as now, was the location of the road in the first 1½ miles west from Ribchester.

If projected, the gentle curve already mentioned would meet the modern road from Ribchester to Longridge (which is approximately on the line of another Roman road to which we shall return) well to the north of Ribchester. Somewhere there has to be a southward turn towards the site of the fort, either along the modern road from Longridge or in the vicinity of Hothersall. The problem is complicated by the existence, west of Ribchester, of several deeply incised tributaries of the Ribble, where post-Roman erosion has apparently removed evidence for the road.

Another factor which complicates consideration of this route is the existence of two three-quarter-mile stretches of notably straight modern road lying exactly in the direct line between Ribchester and Kirkham. They are, firstly, the road through the village of Grimsargh and, secondly, Lightfoot Lane west of the railway in Broughton, north of Preston. These roads may have no significance in Roman terms, and it is certainly true that the road was apparently exposed in excavation near Roman Road Farm, well to the south of the direct line, a few years ago. Here, as elsewhere in Lancashire, there is still much scope for speculation and much opportunity for further research.

When we consider the Fylde, to the west of Preston, we encounter two questions which generate a great deal of heat but little light. These are the alleged naming of the Roman road as the Danes Pad and the question of its destination west of the site at Kirkham. To dispose of these in order: if the name 'Danes Pad' is a genuine folk name (in other words, not an eighteenth-century antiquarian coinage) it presumably implies the existence of a feature resembling a road, the origin of which was uncertain. Such man-made features were often attributed to supernatural beings such as the Devil, or to peoples long since dead. The Danes Graves in the East Riding of Yorkshire, which are Iron Age in date, are a good parallel. A feature must have existed, since it acquired a name, and recent research has concentrated on locating and identifying it. This has not proved easy, and it has been suggested, not impossibly, that the so-called road was in reality a natural gravel ridge. This would accord well with stories of its removal by farmers for use in road-mending, but its having been a natural topographical feature would not preclude the possibility that it was used for the alignment of a Roman road.

As far as its destination west of Kirkham is concerned, the usual candidate is the fabled *Portus Setantiorum*, and we must now address ourselves to the identification of this name with a site in the area of Fleetwood. The name is recorded only once in an original source – in a compilation known as the *Geography* of Ptolemy, a writer who worked in Egypt in the second century AD and used, as was normal in that area, the Greek language. He gathered together a great deal of geographical information and published it in the form of lists of place-names together with their latitude and longitude. He did not produce a map, though Renaissance editions of his work were so adorned. For our purposes we are concerned with just six names from the north coast of Wales and the north-west coast of England.

Working from south to north the identification of the first of these (*Ganganorum promontorium*) with the Lleyn Peninsula of North Wales and the sixth (*Ituna aestuarium*) with the Solway Firth (strictly the Eden) are hardly to be doubted. This leaves four names, all relating to indentations in the coastline rather than to promontories. Three of these are designated, in the Latin version of the work which is almost as old as the Greek, by the word *aestuarium* and, as we have seen, the other by *portus*. This, and the Greek word which lies behind it, means something like 'haven' rather than 'port' or 'harbour'. All that can be said with certainty about these four names, leaving aside abstruse mathematical juggling with the latitudes and longitudes, is that they seem to occur in the correct order. Given that, and the fact that there are more than four significant coastal indentations between Lleyn and the Solway, there is no certain way of identifying which is meant.

It has been common to assume that the estuary *Seteia* was either the Dee or the Mersey, that *Belisama* was the Ribble and that *Moricambe* was Morecambe Bay. There was then little choice but to place the *portus*, lying between the last two, somewhere on the Fylde coast. However, these identifications require their proponents to answer such questions as why one or other of the Dee and the Mersey, both prominent and important estuaries well known to sailors, was omitted. Further, the apparent coincidence between *Moricambe* and Morecambe Bay is entirely spurious, the latter name having only been applied – to what was previously known by such names as Kent Sands and Leven Sands – by John Whitaker in the eighteenth century, precisely as a possible identification of Ptolemy's *Moricambe aestuarium*.

There is, therefore, absolutely no certainty that *Portus Setantiorum* was in the Fylde at all. The implication of this for the road network is that the feature said to have been known as Danes Pad may, in reality, not have been a Roman road. It was said to have run westwards from Kirkham, curving northwards through Weeton to at least Hard-horn, where traces of it began to fade. Because of the double difficulties, with the name of the place and the nature of the 'road', it cannot be used to support the identification of *Portus Setantiorum* as a site on the Fylde coast, nor can the *portus* be used to support the attribution of the road. It may be objected that the discovery of at least one large hoard of Roman coins at Rossall is some confirmation of its existence, but this does not seem logical – the hoard found at Hackensall, on the other side of the Wyre, has not led to suggestions of a Roman road through Pilling Moss.

We have now looked at the evidence for Roman roads running to each of the main compass points from Ribchester. However, one more road is said to have served that fort. This ran north-west, with its initial stages on or near the present road to Longridge: the Roman and modern roads are said to have diverged near the *Cross Keys Inn* to the east of Ribchester Hospital. The road is then said to have run up the southern side of Longridge Fell, down the northern face, and then across the plain in a north-westerly direction to join a Roman road on the general line of the modern A6 near Galgate. Little of the course has been identified on the ground, and because the intervening country-side includes several deeply incised valleys, such as those of the Brock and Calder, together with the whaleback of Beacon Fell, the road cannot have been straight.

One of the most important pieces of evidence quoted for this road is the name 'Street', applied to a farm and nearby bridge over the river Wyre in Nether Wyresdale. While the name may well be derived from a Roman road in the vicinity, one further piece of evidence, often quoted in support, must be rejected. This is a stone bridge abutment some forty yards downstream from the present-day bridge. It has been suggested that this abutment was Roman, and a portion of the road leading towards it was exposed when gravel extraction took place nearby. However, reference to the records of the bridges in Amounder-ness hundred shows that the abutment, and the road leading to it, were those of the immediate predecessor of the present bridge rather than being of Roman date.

Near Galgate the putative Roman road from Ribchester to the north-west would have met a road leading north from the river crossing at Walton-le-Dale to the fort at Lancaster, a road which is represented for long stretches by the modern A6. There are some deviations, where – from the eighteenth century onwards – the modern road has been diverted from its historic alignment, but the general line is not in doubt. North of Garstang the A6 runs to the east of the Roman road line, and this section of the road has produced three more of the county's Roman milestones.

The most southerly was at a minor road junction near Forton Hall. Here, for many years, stood a large cylindrical stone gatepost, with the stone socket of a wayside cross alongside. It was sometimes suggested that the gatepost had been part of the cross shaft, but in fact it would not have fitted the socket, and neither would its cross-section have been appropriate for this purpose. Furthermore, a cylindrical gatepost was itself very unusual. There is little doubt that it was actually a Roman milestone. The local historical society excavated the base of the gatepost, to be certain that there was no inscription on the buried portion and then, some years later, the stone was removed and a more conventional gatepost substituted. The milestone was eventually re-erected beside the road, and is still there.

The other two milestones were found in the area known as Burrow Heights in Scotforth, just south of Lancaster, the first in 1811 and the second in 1834. Each is inscribed with the name and titles of an emperor, but neither gives any other information. This is quite normal, for although some Roman milestones state distances in the fashion of modern examples, many do not. These milestones were erected in the reigns of Philip (AD 244–249) and Trajan Decius (AD 249–251). They are now to be seen in Lancaster City Museum.

The communications system of the fort at Lancaster which com-manded the Lune crossing has proved difficult to reconstruct. There was a road on the south side of the Lune connecting with the fort at Burrow-in-Lonsdale, and a north bank road has also been postulated. The detailed course of the southern road is not clear, although it was revealed at Quernmore and in the Brookhouse area of Caton during pipeline excavation in 1992. This road also produced a splendid mile-stone, found in 1811 in the bed of the Artle Beck at Caton: we do not know precisely where the milestone was found. There is a growing belief that the Lune Valley road did not run directly from Lancaster but branched off the road from Walton-le-Dale at a point near Scotforth and proceeded through Quernmore (where Roman pottery and tile kilns are known) to Caton.

Whatever the truth of that possibility, the Caton milestone is one of the best examples from Roman Britain, and its inscription tantalises with the unfulfilled promise of solving a problem. We do not know the Roman name for Lancaster, and the milestone might have told us. The tantalising near-solution is to be found at the end of the inscription on the milestone, which records, first, its erection in the reign of the Emperor Hadrian, in or after the year in which he assumed the title *pater patriae*. The date is therefore between 128 and his death in 138. Below that is a rectangular panel enclosing the information that the milestone was sited four miles from somewhere, presumably Lancaster, designated only by its initial letter.

The difficulty is that the left end of the panel is ambiguous. The right hand end of the panel is correctly carved to produce what is known as an *ansate frame* – a triangle with one of its apexes touching the centre of the right hand vertical of the frame. At the left end of the frame, however, the horizontal lines of the frame are prolonged to the base of the triangle. To the right are two vertical lines, one of which may be intended for the left vertical of the panel. The second may be the initial letter of the name of the fort and has a near-horizontal line near its base which may be intended to make it L. The most widely favoured interpretation of the inscription is therefore that the milestone lay four miles from L——, which was Lancaster.[8]

If the Lune valley road led close to Burrow-in-Lonsdale, it may well have continued to join the known road from near Ingleton to the fort at Bainbridge in Wensleydale. Likewise, a possible road northwest from near Burrow towards Watercrook (just outside Kendal) may be a continuation of a road running from the Aire valley into the upper Ribble valley and passing the probable site of a fort at Long Preston. If these roads did exist – and the Lune valley courses are all hypothetical – Burrow lies on none of them, a situation described nearly fifty years ago as 'inviting speculation'.[9]

The roads leading from the fort at Ribchester have enabled us to survey the communications of all the known Roman fort sites within the county except Manchester, to which we shall return. We must now, however, deal with the three sites of large-scale Roman occupation which were not forts. These lie on the Lancashire plain – Walton-le-Dale on the Ribble and Wilderspool on the Mersey, with Wigan lying roughly midway between them. This is not the place to discuss the status of those three sites in detail, but all seem to have been more or less industrial and will certainly have been military in commercial orientation. They were linked by a major north–south route, and field traces and excavation have established the line of this with certainty on both sides of Wigan.

The Roman site at Wigan itself was somewhat elusive and ambiguous until fairly recently, but there is no doubt of its existence. Its name remains the subject of debate, and when considering this we encounter a second century document much used in the study of Roman roads and sites. This is the *Antonine Itinerary*, the road book consisting of lists of place names with the distances between them. Its individual routes have been given numbers (which are not in the original) and one of these (*Iter* X) runs through Lancashire. Its first site in the county is *Mamucium*, which is almost certainly the correct Roman name for Manchester. This is followed by *Coccium*, seventeen Roman miles away. A further twenty miles brought the traveller to *Bremetonnacum*, which is certainly Ribchester. Where, then, was *Coccium*? A number of sites were proposed in the nineteenth century, but there are really only two possibilities. First, that it was somewhere roughly midway between Manchester and Ribchester. In that case, it has not been recognised on the ground, and the distances are plainly wrong. Discrepancies in mileages can often be explained by the constant copying and recopying of the text, which gave rise to errors – the addition or omission of an 'x' or a 'v', or the misreading of the one for the other, could soon result in anomalies. Such errors can sometimes be identified and allowed for, though too much juggling with the figures is precluded by the fact that each route, or *Iter*, had a total mileage figure at the end.

The second possibility, if *Coccium* cannot be located between Ribchester and Manchester on the direct route, is that some form of dog-leg is involved, and here the possibility that *Coccium* was Wigan comes into play. A road from Manchester to Wigan was recorded in the nineteenth century, before most traces were obliterated by industrial and urban development, and the distance is close enough to seventeen Roman miles. The route north from Wigan, over the Ribble at Walton-le-Dale and then onto the Kirkham–Ribchester road would involve about the right mileage to *Bremetonnacum*. There may well have been some means of getting from Walton-le-Dale to the Ribchester road without going north through the site of modern Preston to meet the east–west road in Fulwood, but this is speculative.

The Roman fort at Manchester, which has been the subject of extensive research and excavation in the past thirty years, was a very important route centre. Its situation, at the centre of the south-east Lancashire basin and at a focus of valley routeways, made it an obvious meeting-place for roads. There are six roads which are definitely known, and this means that it had better road access than any other Roman site in Lancashire – indeed, it ranks with York, Chester and Carlisle as one of the nodal points of the Roman road network of Northern England.

Manchester lay on the great road which linked the key centres of Chester and York. To the south-west of the fort the line of this route is marked today by Chester Road, which passes through Trafford (recorded as *Stratford* in 1206) and Stretford, both of which mean 'road-ford' and derive their names from the Roman road. Moving clockwise from the Chester road, the fort was served by the probable route to Wigan, which is now obliterated by housing but was traceable in the eighteenth and nineteenth centuries in the Ellenbrook area beyond Worsley. The major route to Ribchester ran north-westwards through Prestwich, and the York road ran north-east, along the line of Oldham Road, to the fort at Castleshaw above Delph. The long straight stretch of Hyde Road marks the beginning of the mountainous road which crossed the northern Peak District via *Melandra*, the fort at Gamesley near Glossop, heading for Templebrough (Rotherham). A major route ran south-east into Derbyshire, passing through Stockport to Buxton and eventually to Littlechester outside Derby.

Discussion of what must surely be Lancashire's most famous 'Roman' road has been left to the end. That inverted commas have been put round the word 'Roman' must not be taken to mean that any conclusion has been reached about Blackstone Edge stretch of the road which probably ran north-east from the fort at Manchester and over into Yorkshire, its destination being Ilkley. It is the short Blackstone Edge section of the road, rather than the route itself, which engenders controversy. On the Edge, two miles east of Littleborough, stone paving and an enigmatic central 'groove' survive. This is either one of the best preserved stretches of Roman road in the country, or is of a totally different date and not Roman at all, according to one's point of view.

Proponents of either view face the difficulty that there is apparently no exact parallel to the features seen on the Edge, whatever their age. That two of the people best qualified to judge considered the road to be Roman is one of the strongest arguments in favour of its being ascribed to that period. They were Sir Ian Richmond, who grew up nearby, and one of whose earliest archaeological papers describes the road better than any other; and I. D. Margary, who might claim to have seen and studied more miles of Roman road in Britain than anyone else.

Thrown back on one's own judgment, there are several points to be made about this road. When seen on the map it does not seem to follow a course which would be particularly logical for a Roman road. Much of its value could equally have been obtained from the road from Manchester through Castleshaw and Slack. On the other hand, its construction is not only unique but was extremely laborious. To cut, transport and lay the pavement of the road, let alone its bed, would have been a great undertaking. That in itself is an argument in favour of its Roman origin, for it is extremely unlikely that such a project would have undertaken in the Middle Ages and, while it would by no means have been beyond the capabilities of the eighteenth or nineteenth centuries, its construction then would surely have left some record.

The road was first drawn to academic attention in the later years of the nineteenth century by Dr H. Colley March. His paper cited the existence of a number of paved 'packhorse roads' on the moors, but the very considerable differences between these well-attested examples and the Blackstone Edge road increases the likelihood of another (and therefore presumably Roman) origin. One man, James Maxim, devoted many years of study to the problem, but his researches were published only after his death from a working-up of his notes,[10] and his conclusion that the 'Roman' road dates from the same period as the stone 'packhorse roads' on the moors does not carry conviction.

A final word may be added about the road network which has been considered in this chapter. The Roman roads of the north of England were constructed and maintained over a period of at least three hundred years. Many changes must have taken place over that time. Just as in our own times, roads fell into disuse, were renewed, reconstructed or added to as the demands of the local population, and military or economic requirements dictated. And these very roads we can identify only by a combination of their direction and their construction. This is the basis of the controversy about Blackstone Edge – neither its direction nor its construction is *certainly* Roman. Whatever else happened during the Roman period in the area that was to become Lancashire, we may be sure that there was a great deal of agricultural activity, and this will have been served by an extensive network of small roads which were scarcely 'constructed' at all. They must have differed little from present-day farm roads, and we can never hope to recover more than the odd fragment of these. We must remember that what we draw on a map, with solid lines for certain routes and dotted lines for doubtful ones, is a palimpsest of three centuries of activity, and a picture as partial as that in any small-scale map of the present day.

APPENDIX IA

Roman Roads in Lancashire with their 'Margary' numbers

7b	Manchester – Ribchester
7c	Ribchester – Low Borrow Bridge (Cumbria) [Lancashire boundary just north east of Burrow-in-Lonsdale fort] – (Carlisle)
70b	(Middlewich) – Wilderspool – Wigan
70c	Wigan – Walton-le-Dale
70d	Walton-le-Dale – Lancaster
72a	Ribchester – Ilkley (West Yorkshire) [Lancashire boundary north east of Barnoldswick] – (York)
702	Manchester – Wigan
703	Ribchester – Kirkham (and beyond?)
704	Ribchester – Galgate
705	Lancaster – Burrow-in-Lonsdale
706	Burrow-in-Lonsdale – ?Watercrook – (Ravenglass)

In addition, small portions of the following roads lay in the county:

7a	Chester – Manchester
71b	Manchester – Buxton – (Littlechester)
711	Manchester – Brough – (Templebrough)
712	Manchester – Tadcaster – (York)

APPENDIX IB

The name 'Watling Street'

This name occurs in two medieval deeds in the de Hoghton collection at the Lancashire Record Office, with reference to [English] Lea to the west of Preston. In the first (DDHo/H 433: n.d., 1284–1285) it is *Wattelingestrete*, and in the second (DDHo/H 435: n.d., 1288–1302) it is *Wattelingstrete*. The name is discussed at some length in *The Place names of Bedfordshire and Huntingdon shire* (p. 6), where it is stated that it was 'a name of purely local and limited application gradually extended in its use', and that it must be associated 'with the Old English name for the Roman settlement at Verulamium'. Further, 'by 973 the name was applied to other stretches of the great Roman road from London to Wroxeter, and by the time of William the Conqueror it had its present full extension, and later writers like Henry of Huntingdon and Robert of Gloucester so define it'. As a name for parts of the Wroxeter road it also appears in the place name volumes for Hertfordshire, Middlesex and Warwickshire.

However, the name is also quoted as in use for parts of the Stainmore road (Brougham–Scotch Corner) in the Westmorland place name volume (p. 19) with the gloss that 'Watling Street is a name frequently transferred to other Roman roads from the famous Watling Street'. The only quotation given to support the use for the Stainmore road is from John Leland, as late as *c.*1540, while the 'frequent' transferal of the name is supported by a reference to its use for part of the Great North Road in Allerton Bywater (*Place names of the West Riding*, vol. VII, p. 145), already noticed briefly in the North Riding volume (p. 2). In the West Riding volume this stretch has three sixteenth-century references, but it also has two thirteenth-century references, one of them prior to 1218. The 'Ferrybridge Loop' of the Great North Road also appropriated the name Watling Street, with a fifteenth- as well as sixteenth-century instance. Nevertheless, the two Lea examples mentioned above precede any others quoted in English Place Name Society volumes except those at Allerton Bywater.

Medieval sources often indicate former Roman roads by distinctive terminology, or by the use of particular names. In this document of 1284-5, from Lee Angl' [Lea, near Preston], the Roman road from Kirkham to Ribchester is named as Wattelingestrete; the name is the seventh word on the third line (*LRO DDHo H433*).

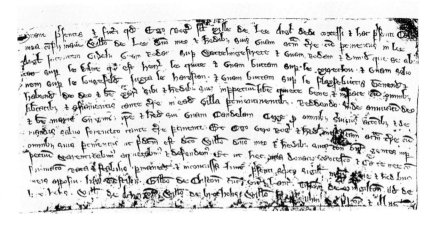

APPENDIX I C

The term *strata ferrata*

References in medieval deeds to a *magna strata* (e.g. Lancashire Record Office [LRO] DDHo/B 64: Lea, *c*.1190) are frequently taken as at least a *prima facie* case for the continued existence of a Roman road. A number of cases can be cited, however, where the adjective qualifying *strata* is *ferrata* (e.g. LRO DDF 526: Hutton 1236–1242; DDPt 5/8: Billington). *Ferrata* does not occur in the *Medieval Latin Word List*, and there is no reason why it should, since it is straightforward classical Latin, meaning 'furnished or shod with iron'.

However, roads were not usually, or ever, shod with iron in a literal sense. What, therefore, does the term *strata ferrata* mean? It is clear that many writers of medieval deeds, though writing in Latin, thought in English, and this prompts the idea that the word translated as *ferrata* was 'metalled', or a Middle English predecessor of it. *The Oxford English Dictionary*, perhaps surprisingly, gives no example of the use of the verb 'to metal' earlier than 1819, which would appear to negate the suggestion made above. Nevertheless, the Dictionary does give, as a substantive sense separate from 'broken stone used in macadamizing roads', the meaning 'material, matter, substance, esp. earthy matter'. As an illustration of this meaning, the quotation given is 'Two skepfull of sande; no other mettell, stone, clay or rubbish'.

It does not seem likely that 'mettell', coming in the quotation between 'sande' and 'stone', would have a meaning as general as 'matter, substance', but rather it must surely have implied some sort of broken stone, perhaps what we would now call gravel, though that word itself had a considerable ancestry. Since the quotation is dated *c*.1570, there is at least a possibility that 'metal' in the sense of gravel or something similar may have a medieval ancestry which would explain *ferrata* as an adjective for roads. *Strata* itself is not grammatically a noun, being an elliptical use of the feminine past participle of *sterno*, for *via strata,* 'paved road'.

2

The Roads of Dark Age
and Medieval Lancashire

THE THOUSAND YEARS which elapsed between the end of the
Roman occupation and the beginning of what might be thought
of as modern Lancashire pose problems for anyone investigating the
history of roads in the area. The Roman military road system, with its
fixed alignments and clearly identifiable surfaces, which continued in
use long after the Romans left, had been imposed upon the countryside.
As noted in the previous chapter, it formed only part of a more dense
and intricate communications network, because alongside the former
Roman roads there were other 'organic' systems which met the needs
of the local populace. These developed – or fell out of use – as fashion
or demand dictated, throughout the Dark Age and medieval periods. If
one route became too boggy through over-use, another one, often
parallel, would come into use until that, too, became impassable and
had to be abandoned in favour of yet another alignment or of the original.

Then, as now, roads could be legally moved. In July 1353, for
example, the king granted a licence to the abbot of Croxton, near
Leicester, which allowed him to move a section of Lancashire road for
housing development! That document is additionally interesting because
it gives information about the width of roads, indicating that, although
the dimensions of most routes varied widely in practice, there were
serious attempts to impose standards. It also confirms the emphasis put
on protection of 'right of way' in the medieval period. The abbot was
permitted to 'inclose a certain way which leads from the dwelling-place
of the vicar of the church of that town [Cockerham] to the dwelling
place of John le Marchal, for the enlargement of the latter's dwelling
place . . . on condition that the abbot shall cause to be made in the
place of the said way, a certain other way of the same length and
breadth for those passing through his ground there; the said way contains
in length 140 perches of land and in breadth 30 feet'.[1]

Other comparable developments, such as the building of a new
bridge to replace one further upstream, could divert a road, and often
part of a route could be left as a 'green track'. Such changes must have
happened many times and in many places, and as a consequence both
the positive identification and the dating of roads is fraught with

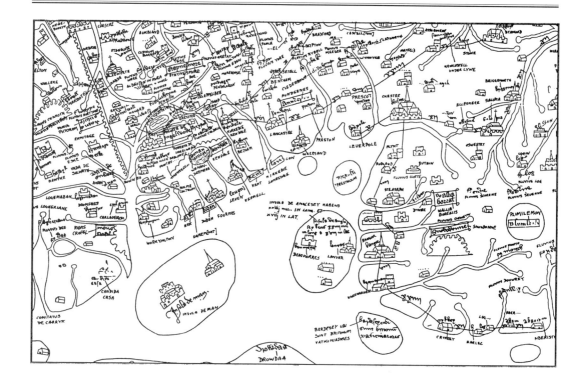

difficulties. What is certain, however, is that there was a complex and surprisingly sophisticated system of roads throughout the period under discussion, and that this did meet the needs of the Lancastrian population.[2] This was a population which, contrary to the very widely held popular belief, did travel frequently and often over long distances. Our forebears were far more mobile than is usually appreciated.

The major problem for the local historian is finding firm evidence for the roads and tracks on which the medieval inhabitants of the county moved. Such research has to rely a great deal on the evidence afforded by the cartularies (collections of deeds, charters and documents relating to grants of land) of the Lancashire monastic houses. Although by definition they are biased towards the holdings and activities of religious houses, these cartularies are invaluable because they actually state that certain roads existed at a particular date. The records of Cockersand Abbey, which had holdings in some forty separate places in Amounderness hundred, together with over eighty places south of the Ribble in Leyland, West Derby, Makerfield and Salford hundreds, have been particularly useful.[3]

Many early roads have, of course, continued in use to the present day, their earliest surfaces being masked or obliterated by centuries of repairs and by toppings of tarmac and concrete. Even the physical remains of those roads and tracks which went out of use as major

The so-called Gough Map was a road map of Britain drawn in the mid-fourteenth century showing major routes and significant places on them – particularly monastic houses, which were important stopping-places for travellers. In Lancashire it shows the road from Warrington through Preston to Lancaster, together with the Skipton to Kendal road, and it also depicts a number of monasteries and other towns such as Cockersand and Manchester.

routeways – and which are thus comparatively undamaged – are almost impossible to date, even if they survive as green tracks, sunken roads, or 'hollow-ways' eroded by traffic and rain water. Therefore the field evidence can be ambiguous and difficult to interpret with confidence, and one has to rely on other sources. For later centuries we have cartographic evidence, but there are no local maps for the medieval period. However, for medieval England as a whole there are a few maps.

The most important of these is the Gough Map, which was compiled in the mid-fourteenth century 'as an official map for government use, probably intended for use by royal couriers, royal officials and the judiciary, the people most likely to travel around the country as a whole'. In a recent article it was suggested that the roads shown on that map were in fact those former Roman roads which had continued in use into the medieval period.[4] The northern stretches of the road on the Gough Map which was identified by Parsons[5] as 'M4', linking London with Carlisle via Newcastle-under-Lyme, Warrington, Wigan, Preston, Lancaster, Kendal and Penrith, correlate well with a Roman route to the north identified by Margary and discussed in the previous chapter.[6]

One road on the map which did not receive detailed attention in the 1993 article was that shown as coming into Lancashire from Bristol, via Shrewsbury and Chester, to cross the Mersey to Liverpool.[7] It is likely that this was also a former Roman road. The crossing of the Mersey would have been by ferry. Bagley and Hodgkiss suggest that in the medieval period travellers would have been able to use the ferry operated by the monks of Birkenhead Priory and then 'as they did in later centuries, continue along the shore towards Crosby and then cut eastwards via Ormskirk and Burscough to Preston'.[8] Although superseded by other river crossings the memory of the route survives in the place-name Monks Ferry on the Wirral side of the river.

The early importance of the route from Liverpool to Preston via Ormskirk is supported by several documentary sources. Bagley and Hodgkiss quote a fourteenth-century reference to the *iter regale* – the king's highway – in Ormskirk, a reference, dated 1348, to the king's highway from Preston to Ormskirk, and a mid-thirteenth-century reference to *stratam ferratam* – the metalled road – at Hutton. In the cartulary of Burscough priory is a grant of land dated from between 1230 and 1260 referring to *regiam viam*, the king's highway, in Melling.[9]

References to the 'king's highway' do not, of course, indicate that any king had necessarily ridden over a road but, as Hindle notes,[10] 'such a name implies a certain degree of importance'. It is possible to provide additional evidence for this medieval route from Liverpool. Land in Melling granted to Cockersand Abbey[11] was said to lie 'between the highway [*inter magnam stratam*] and the boundary of Simonswood, which said road crosses Alt at the wath [ford] which is between Melling and Thorp'. Taken in conjunction with the reference to the *stratam ferratam* [12] in Hutton, which would seem to indicate a Roman road, and given that other roads on the Gough Map appear to be of Roman origin, it seems a possibility that the route north from Liverpool (roughly followed by the modern A59) falls into the same category. The presence or absence of Roman occupation in south-west Lancashire has long been a subject of debate – no significant Roman sites have been found, and the road map is a blank, but the question deserves further consideration.

Whether the 'metalled road' mentioned at Hutton went on to Preston, as part of the 'king's highway', or headed due north to cross the Ribble (or, indeed, whether both routes were used) is unclear. In an admittedly oblique reference to the existence of a crossing to Lea from Hutton at the beginning of the thirteenth century, the Cockersand cartulary refers to land in the townfields of Hutton 'lying on the marsh between the lands of the river-guide of Lea and the land of Abel'. [13] The income derived from this land was presumably used for the maintenance of the guide, and there may even have been a shelter there for the occasions when he was stranded 'at the wrong side' by the tide. [14] This river crossing, although recorded here in the early thirteenth century, is unlikely to have been a new venture at this date – the low-tide fords at Lea and lower down the river were very extensively used until the dredging of the channel in the 1880s destroyed them, and there can be little doubt that they had been known for thousands of years. They linked with routes using the Kirkham moraine and other low-level ridge routes in the Fylde, some of which had been in use since at least Roman times.

Another 'Roman' road, not shown on the Gough Map but which was unquestionably in use in the medieval period, is that from Ingleton to Wennington and the Lune valley. The county boundary on the Wennington-Ingleton road [15] would appear to be the *Ravencros* mentioned in Robert de Holand's inquest post mortem of 1323, [16] in which Edmund de Dacre was said to hold the manor of Heysham by the service of sounding his horn at Ravencrosse when the king came into Lancashire. Presumably this was a survival of the service owed by Vivian Gernet about a century earlier – he held two carucates of land in Heysham by 'the service of meeting the king at the bounds of the county with his horn and a white rod, and of leading him into the county and to be with him and to conduct him back again'. [17] The route which kings would take to enter the county from Yorkshire at Ravencrosse was the road which in 1293 was described as *regia via* and *regia strata*. [18] Because of the context of the references it can safely be identified as the Roman road [19] from Bainbridge over Cam Fell to Ingleton. The medieval evidence suggests that the extension of this Roman road from Ingleton via *Ravencros* and Wennington to the Lune valley continued in use as a true 'king's highway' for a long period.

In grants of lands in Stalmine-with-Staynall, north of the Wyre, there is a tantalising set of references which *might* indicate the presence of a putative Roman road. It is clear that the same route is being described in references which include mention of a 'stone bridge', and to the *magnam stratam*, *regiam viam*, *magnam stratam regiam* and (fortunately, since it allows the exact location to be pinpointed), to *stratam quae vocatur* [road which is called] *Alsergate*.[20] Alsergate has been identified as High Gate Lane, shown on modern maps, which bypasses the settlements of Staynall and Stalmine and takes a very direct route parallel to the Wyre northwards, heading for the coast, towards Preesall, where it now joins the main road.

This bypassing of settlements by a major road which could conceivably be of Roman origin, or by a 'king's highway', was far from unique to the Over Wyre district. The *stratam ferratam usque Cliderhow*[21] might have been expected to be the sole 'king's highway' in the Clitheroe area, but it apparently shared this status with another road on an almost parallel alignment less than a mile away. It linked the *caput* (head) of the medieval honour of Clitheroe, held by the de Lacy family, with their major administrative centre at Pontefract, via the trans-Pennine road system clearly shown on the Gough Map. However, the former Roman road probably failed to satisfy local administrative and economic requirements, and a second 'king's highway' developed to serve these needs. Whether this was a completely new road, or represented a change in status for a road already in existence, cannot now be ascertained. It is significant, though, that this was one of several routes – others of which were also designated 'king's highway' or 'king's causeway' – which appear to have focussed upon Whalley, which was the mother church of an extremely large ecclesiastical parish and so was a place of great importance in medieval east Lancashire.

The alignment of the alternative 'king's highway' runs along the lower northern slopes of Pendle. This road, like Alsergate, bypasses settlements – in this case Wiswell, Pendleton, Great and Little Mearley, Worston and Downham. They are located just off the line of the road. One alignment continues forward to join the Roman road, while another swings to the south, to curve round the 'Big End' of Pendle and enter the medieval Forest of Pendle at Annel Cross. All over the north-west there is a pattern whereby crosses were placed as markers at the points where a route passed into a forest.[22] At these crosses forest tolls such as *cheminage* were collected – this was levied on those who wished to pass through a forest with carriages, carts or pack-horses,

The ancient 'king's highway' from Whalley to Downham and beyond is marked today by a green lane and track which runs along the foot of Pendle. Here the lane is seen between Pendleton Hall Farm and Mearley; note the width of the highway and the very deep wide ditch to the left [north] side *(author)*.

Nearer to Mearley Hall the width of the road, here a true 'green lane', is still apparent, as are the substantial trees which line the route for most of its length. These include holly, which was much favoured for cattle fodder and is a characteristic of stock tracks such as this *(author)*.

the restrictions officially being applied during the 'Fence Month' or close month, when the deer were fawning and had to be disturbed as little as possible.

From Wiswell the route of the 'king's highway' is virtually that of the modern road to Pendleton but, as Pendleton village is approached, the modern road turns away sharply to the left into the settlement. Here a footpath marks the old line of the 'king's highway', which carries straight on across the field directly ahead. The ford across the Pendleton Brook can be identified, but recent encroachment (and slurry!) make the next section, round the back of the nineteenth-century All Saints' Church and modern housing, difficult to negotiate. Beyond the houses the route re-joins the present road as far as the road to the Nick of Pendle from Clitheroe. There is a right-of-way through

Beyond Mearley Hall the road enters a very impressive stretch of hollow way, cutting through the shoulder of a small stream valley *(author)*.

The landscape, and the nature of the road, change very noticeably east of Little Mearley Hall. The 'king's highway' emerges into an area of unfenced grassland, which place-name evidence suggests has been pasture for at least a thousand years *(author)*.

Pendleton Hall Farm (not on a medieval alignment) and once the final yard gate is cleared the road is very obvious, although its character changes several times in the next couple of miles. There are stretches of wide, banked track, often with holly in the hedges (hinting at stock movement[23]), a very impressive deep hollow-way for a short distance, and a section where the unfenced road crosses an area of open grazing which would appear to be of some antiquity, as the next farm which the highway bypasses has a most significant name – Angram Green, meaning 'at the pastures'.[24]

The farm road, now tarmac-surfaced, swings left to join the modern road from Worston to Downham, but here, too, the line of the medieval 'king's highway' is marked by a footpath which carries on in a direct line north-east of Angram Green before joining the modern road for a short distance. From here the alignment is less clear, but it is possible that the old road followed West Lane to within a short distance of Downham. As at Pendleton, the lane makes a sharp right-angled turn into the village, with the former alignment of the 'king's highway' continuing in a straight line towards a junction with the Pendle road, which is probably a much narrower road than it would have been in medieval times. This route has been described in some detail, to illustrate the way in which a major medieval road, now long forgotten, can survive as back roads, lanes and field paths – to trace such a route on the ground can offer a fascinating exercise in historical reconstruction. Throughout, the lack of settlements on the road is very marked. This could have been a distinct advantage, both to the inhabitants of the villages who may have thought, as Hindle [25] suggested of Roman roads, that 'those routes would only mean trouble', and also to those using the road, who would not want to be tangled up in the congestion of local traffic. The 'king's highways',

On the western approach to Worston the modern surfaced lane turns sharply to the left and heads for the village, while the ancient 'king's highway' continues – now only as a footpath – heading eastwards to Downham. Medieval main roads very frequently bypassed settlements in this fashion *(author)*.

whether former Roman roads or 'new' roads, would tend to be used for long-distance movement of people and goods.

Salt was an essential commodity, the carriage of which was important for many centuries. Taylor [26] considered that the term *saltway* was a useful indicator of long-distance routes in the Saxon period – and by implication in the Middle Ages as well. Hindle [27] rightly points out that the trade is so essential that it was certainly carried on long before, and salt routes may therefore be of great antiquity. Salt for use in medieval Lancashire would have been obtained from two sources – from salterns on the coast and from the major inland centres or *wiches* such as Northwich and Middlewich in Cheshire. It is likely that the *Saltersgate* mentioned in Withington *circa* 1184[28] was one of the routes used by salt traffic from Northwich into Lancashire, and it is known that Manchester market was a centre for the sale of Cheshire salt – in 1286 traders from Wakefield were buying salt there.[29] Other salt routes may be recognised by place-names such as Saltersford.

The Domesday record for Cheshire [30] gives a good account of what the traffic using the salt routes might have been like and, by inference, the character of the roads which were intended to take such traffic.

Whosoever carted purchased salt from these two *Wiches* [Northwich and

Middlewich] paid 4*d*. in toll if he had four or more oxen to his cart; if two oxen he paid 2*d*. toll . . . A man from another Hundred paid 2*d*. for a packhorse load but a man from the same Hundred paid only ½*d*. for a packload of salt . . . Men on foot from another hundred who bought salt there paid 2*d*. on 8 manloads; men of the same Hundred paid 1*d*. on 8 loads.

It can be seen that the salt-ways – which would, of course, have been used for other traffic as well – were, at least close to the production centres, expected to carry heavy cart traffic, packhorse trains, and laden men on foot. That hauliers have not changed much in a thousand years can be deduced from the subsequent clauses which state that

anyone who so overloaded a cart that the axle broke within one league of either *Wich* paid 2*s*. to the officer of the King or the Earl, if he could be caught within the league; similarly anyone who so overloaded a horse that it broke its back paid 2*s*., if caught within the league; beyond the league nothing . . . Anyone who made two packloads of salt out of one paid a fine of 40*s*. if the officer could catch him.[31]

There were many salterns where sea-salt was produced along the Lancashire coast – in Furness, the Warton area, Pilling and Preesall, Lytham and south of the Douglas. These, too, would have meant long overland journeys for many users. For example, Salley Abbey was granted *unam salinam* in Meols,[32] which would have involved a round trip of at least sixty miles to get the salt back to the monastery near Clitheroe. On the other hand, Salthouse in Dalton parish [33] may have been a saltern belonging to Furness Abbey and would have been quite conveniently placed. Although the existence of monastic salterns is easier to establish, others must have been in private hands and salt was traded on the open market. The de Lacy *compotus* [account] for 1305[34] includes an item of 7*s*. 9*d*. spent on 'salt bought for salting the game'.

It has often been suggested that the route from Hornby to Slaidburn via Roeburndale, known as the 'king's highway' from Lancaster to Clitheroe in the seventeenth century,[35] is a former salt route because of the 'Salter' farm names in Upper Roeburndale. However, the position of these farms within the medieval Roeburndale Forest is significant, when considered with local field names which indicate that the area around Salter was a deer-feeding 'station'.[36] 'Salter' also survives as a field name within Cawood Forest,[37] quite close to the boundaries of Locka, which in 1292 was a small park held by the abbot of Croxton.[38] This could suggest that an alternative and preferable derivation of 'salter' in these two instances might be found in *salterie* – a deer-leap.[39] Although the route is obviously an important and ancient one, and may well have been used by salt traders at some time, it must be accepted that the group of 'salter' names in

Roeburndale is unlikely to be the 'salt-way' indicator which it is popularly thought to be.

Many goods other than salt would of course be moving along Lancashire roads. Some would have been produced locally and would have been for local consumption, others were imported into the area, and Lancashire goods were sent to markets outside the county and even overseas. Goods constantly had to be moved to market or for other purposes: the service obligations of the people of Grindleton included the making of three cartings a year to their lord's estates at Pontefract.[40] Even van hire is nothing new, for one could hire a wain complete with drivers! For example, the abbot of Furness hired out one wain and two waggons to Thomas, earl of Lancaster, for twenty-eight weeks, the hirer apparently buying a new pair of wheels and tyres 'and other things'. The total cost of hire (including spares and replacements) was 75s. 2d.[41]

The de Lacy *compoti*, mentioned earlier, give examples of the goods, other than agricultural produce, which were being moved from the Clitheroe area. Some of them are rather unexpected.

Bringing 190 li [£] safely from Cliderhowe to Buckeby [near Daventry, Northamptonshire] and carrying money 5 times to Pontefract

Carrying letters to various places

Taking 400 marks to Pontefract at various times

Carrying a hind to Burton juxta Lincoln by precept of the Earl

Carrying alms cloth from Pontefract to Cliderhou

Carrying 3 stags and 12 does to Pontefract [presumably dead]

Carrying 7 loads of lead from Baxenden to Bradford

Expenses of 16 hawks at Clitheroe, and of grooms carrying them to London, with cocks bought for them [as snacks on the journey?]

Carrying the Earl's bed to Denbigh

Although these examples are taken from the accounts of only one estate, they are probably representative of the period. Too often our ideas about the difficulties of travel in the past are culled from what might be termed the 'popular press', which then, as now, tended to deal with the unusual and the dramatic rather than the more commonplace and routine. The case of the glover from Leighton Buzzard who, together with his horse laden with panniers full of gloves, drowned in a large hole in a road near Aylesbury was quoted by Hadow[42] as illustrating the generally poor state of medieval roads. The hole, ten feet wide, eight feet broad and eight feet deep, was allegedly dug by two servants of a local miller, who needed the clay for mill repairs!

However, the glover had gone with his wares to Aylesbury for the market, held there before Christmas Day. This was a distance of eleven miles, and he was returning home in the dusk. Some things do not quite add up – either the servants were exceedingly quick workers to have dug a such a huge hole in the limited daylight around Christmas (after the glover had passed by in the morning) or the size was exaggerated. Surely the glover would have noticed this great pit on his return – or had his Christmas festivities started rather too early? If road conditions were so universally bad, as is alleged, why did he – or anyone else – even contemplate a round trip of over twenty miles to attend a market? Despite stories such as this, the weight of the evidence points to the conclusion that conditions, although not especially good, were probably acceptable most of the time.

This view is reinforced by the fact that winter travel was quite common. The royal household travelled regularly in the winter, and expected its subjects to do likewise. Two orders sent to the abbot of Salley help to illustrate this.[43]

> 30 December 1299 To the Abbot of Sallay: Order to send to the chancery at York a strong horse by one of his men before 14 January next, as the king much needed a good and strong horse to carry the rolls of chancery

> 3 November 1304 To Sallay: The war of Scotland having come to an end, the king willed that the exchequer should be transferred to Westminster, and as it was necessary that he should have horses and carts with their harness for the carriage of his treasure thither, he ordered and requested them to aid him with a cart with four horses and their harness and with two men to take the cart thither at the king's expenses and to bring it back again, so that they should be at York at the latest on Friday before St Nicholas next [6 December]

A more general picture of the commodities which might have been moving around in the first half of the fourteenth century may be found in a list of goods on which pontage [a bridge toll] was authorised for two years at Edisford near Clitheroe.[44] The bridge there had been damaged in floods, and letters patent were obtained from the king permitting the collection of tolls to pay for its repair. The list is so comprehensive that it must have been a standard one, used whenever a grant of pontage was made. The grant illustrates the importance attached to the crossing points of rivers in the medieval period. That this was not a new phenomenon can be seen from the suite of words which were used with great precision, in the pre-Conquest period, to describe types of crossing. Besides the OE *ford* and its ON counterpart *wath* (which frequently seems to have been applied to fords where Roman roads crossed), names with OE *staep* (step or stepping-stones) point to places where foot-travellers could cross safely. Bridges were of various kinds. A *plat*-bridge was made of laths or flat planks; a *stoc*-bridge was of wood; and a *spenne*-bridge was one which spanned – probably a small footbridge.

A type found in several Lancashire place-names and in medieval documentary sources is the *hrisen*-bridge. This was one made of brushwood or, alternatively, was a causeway through marshy ground. The *Risegreve* [brushwood-grove] next to a road in Staynall may have been a place where brushwood was deliberately cultivated for use as road material.[45] Rising Bridge, near Haslingden, is probably an instance where the term was applied to a causeway through marshy ground. At this point Black Lane leaves the 'king's highway' just south of Stone Fold and crosses the valley in the direction of Moor Lane, south east of Friar Hill. The valley at this point may well have been very wet – hence, perhaps, Black Lane – and so a causeway was required. It is probably significant that the route described as the 'king's highway' takes a consistent line well above the valley floor for much of its length between Huncoat and Rossendale,[46] between 900 and 1000 feet above sea level – it was easier to keep to one high-level route than to descend to wet and ill-drained valleys.

The 'Risen-bridge' mentioned in Cockersand charters for both Wrightington and the adjacent vill of Parbold may have been a brushwood bridge, possibly over a boundary stream. The relevant section of the Wrightington document states that the boundary runs 'up that clough between Robert's house and Hugh's land unto Risen-bridge, now across Vivenhac [Vivian oak?]',[47] while that for Parbold describes it 'from the Risen-bridge going down the Wain-gate to land of St John [of Jerusalem], following that land to the syke which is the boundary of the land of Robert de Linleys, and so going up that syke to Risen-bridge again'.

Few medieval bridges survive in Lancashire, because the road network of the county has undergone such immense changes in subsequent centuries. As the next chapter shows, already by the sixteenth century there was strong pressure for older wooden bridges to be rebuilt in stone, a process which was well under way by the mid-seventeenth century. Thereafter the growing traffic burdens imposed by urbanisation and industrialisation meant that older bridges were quite inadequate. There was extensive new construction in the eighteenth and nineteenth centuries – on main roads the turnpike trusts were active in this area and from the late eighteenth century the county bridgemasters pursued a policy of reconstructing older bridges. As a result the historic county has an exceptionally fine series of bridges from 1700 onwards, but good medieval examples are scarce.

The first reference to a bridge at Lancaster, on the key crossing of

In the late nineteenth century building work close to Manchester cathedral revealed the very well-preserved remains of the medieval Hanging Bridge, which had crossed the ravine known as Hanging Ditch to link the parish church with the market place. The bridge was excavated and consolidated, and these drawings, made in the 1880s, show its elevation and details of the plan *(from T.L.C.A.S. vol.8 (1890), p. 96).*

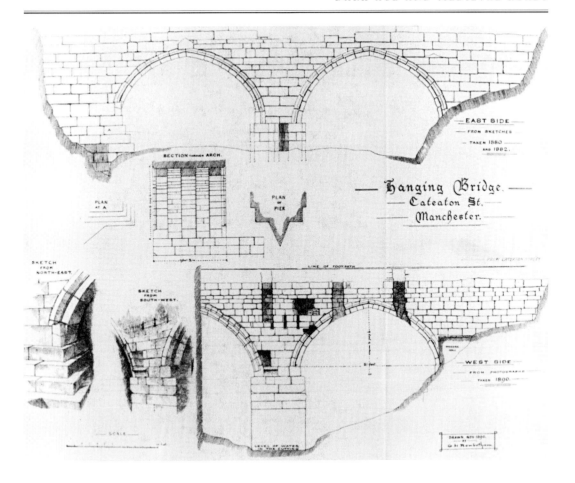

the Lune, dates from 1215, when timber was granted by King John for the repair of the adjacent fish-weir. The bridge itself was also of timber and – not unexpectedly in view of the heavy traffic and the strength of the river and estuarial currents – it required constant maintenance. In the fifteenth century it was replaced by a four-arched stone bridge, described in 1634 as 'a fayre, lofty, long archt' structure. The medieval bridge was demolished in the nineteenth century, although traces of its foundations survive.[48]

One of the most remarkable, and least known, of the surviving medieval bridges is the Hanging Bridge, which linked Manchester parish church and town centre with the market place and the road to Chester, across what had been the deep defensive ravine of Hanging Ditch. The fourteenth-century bridge, which had two main arches, was eventually buried beneath rubble and buildings as the ravine was filled in – it was partially uncovered in the late nineteenth century, and part of it can be seen, amid a sorry mess of rubbish and litter, just south of the cathedral.[49]

The 'Risen-bridge' between Wrightington and Parbold, referred to above, linked two sections of a wain-gate, a term used to describe a road capable of use by heavy carts. This might seem to imply a former Roman road – since these would clearly be of strong construction – but in fact many medieval roads were perfectly capable of carrying heavy traffic. There is, for example, a reference in documents relating to Clayton-le-Woods which shows that the 'king's highway' (*regia strata*) and the *Weingate* were two quite separate roads.[50]

In the Norman period the need to control routeways and river crossings was clearly understood and the disposition of mottes (earthen castle mounds) built in Lancashire by William I clearly shows his understanding of this strategic requirement.[51] Thus the motte at Penwortham, which still survives, and its now-vanished twin at Tulketh on the north bank of the Ribble, commanded a series of convenient fords on an old north–south routeway which ran from Cadley in Fulwood, south towards Hutton and Farington – a 'Preston western bypass' of the pre-Conquest period. The deeply-cut hollow-way by which this track descended to the ford can still be seen alongside St Mary's Church in Penwortham, even though the ford itself now lies deep beneath the Preston dockland.[52]

The Hanging Bridge, shown here in a drawing made not long after its discovery, can still be seen just south-west of the cathedral, though today it is again almost buried – in litter, debris and abandoned furniture (*from* T.L.C.A.S. *vol. 8 (1890), p. 107*).

Travellers of all kinds would need to know where fords and bridges were. The Gough Map shows clearly all the major rivers – even if they are all depicted as issuing from large lakes! Some people regularly made long business journeys: the seneschal of the honour of Clitheroe, for example, claimed expenses for visits made to Denbigh, York and London while looking after the earl of Lincoln's affairs [53] and the major roads, such as those shown by Gough, would have been used for these. There were, however, countless other journeys made regularly during the course of local business, commerce or pleasure. The mobility of medieval man should not be under-estimated. Just as the seneschal visited the estate centres at Pontefract and Denbigh, so the local people would be required to visit the *caput* of the local estate, to render service dues, pay rents and attend courts.

Within each secular lordship there would have been a cornmill (and possibly a fulling mill) and the inhabitants would have had no alternative but to use its facilities. The road to the mill was one with which every community would be familiar – not least because re-pairing the road was likely to be one of its feudal obligations – and its importance is often reflected in modern street names. In the very heart of Manchester the name Long Millgate reminds us of the road which led from the great market place, past the parish church – now the cathedral – and the manor house (today miraculously preserved as the great hall of Chetham's Hospital) to the town mills on the river Irk. The mills themselves are long gone and their site lies under Victoria Station, but the name of the street and its winding course, recall a medieval road of fundamental importance to the townspeople.

The road to the church was another highway with a real and a symbolic significance. Regular journeys to church were part of the weekly and yearly round of activities, and processions for baptisms, marriages and burials were part of the cycle of life. Examples of church roads have already been mentioned in the discussion of highways leading to the pre-Conquest ecclesiastical centre of Whalley, but there are numerous other instances. There was a great road [*magna via*] running between Rawcliffe and the church of St Michael on Wyre.[54] All across the county were routes such as this. There was a Kirk Lane in Melling near Ormskirk.[55] The boundaries of land in Pennington [Salford hundred] granted in 1246 were defined in part by the access route to the parish church at Leigh: 'from Oldmiln-ford going up to the road which comes from Bedford, following that road towards the church to a certain ditched place'.[56] All churches extant in the medieval period would have been the focus of a network of roads and tracks.

Roads to markets were, of course, of fundamental importance to trade and commerce, and to all agricultural communities. If the list of goods on which tolls were payable at Edisford Bridge in 1339 is analysed (Table 1) the great range and variety of commodities which were regularly transported is easily appreciated. The dense network of small lanes and tracks surrounding, and focusing on, the Chipping area still testifies to its importance as a local retail centre in pre-Conquest times – the name means 'market'. In the post-Conquest period there was a formalisation of trade to maximise the profits which the lay and monastic lords could obtain from their lands and charters were obtained for boroughs, markets and fairs. Although these had differing functions, a good communications network was necessary for each to survive and thrive. There appear to have been between fifty and sixty boroughs and markets in medieval Lancashire,[57] each serving a hinterland of some five miles radius, the distance which could be walked to or from the market centre in a day, allowing time for trading, for droving of animals if necessary and for the return journey. However, the major centres, such as Lancaster, drew custom from further afield and Crosby[58] has demonstrated both the influence which Preston exerted and the effect the road network apparently had on this in the fourteenth century.

Many medieval roads were well-used by wheeled vehicles, and it is misleading to suppose that all were narrow and winding; in the twentieth century many lanes which are now no longer maintained for this purpose have become overgrown and reduced in width, and are now merely footpaths. This view shows the medieval hollow way known as Written Stone Lane, on the slopes of Longridge Fell; among its uses was the hauling of stone from the small quarries on the fellside (John Whiteley).

Table 1:
Analysis of Goods on which tolls were payable at Edisford Bridge, Clitheroe, in 1339

a) Foodstuffs – produced locally
   ale, bacon, barley, beans, butter, corn, cheese, flour, honey, oats, onions, peas, fresh salmon
b) Foodstuffs – probably imported
   almonds, cumin, figs, garlic, oil, pepper, raisins, wine
c) Foodstuffs – from the coast
   herrings, salt, sea fish, lampreys
d) Animals
   horse, mare, ox, cow, sheep, swine, goat
e) Animal products
   hides, fleeces, grease, tallow, skins of lambs, rabbits and hares, Cordova shoe leather
f) Textiles and materials
   wool, linen web of canvas, whole cloth, for textile processing, alum, woad, hemp, teasels, cloths of Galway, Man and Ireland, worsteds
g) Metals and metal products
   lead, steel by the sheaf, copper, roof nails, horseshoe and cart nails, all other sorts of nails
h) Miscellaneous items
   wax, grindstones, tan (bark), caldron and lead for brewing

Fairs were often held on the patronal festival of the local church.

For example, Margaret de Nevill produced a special writ from the king to support her claim to hold a fair at Hornby on the vigil, feast and morrow of St Margaret the Virgin – that is, 19–21 July annually.[59] Although no doubt attractive to people in the middle Lune valley, this was not one of the great fairs which drew people and goods from a very wide area. It certainly did not match such great events as the fair of St Egidius [St Giles] at Pontefract, which began on 1 September and lasted eight days.[60] At the Pontefract fair, in 1296/7, the Lancashire officers of the earl of Lincoln sold some of his stock – probably old cows and other cattle surplus to requirements, and not a complete autumn cull as is often believed.[61] It was by the cross-Pennine links represented by this fair, and the strong Pontefract connection which the Clitheroe area enjoyed, that the Robin Hood legend was transmitted to Lancashire and transmuted here – it was not only goods which travelled by road, but stories, news and popular culture as well.[62]

Documentary evidence shows that cattle from east Lancashire travelled much further than Pontefract. It is on record that sixteen old cows were 'sent to the Queen's larder at Rising [Castle Rising, Norfolk]' together with seventy-four oxen 'each sent to Rising for the larder' from the *vaccaria* [cattle-farms] of Queen Isabella in the Forest of Pendle in 1341.[63] It must be assumed that these animals were walked down to Castle Rising to be butchered there. The accounts of the Pendle *vaccaria* have amounts credited for the animals which were sent, however, and for the value of the 'empties' – the hides!

To allow surplus agricultural produce to arrive at the markets of Lancashire and further afield, the predominantly agricultural county had an intricate network of roads and tracks – the rural road network, the descendant of which we see today in the lanes and paths of our countryside. It is possible to identify some elements of the medieval network from the place-names which were used to describe them. Words which to us in the twentieth century have little specific meaning would not have been used loosely in the pre-Conquest or medieval periods: they were precise technical terms for individual features. For example, medieval people knew exactly what a *stig* was, and what to expect when they came to one. In the north of England a *stig* was often 'a narrow [climbing] path'[64]: the Hunter's Sty in Claughton[65] was close to Claughton Hurst (*hyrst* – a wooded hill) – just the place for a narrow path climbing uphill, with game for the hunter.

There must have been a road which led out from enclosed land into open country at Lydiate, for this distinctive place-name is from the OE *hlidgeat*, a swing-gate. As the settlement of Lydiate, in Halsall parish, was mentioned in Domesday, the track which led out from the enclosed lands around the village onto the open grazings must be an ancient one. Here, as doubtless in all occurrences of the 'Lydiate' name, the gate would have been there to prevent the stock from the moor grazings doubling-back down the track and getting into the crop fields or hay meadows, where the beasts could wreak havoc. Access for stock movements to moor, hill and moss grazings, or to the woods for pannage [grazing in the underwood], was an integral part of the medieval economy, and this is reflected in the number of tracks and roads which were available for this purpose.

In the areas of the county where the topography might be described as one of 'low relief', such roads and tracks are often referred to as 'Houtlone'[66] or 'Outlane'.[67] The term *hraca* – cattle or sheep walk (rake) – is usually applied to the steep track which the animals used to reach the hill grazings, and the terms 'Rake Head' and 'Rake Foot' are very common Lancashire place-names. Rakehead, at Stacksteads in the Rossendale valley, is just one example. A typical 'rake' gave its name to an inn at the foot of a hill on an old road out of Littleborough and this is now the proud possessor of a pub sign showing a man clutching a hay rake – such terminological misunderstandings would not have happened in the medieval period. The 'high road in the Rakes' in Longworth, near Bolton[68] was in hilly country where a rake would be very characteristic. This makes the mention of 'Hutrakes' [out-rakes] in Staynall[69] seem rather surprising, but in this area of low relief even a small elevation would be given greater status than it would warrant elsewhere – the farm name Height o' th' Hill near Stalmine Grange, at all of 50 feet above sea level, testifies to this.

Where communities had rights of turbary – that is, the right to cut peat or turf in the summer to dry for winter fuel – there was a need for a track to the turbaries on the moss or moor. On Parlick near Chipping, and in other upland areas, the track often took the form of a steep incline down which turf sleds could be lowered to more level ground below. In flatter areas, such as the Fylde, cart roads were often used, as these would make movement of heavy loads of turves easier. The 'waingate' which went 'towards the moss' in Stalmine was probably used for turf-carrying.[70] In Greenhalgh, too, it was possible to get 'to the Whinnyhowe Turbary on the road' and go 'up from Medlar to the turf pits on the moor' by road.[71]

These turf roads were usually carefully defined, and in areas where several townships shared a common mossland the routes by which the people of each could cross the moss were jealously guarded. In 1527 the Duchy Court heard a case in which the abbot of Whalley and his tenant, Robert Heyton, sued Sir Thomas Langton. It was stated that for many generations Heyton and his ancestors, who lived in Walton-le-Dale, had 'taken turves for ffewell' in Penwortham Moss, and that to reach the moss they had used a specified common right of way through Walton. This had now been stopped up by Langton, without leave. The dispute dragged on, without result, until the Dissolution put an end to the abbey itself.[72] It is, however, unlikely that the *Timber-gate* road in Claughton-on-Brock was used for material for fuel.[73] Indeed, the cutting of timber (in contrast to the taking of fallen wood, the right of estovers) was the prerogative of the lord of the manor, whether lay or ecclesiastical, so the specialist use commemorated in this particular road-name would not have been one which involved the community at large.

In all communities there was a network of tracks round those fields used for crop-growing and hay. Unlike the stock-tracks and the turf roads, these seldom have names which allow them to be identified – but their existence is made plain by hundreds of references in medieval deeds, because it was these roads which served as the landmarks by which the boundaries of property holdings were described. For example, certain arable strips [selions] in Thistleton were said to be 'on the road leading to Singleton', and the boundaries of land in the town-field of Hutton included the *Meingate* – a shared road.[74]

In about 1213 certain lands in Ainsdale were said to 'extend to Westgate' and to lie between 'two roads in the northern part of Atefield', with a butt 'on the south side of Halsteadhow, whereof the eastern head extends to the road'. There is also a reference in the same document to two oxgangs in Scartherwolmer, in Waingate.[75] Even if the two roads in the Atefield were Westgate and Waingate, which seems very unlikely, Ainsdale had at least two roads of reasonable status. That such roads were often substantial is indicated by a deed in the Burscough cartulary, dated between 1258 and 1292, which refers to 'the road along which the prior and canons were accustomed to go . . . with their waggons and carts and beasts and men leading them, for the carriage and removal of their tithes of all kinds of grains'.[76]

The impression obtained from the documentary evidence is that much of Lancashire was well-served with roads and tracks which met the needs of the local population. The network was not static and unchanging: as economic and social circumstances changed, the road pattern appears to have altered. Probably the greatest influence for change was the granting of lands to monastic houses. The Cistercian and Premonstratensian orders were supposed to accept land only if it lay within one day's journey of their abbey, but this rule was swiftly overlooked and it certainly did not appertain in Lancashire. Furness Abbey, for example, had extensive holdings in Cumberland; at Ingleton, Newby, Horton, Clapham and Winterburn in Yorkshire; and, of course, in Furness itself. As has been demonstrated, Cockersand held lands all over the county, and even small and impoverished Burscough had properties as far afield as Bury and Ellel.

The abbeys and priories were therefore important users of the already-established major road network, both within and outwith Lancashire. In the case of the great and immensely wealthy abbey of Furness, monastic herds and flocks would have been moved around the countryside from *vaccaria* and *bercaria* (sheep farms) in the Lake District and the Ingleton area, and it has been suggested that the monastic wool clip may have been brought from the sheep shearing stations to the abbey wool-shed (*lanaria*) in sacks by packhorse. There it was cleaned, sorted and re-packed in sacks, and sewn up into canvas containers weighing, when full, over three hundredweights. These would then have been loaded on carts if the wool was being sold and the already established network of 'king's highways' was used for the journeys across country.

The religious houses not only needed to keep in touch with their own rather far-flung estates, but also maintained contact with other houses of the same order in this country and abroad. They also had regular and important dealings with merchants abroad: Furness had contacts with, for example, merchants in St Omer (1212) and Florence (1294).[77] The network of major cross-country roads was normally used for the delivery of the wool to the port for trans-shipment overseas. Only certain ports were licensed for such exports, in general those which were convenient for the buyer being the ones used.[78] This was not the hardship it might seem, for most monastic houses had been granted important toll exemptions and so road transport was less expensive than it might have been. Furness maintained a 'chain of stations' at which the journey could be broken, including a house at York (*a regia strata de Skeldergate ante usque ad aquam de Ouse retro*), between the abbey and the port of Boston.[79] Beverley was another destination for Furness wool, but whether it was to be exported from there, or used for the woollen textile industry in Beverley itself is not clear.

Efficient agricultural exploitation of the estates, large and small, which the monastic houses had been granted within Lancashire have also affected their requirements for roads. These existing routes would have been adequate for local people but they would not necessarily serve the needs of the monastic community. Not only were there potential problems of access, but contact between the religious community and the lay population may have seemed undesirable. This was partly the reason why the monks liked to acquire their own mills – they could work more quickly and return to their real work of prayer and would not meet local people, including women, at the mills and be led astray. The construction of new or improved roads was sometimes negotiated when grants of land were being made. For example, Lady Christiana de Lindsay made a composition in 1320 with the abbey and convent of St Mary de Pré, of Leicester, respecting common of pasture in Wyresdale and, as part of the final agreement, it was stated that 'the driving ways and roads to the said pasturage, which are of insufficient width, shall straightway be increased to the width of sixty feet'.[80] The definition of the minimum width of stock tracks in this and the next example is an indicator of the importance of the availability of herbage along the wayside as animals were being moved:

> the said John [the tailor, of Kirkland near Garstang] further granted to the said abbot and convent a competent road [*viam competentem*] through Kirkland Wood to Fildyngford and thence in a straight line to Pilling Moss, five perches wide, for driving and re-driving their beasts and fetching and carrying their turves and other necessaries, and a further good and sufficient road from their manor and church of St Ellen of Garstang to the said improvement at Hallhurst and elsewhere, for the carriage of dead wood to their said manor.[81]

The reference to 'Fildyngford' is interesting, suggesting that this was the point where an extension of the road called *Fildingate* which is recorded further north, in Ashton township,[82] crossed an important ford in the vicinity of Kirkland wood. The presence of these two names gives an insight into the medieval landscape of the area. There is a similar name in Bolton-by-Bowland, *Fildingate*, and both mean 'the road through open country'. The name is also found elsewhere in the country, as at Fieldon Bridge in Warwickshire – the bridge in or leading to open country.[83] The area between Ashton and Kirkland must have been an unenclosed and open landscape, characteristic of the lower parts of the Amounderness plain: the alternative name for the district, which has now become generally used, was the Fylde, which is derived from the same source. *Fildingweynegate* in Eccleston near Leyland is a similar name.[84]

That neither *Fildingweynegate* in Eccleston nor *Fildingate* in Ashton appears to be the same as the former Roman road (Parsons 'M4') suggests that here, as at Clitheroe, there was an alternative stretch of 'heavy duty' road running on an almost parallel alignment: such parallel routes have been noted in several examples above. Some of the earliest Lancashire maps, made during Elizabeth's reign, reveal this same phenomenon, and it is quite clear that when mapped they were already ancient. The Farington Collection at the Lancashire Record Office includes a fine plan of part of Penwortham, drawn in about 1590 as evidence during a boundary dispute. Between Tardy Gate and the river Ribble it shows the present main road from Preston to Leyland, the B5254 Leyland Road, as a broad band labelled 'the waines waie to penwortham'. Parallel with it, and just to the west, is 'the cawsey or horsewaye to Preston'. The latter crossed the open moss and was much narrower – on the tithe map of 1840 its memory survived in the names such as Padway (pathway) Field, although as a right of way it had disappeared. In 1837 part of this medieval causeway was unearthed at Marshall's Brow, Middleforth, and was described as 'a compact pavement of blue Boulder stones . . . about four feet wide'.[85]

The dead wood which was allowed to the monks of Cockersand by John the Tailor of Garstang would have been used as fuel: because of its exposed position Cockersand must have had an insatiable demand for turf and timber. Elsewhere in the district turbary and timber rights were exercised by the abbey: William le Boteler, for example, gave a grant of 'sufficient peat moss from the great moss of Marton for graving [digging] and drying their peats, for fuel for their Grange of Trefield, and *an adequate road for drawing the same from the moss to the said Grange with wagons [sic] and carts*'.[86] Here there is possible evidence for the construction of a new road.

Any discussion of Lancashire roads must include those which Hindle[87] categorises as unusual roads, such as the sands routes where travellers commonly left *terra firma* and travelled across bays and estuaries to save time. The savings could be considerable: according to a milestone in the centre of Cartmel the distance to Lancaster over sands would be 15 miles, whereas by modern road it would be 25 miles. To cross the Ribble from Lea to Hutton would involve only a quarter of the distance of the road via Preston.

As with this crossing of the Ribble, guides were essential for any journey across Morecambe Bay with its treacherous, shifting sands and even with guides the journeys could be hazardous. The abbot of Furness, in support of a petition in 1325 'for he and his successors to have a coroner in their lands and fees of Furneys ' stated that 'in crossing over the sands between the parts of Furneys and the town of Lancaster at the ebb of the sea many men of the parts of Furneys in making the crossing towards that town and thence returning oft times past have stood in danger in that crossing by such cause'.[88]

This was a long-standing problem: in 1246/7, for example, Gilbert of Ulverston was drowned from a horse on the sea beach – the horse was drowned with him – and Ivo, a lay brother of Furness, was drowned from a horse in Leven water.[89] An inquest at Lancaster agreed that it would be 'to the great alleviation and safeguard of the people' if the abbot of Furness and his successors could have their own coroner. The duties of a medieval coroner were very much the same as those of his modern successors – to hold inquests on the dead – and just how this would have safeguarded the living travellers crossing those hazardous sands is something of a mystery! Nevertheless, despite the perils, the sands route remained attractive as a short cut and was well-used throughout the medieval period.

The routes in the vicinity of Morecambe Bay are well attested, but the existence of an over-sands way across the estuary of the Cocker is not as familiar. The grant which mentions this route specifically notes that 'beasts should pass over the sands in summer time, or when they had need or desire, to Cocker [from Pilling or Preesall]'.[90] This could either imply that it was a particularly difficult crossing in winter or – more probably – that this was the most likely time for animals to be moving between the home farm and the abbey's out-pastures, such as the ones discussed earlier in Garstang and elsewhere in Wyresdale.

Hindle does not mention the shore routes, which were commonly used in Lancashire because they were often faster, more convenient and more direct between coastal locations: the use of the shore between Liverpool and Crosby has already been mentioned. If the route used by the monks of Cockersand to reach their grange at Stalmine is traced it can be seen that a shore-line section is an integral part: 'when they had need or desired to do so, their carts should pass and repass without let from henceforth *by the sands below the bank*, and by Hackensall Knot to his mill (a tide-mill belonging to Geoffrey de Hackensall[91]) and so to the highway'.[92]

Provided that weather and tides were favourable, the route would take the monks and their carts westwards from the Cocker crossing along the shore towards Knott End and then 'by Hackensall Knot' – that is, due south under the cliff of the Knot below Hackensall Hall, leaving the shore close to SD 346467. From here a route past Breckells (SD 355466) called 'the Monk's Lane' – clearly named and shown as a track on the 1st edition OS 6-inch map but now reduced to a single field boundary for part of the way to Higher Lickow (SD 360463) – would take them to the highway called Alsergate discussed earlier. From here it would have been a short journey to Grange Lane and Stalmine Grange. Note that the shore route was not used only for foot and horse traffic – carts, too, could use the beach as a roadway.

The documentary evidence examined has demonstrated that even in those parts of the county such as Over Wyre, where travelling is often supposed to have been difficult and road provision rudimentary in the past, there was apparently a sophisticated and complex road network serving the needs of the local population and of longer-distance traffic as early as the thirteenth century. There is no reason to believe that the rest of the county was any less well provided with roads – indeed, in some parts of south and central Lancashire the density of roads in the medieval period is likely to have been much greater than in Over Wyre.

Then, as now, there was a hierarchy of roads for different purposes, and these were clearly understood and managed and defined accordingly. At the lowest level there were the roads and tracks within settlements, the lanes and weinds among the houses and buildings. There were the tracks leading out to the fields and the stock tracks which extended long distances to the open grazings. The mills, the churches, the markets and the local administrative centres were served by a road network which was vital to trade, commerce, government and spiritual life. The trunk routes were the 'king's highways', the top-class roads which were often, but not always, former Roman roads. Alongside these – often literally – were frequently to be found wain-gates, the lorry routes of the medieval period, capable of coping with heavy traffic but without the high status traffic which used the 'king's highways'.

John of Gaunt, when visiting Ightenhill near Burnley (probably to check on his *equicium* or stud there, rather than for the hunting as Goodman suggests[93]) would have used the 'king's highway', not a wain-gate. The county was linked with the rest of the country by a series of long-distance routeways, which in the medieval period in east and central Lancashire tended to emphasise trans-Pennine connections with Yorkshire rather than routes to the south. New roads and re-alignments of existing roads were developing not only by 'organic' means but also by the deliberate decision-making of manorial and monastic lords. The long-established framework of key roads, which had its roots certainly in the Roman period, gave Lancashire a sound basis for the development of its future road pattern, but we should not minimise the contribution which was made by medieval Lancastrians, or underestimate the scale, significance and importance of their roads and road traffic.

3

Roads of county, hundred and township, 1550–1850

Dᴜʀɪɴɢ the sixteenth and seventeenth centuries the development, and to some extent the upgrading, of the Lancashire road network proceeded apace. This was a period of major change in the economy and society of a county which saw significant industrialisation and urban growth. Coalmining in the Wigan area, Rossendale and the Manchester region, and engineering and metal-working in Wigan and Makerfield, began to develop on a larger scale, while in south-east Lancashire textiles were of ever-increasing significance.[1] The port and town of Liverpool became much busier as the silting of the Dee and the increasing size of vessels forced shipping to abandon the port of Chester. In most parts of Lancashire the population grew rapidly throughout the sixteenth and seventeenth centuries, so that there was a rising demand for building materials, fuel, foodstuffs and consumer goods – some supplied from local sources, others brought from further afield. Town growth was also rapid, and the formerly rural county was becoming increasingly urbanised. The booming, sprawling expansion of Manchester, Bolton, Rochdale, Liverpool and a host of other towns was under way well before the mid-eighteenth century.[2]

All these changes and developments had an immediate impact upon the road network, which was used by a rapidly growing volume of traffic and was of crucial importance to the expansion of the new industries. There were no canals, no railways, and only the most limited opportunities for river navigation, so growth in imports and exports, movements of coal and manufactured goods and the supplies destined for markets, and the increasing quantity of inter-urban business and commercial passenger traffic were entirely dependent upon the road network.

Against this local background – a road system of ever greater significance in the commercial life of a fast-growing and increasingly prosperous county – may be set another major development, one which was national in its impact. This was the gradual transition from an entirely arbitrary and voluntary arrangement for road and bridge maintenance to a system which had a rudimentary statutory basis, in which local communities acquired important responsibilities for the financing and upkeep of the road network. In many respects the procedures remained fickle and frail and lacked uniformity, and there was much scope for the evasion of responsibilities both by the authorities and the individuals concerned, but by 1700 a basic pattern was in place. As the population grew and the economy expanded this came under ever-greater pressure, but nevertheless the system operated until the late nineteenth century.

RESPONSIBILITY FOR HIGHWAYS

In the medieval period the maintenance of highways had been essentially a manorial responsibility. Manor courts were nominally in a position to supervise the repair and improvement of roads within their area and to enforce action on the part of tenants and manorial freeholders. In practice this was often an ineffective procedure, not least because a manor was not necessarily a coherent block of territory – it could consist of widely scattered pieces of land linked only by their ownership. The ability of manor courts to enforce their decisions and the vigour with which individual courts pursued the goal of highway repair, were also variable. Generally, too, the only matters of concern were of entirely local interest – an awkward pothole or an overflowing ditch – and there was no feeling that the roads were part of a greater highway network.

The Statute of Winchester of 1285 had recognised the manor as the unit for highway administration and had given specific responsibilities to the constable (an office which was originally a manorial appointment). Some historians have considered that the manorial system worked tolerably well, but others have argued that increasing traffic – and especially the growth of wheeled traffic – in the fifteenth and early sixteenth centuries rendered it quite inadequate. Another factor in the near-collapse of efforts to maintain highways was the dissolution of the monasteries. As Mary Higham notes in the previous chapter, the religious houses were major generators of traffic and, as large commercial enterprises, had an interest in keeping roads up to standard. The major monasteries were important contributors to bridge repair and construction, and they gave valuable financial support and manpower for road work. Their disappearance in the late 1530s undoubtedly threw a substantial additional burden onto the creaking manorial system and increased the pressure for a more coherent and effective arrangement to be devised.

The government of Mary I eventually took action and in 1555 the Highways Act was passed, to give – for the first time – a reasonably clear and coherent statutory basis for highway work. The 1555 Act remained the basis of highway law and practice for almost 300 years, although it was eventually paralleled by the legislation governing the turnpike network and by various *ad hoc* local practices. Under the Act the responsibility for highways and their maintenance was transferred from the manorial courts to the parish or (as in Lancashire) the township. In other words, roads became a public, not a private, responsibility: although many manor courts continued to tinker with highway matters, thereafter the burden of administration and supervision was in large measure laid upon the shoulders of public officials, while the financial burden was borne by the ratepayer.

The choice of the township or parish as the administrative unit was innovative. There was no existing system of local government which could be given the new powers and duties, since local administration as we understand it scarcely existed. Instead, the 1555 Act was one of the pioneering developments in the creation of such a system, and its significance extends well beyond highways alone.[3] The townships had no paid officials of any sort so their work was to be entirely by communal effort. A crucial section of the Act required that all occupiers of ploughland, and every person who kept a plough and a ploughteam of horses within a township, was to provide a cart, a horse and the labour of two men, for four days each year. The horse and cart were intended for the transporting of highway materials, while servants or farm labourers working for the landowner or occupier would provide the manpower. All other householders, cottagers or labourers were to provide four days' labour, or to send a substitute by their own arrangements. Under legislation later in the sixteenth century the period of four days was increased to six.

The work of the 'volunteer' highway labourers was overseen by the surveyor of the highways and each township had at least one such official. This office was unpaid and its holders had no training – the success of their work depended on experience, observation and common sense, but these attributes were often conspicuously absent. The surveyors, who held office for one year, were nominated and chosen by the ratepayers of the township. After 1691 the justices of the peace usually confirmed these appointments and they at all times exercised a supervisory authority, not least because they arbitrated in disputes between neighbouring townships, confirmed the rates levied for highway and bridge purposes, and resolved – or attempted to resolve – differences of opinion between the surveyors and other involved parties. It is important to appreciate that the system was run entirely by unpaid amateurs who served only a brief period in office, who had other full-time jobs and who usually served only on sufferance or after much pressure from their neighbours and colleagues. The system was almost guaranteed to produce examples of incompetence, neglect, inactivity, financial irregularity and overall ineffectiveness.

The role of the justices of the peace was crucial – and became more so. It also provides us, via the quarter sessions records, with much of the primary documentary evidence for the condition of the roads and bridges of Lancashire before 1800. The justices, meeting four times a year at the quarter sessions, checked and regulated – often in a somewhat desultory fashion – the activities of the surveyors, churchwardens, overseers of the poor and constables of each township. The justices were unpaid and had no formal training, but they did at least have the experience of administering the law, both civil and criminal, and could draw on the advice of local experts and specialists if required.

They approved the levying of rates for highway purposes and, where cases crossed township boundaries, they acted as the higher authority. They had a specific responsibility for the so-called 'county bridges' – those on the major regional highways which were of special strategic significance – and they exercised a close supervision of the second-rank 'hundred bridges'. They received and adjudicated upon many highway matters – petitions from local surveyors asking for help with particular problems, such as damage to roads from industrial traffic, appeals from those who were suffering financial problems as a result of non-payment of rates, similar grievances where money destined for highway work had not been delivered and the complaints of contractors who had not been paid by the surveyors for work completed.

The duties of the surveyor began with receiving, from his predecessor, the cash balance from the previous year – although there were many instances where the surveyor had to begin by trying to track down money which was not forthcoming. He then had to establish the source and purpose of the moneys, and how the accounts – if any – had been kept. During his term of office he had to view the roads several times, to take appropriate action on any specific problems and to make to the justices a general statement of the condition of the highways if they required this. If there were problems which needed immediate and expensive attention he had to request the levying of a rate, usually seeking the approval of the justices (and after 1691 invariably doing so), and he also had responsibility for spending the money so raised. For the annual period of highway labour he had to issue instructions to the men who gathered to work, ensure that the materials required were obtained and carried to the site, and supervise the various repair jobs undertaken – all, be it noted, without any training in such tasks.

Examples of such labour are numerous, although they began to diminish by the mid-eighteenth century as individuals increasingly paid small sums as a monetary alternative to hard work. The system was cumbersome and awkward so it was often easier for surveyors of the highways to gather money as 'fines' and then to use this for contract work. At Alston in 1685 the manor court was dissatisfied with the way

Part of the village street of Waddington (then in the West Riding but now in Lancashire) drawn in 1842, showing an un-surfaced and rutted highway which was typical of all but the turnpike roads in rural areas. The stream still runs down the centre of the village of Waddington, al-though it is now confined by high stone banks *(Redding and Taylor,* Illustrated itinerary of Lancashire *(1842), p. 213).*

in which the surveyor was carrying out his duties. The court instructed him 'to summon the inhabitants of the said township to repair the cartway in the booght lane upon fryday next', or be fined 3s. 4d. by the manor court. Boat Lane led down to the ferry over the Ribble, linking Alston with Balderstone, and was an important part of the local highway network. The court further ordered that every inhabitant who failed to undertake his statutory labour was to be fined twelvepence. A later marginal note states that 'tis done', so at least these threats worked.[4]

The surveyor had to check the traffic which passed through his township – a responsibility which was often, maybe even generally, evaded or avoided – and to attend the quarter sessions to report to the justices as required and to present cases. It was, for most incumbents, a thankless, arduous and wearisome task, and it is scarcely surprising that many holders of the surveyor's office were very neglectful of their duties, waiting only for the year's end. The list of duties outlined above remained, in many cases, entirely theoretical – many surveyors undertook few, if any, of these tasks. The opportunities for diversion of funds were considerable and the giving of contracts to friends and neighbours must have been ubiquitous. All surveyors must have dreaded the onset of winter storms which undermined bridges, or the receipt of a complaint from one of the local gentry about the condition of the roads, for these would inevitably mean more work and a hard time. Perhaps the most remarkable feature of the highway maintenance system during the three centuries after 1555 is not that it frequently failed, but that it ever worked at all – the roads of Lancashire were, despite many problems and manifold inefficiencies, surprisingly adequate for the tasks imposed upon them, and certainly were no worse than those elsewhere in England.

Few sets of surveyors' accounts have survived from before the eighteenth century, but thereafter there is a good deal of detailed evidence to show how the system worked. For example, the income and expenditure accounts of the highway surveyor of Waddington, in the Ribble valley, survive from the 1730s and 1740s.[5] The sums involved were small – this was a thinly-populated rural parish and there were no major through roads to increase the need for highway repair. That which was done was therefore very modest and very localised. The income for highway purposes in 1740 totalled only £5 15s. 3d., of which £1 3s. 0d. was received, in sums ranging from 1s. 6d. to 4s., from ten men who compounded their labour – that is, paid money instead of doing the statutory six days' road work. In the same year the outgoings were as follows (and note, the figures do not add up!):

	£	s.	d.
paid James Read for paving on road in Southel Lane 2¼ yards wide at 1s. 8d. per rood ★	0	18	04
and for pulling up 3 rood	0	01	00
paid Robert Parker and Thomas Tomson for paving 13 rood at 1s. 6d. per rood 2 yards wide	0	19	06
paid Thomas Chatburn for mending hippins† 25 of March	0	02	04
Spent when the hippins was test ‡	0	02	00
paid Thomas Chatburn for setting hippins 9d. per hippin 32 hippins	1	04	00
Paid Thomas Chatburn for work above the frame §	0	15	00
Paid for ale at Earnshaws	0	02	06
Paid to ten men for finishing a causey in Southel Lane	0	01	10
Paid to Thomas Gardner trespass for leading all the sand into Southel Lane ¶	0	05	07
Paid Thomas Parker, for leading stones two days	0	05	00
2 gates to the sessions ★★	0	03	00
2 bills	0	01	00
	4	11	01
paid James Read for four days work	0	03	04
	4	14	05

* 'rood' = 'rod', a measure of 5½ yards (5.03m)

† 'hippins' are stepping stones: the brook ran along the middle of the village street, as it still does, and stones were the only convenient way across

‡ 'test' = tested for stability

§ the 'frame' was the temporary structure in the stream bed used for fixing the stones in place

¶ 'trespass' means allowing passage across his private land

** i.e. two visits to the quarter sessions

These accounts may be taken as characteristic of the period and place. Apart from the special expenditure on the hippins the road works carried out during this year amounted to nothing more than the rather casual repair and resurfacing of sixty yards of road seven feet wide. In the previous year expenditure included 3*d.* for a pick-shaft and small sums on fencing, and the length of road mended – thirteen roods – was roughly comparable. The small scale of such work is well indicated by an order to the inhabitants of Flixton in 1629, that 'the highe waies and commen faring wayes . . . shall be amended and the ditches . . . scoured as alsoe all the watercourses issueing from the said wayes to bee scoured and clensed and the bushes cutt downe'.[6] Nevertheless, if carried out effectively at least such work would maintain a minimum standard for road repair and drainage.

THE CONDITION OF LANCASHIRE'S ROADS

It is not easy to ascertain exactly how good the roads of Lancashire were in the years 1550 to 1800, and even harder to establish whether or not the work of the surveyors represented a real improvement. Not until the arrival of the turnpikes, after the 1720s, does the volume of information begin to increase appreciably. Travellers and visitors often gave lurid descriptions of the appalling state of the highways, with fearsome stories and much use of colourful adjectives, but we must remain sceptical and take their stories with a good pinch of salt. As Mary Higham notes, some of these stories were written by the equivalent of the tabloid journalists of the day, while other opinions were coloured by the alarm which travellers felt at being in – as they saw it – this shockingly remote and primitive county. Detailed descriptions are given by local highway surveyors in their numerous petitions to the justices but these, too, must be regarded with a certain caution – the surveyors were pleading their own special cases and emphasising how deserving they and their townships were, so pardonable exaggeration may have crept in.

Nevertheless, three examples of early seventeenth-century petitions to the justices may serve to give a flavour of the complaints and pleadings of local highway surveyors, and to indicate at least one attitude to the state of the roads. Of Over Wyre, in 1627, it was said that 'the waie leading from the towne of Rawcliffe and diverse other places to the parishe churche of St Michaell upon Wyre, and so the market town of Garstinge, is in great decay, for want of repaire, and especially betweene Rawcliffe Marshe and the said church, and that it is daungerous and almost impassable for his Majesties subjectes to travel that waie on horsebacke'.[7] Two years later, in the south-west of the county, it was claimed that 'the Lane leadinge the markett roade betweene Huyton and Prescott called the Shepheard Lane is in much decay for want of repaireing and scowreing the diches',[8] while a lane in Pemberton was said in 1633 to be 'soe ruinated and decayed that a horse cannot passe but in greate danger to be overthrown' – and that lane was the main road from Liverpool to Wigan.[9]

Claims such as these are legion. At every sitting of the quarter sessions there were several dozen from across the county, and many of the individual cases appear time and time again – much was said, much paperwork produced, many decisions made, but on the ground either nothing was done, or that which was done was done badly and needed repairing within a short time. Certain themes occur constantly – the damage done in the winter rains and snows, the effect of heavy traffic (often blamed on industry or on people from outside the area), the problems of roads in the mossland areas, and the havoc wrought by serious flooding and erosion by rivers. Many bridges were being rebuilt or upgraded during the seventeenth and eighteenth centuries, and the descriptions given of the problems encountered in these works are particularly vivid and often dramatic. In retrospect a striking feature of the complaints of two and three hundred years ago is their similarity to the grumbles and grievances of the late twentieth century – the circumstances and the degree may change, but the problems and the public attitudes to them remain surprisingly familiar.

Some of the complaints, and some of the problems, would have been familiar throughout the country in the early modern period, but others were particularly serious in Lancashire. The available evidence suggests, for example, that although the roads were not markedly worse than elsewhere, there were serious difficulties with Lancashire bridges during the century and a half up to 1750. Industrial traffic was clearly of greater significance in this county than in almost any other part of England and by the early eighteenth century was posing a genuine problem. By the second half of that century a more effective system of road (and especially bridge) administration was beginning to emerge, as the county justices appointed the first professional surveyors and bridgemasters and began to exercise a positive role in highway management.

Cotton bales being transported by horse-drawn waggon at Holcombe, near Bury, in 1873. Despite the growth of the railway network the roads remained of crucial importance for local short-distance traffic and for transport to railheads. Throughout the nineteenth century they continued to carry very large quantities of industrial and commercial goods in areas such as south-east Lancashire, and when motor vehicles took over from horses in the early twentieth century there was already a sizeable road haulage trade (Barton, History of the Borough of Bury (1874), p. 222).

Many roads were very narrow – no more than pathways by modern standards: in the mid-1630s the lane up to the church at Penwortham was described as being 'two yards wide', but it was said (with some exaggeration) that it was twice the breadth of any other road in the township. The familiar phrase 'packhorse route' is over-used in local history writing and there is a tendency to give this label to all narrow roads, particularly in upland areas, irrespective of their origin. It is often claimed that wheeled traffic came late to Lancashire but the documentary evidence shows that the county was not notably backward in this respect. In any case, before the advent of wheeled vehicles on any significant scale, all roads must of necessity have been 'packhorse routes'. The more recent use of the term relates to those high-level routes, often causewayed with stone slabs, which cross the high moorlands from valley to valley in the Pennine areas of Lancashire and Yorkshire. Here, wheeled traffic was much less common, because of the unfavourable geography, and the large-scale use of horse transport flourished well into the nineteenth century. More detail about these routes is given in the following chapter.[10]

On lowland roads wheeled traffic was widespread by the late sixteenth century – although not, of course, to the exclusion of horse or foot transport. By the 1580s references to wheeled carts appear frequently in probate inventories and other sources, and it is quite apparent that long-distance road transport was perfectly feasible. However, lumbering carts churned up poor surfaces – not least because stone for paving was less readily available – and in winter swollen rivers and streams damaged and destroyed bridges already weakened by the weight of heavy road traffic. The destruction of road surfaces by goods vehicles is an old complaint: modern lorries have their counterparts in the great freight waggons of the past and the constant stream of vehicles serving industrial plants has its parallel three hundred years ago. In 1633 at Burtonwood the highway surveyors rebuilding the significantly named Causeway Bridge made sure that the approach causeway, which was paved for use by horses and other animals and pedestrians, was railed off to prevent it being damaged by wheeled carts.[11] This practice was widespread, and the segregation of pedestrians and wheeled vehicles in this way was found on many routes.

Damage to roads, lanes and boundary hedges or walls could be caused by anybody – even the road menders themselves. In 1633 Alice Holland, who owned land beside the Mersey in Barton on Irwell, claimed to have suffered because 'the parishioners . . . of Eccles have comen through [her] court[yard] and soe alonge through her corne feild & soe alonge downe unto the water syde to fetch stones & other ma-terialls . . . towardes the repaire of the highwayes'. As a result of this trespass she had 'her yates [gates] broken, and cattell letten & put into her corne, and her grasse shorne & growned & given to there horses'. The magistrates ordered the parishioners to find another source of road material.[12]

If the problem was excessive use of the road by 'strangers' from outside the area – that is, if the highway in question was a main regional or even national route and was therefore used by long-distance traffic – the magistrates might permit the surveyor and the constables to take preventive action, or to try to raise money by levying tolls. In July 1633 the surveyor of Cronton near Widnes petitioned that 'by reason of many strangers which doe travell that waye with cartes and other carragees' the highways in his township were 'sore beaten out & gone to decay'. He asked for powers to prevent strangers 'cominge that waye at difficult tymes or elles may contribute and give a Certayne some of money to wardes the repaire there of'. He was authorised to 'sett stoopes' against the offenders – to bar the highways against out-siders.[13]

A particularly vivid example of the same procedure dates from the same month, when the surveyor of Tyldesley reported on the condition of Makant Lane, the road to Hulton, which 'in the tyme of fowle weather and when the same hath beene unseasonable for passage hath usually beene stopped soe that cartes cold not passe [because] the same way lyeth very lowe & that the groundes are wet soe that the same wilbee much annoyed if Cartes should passe in wet weather'. The township had previously had powers to prevent the use of particular roads at times when the surveyor felt the surface would be ruined – in this case because Makant Lane crossed a flat boggy tract of ground, prone to waterlogging and flooding, and would have turned into a quagmire when churned up by wheels. The request in 1633 was for a renewal of these powers, which had involved 'postes & Railes standing & beeing neere unto the dwelling house of Thomas Mean at the Entry into the same way', which were 'kept lock up for the preservacion of the said way'.[14]

In 1628 the inhabitants of the township of Cheetham, just north of Manchester on the main road to Bury, Rochdale and Yorkshire, were in no doubt as to why their main roads had deteriorated. They blamed – probably quite justifiably – the rapid growth of Manchester, and its insatiable demand for building materials, fuel and other goods: 'of late the same waye is of farre greater use than heretofore, with Cariage of Coale, Turves, Cannell, timber, wooll, Slate flagges, Stounes and other thinges for the use of the said Towne of Manchester (divers Coale Mines beinge of late found neere unto ye said high way, . . . which way sithence [since] through the extraordinarie use thereof is much decayed, and the Townshippe of Cheetam being but a small Towne-shippe and haveinge very fue Inhabitants . . . there are not sufficient carriages nor other meanes for the necessarie repaire of the said way'. The magistrates were asked if the inhabitants of Manchester parish, as the main cause of the very heavy traffic, could give a financial con-tribution and their plea was accepted in part – the four townships of Manchester, Salford, Broughton and Crumpsall were ordered to pay £5 between them (which would not have done much good!).[15]

In the same year the people of the rural township of Openshaw, just east of Manchester, complained about the burden of having 'two miles in lenght or there aboute of Causey to bee paved and mended: And being a way that is much traviled being the high way betwixt Ashton under Line and Manchester; and also being far from stones or gravell for the repaire of the same'.[16]

The inhabitants of Chorley, a prosperous and fast-growing market and industrial town, thought that it suffered from being on a major inter-urban route and felt deeply aggrieved because they had – so they claimed – been very assiduous in mending the highways in the past, 'to the greate ease of our Counntrie, and others who have occacion to travell, in, and by, the said waies'. Now, the people of the town complained, the discovery of coal in the vicinity had been the cause of much damage to the roads – not because of local merchants, but 'persones of other townes, and places, being strangers, and farr remote [who have] spoiled, decaied, maid foule and many of our Cawrseyes broken, by Carreing, and Carteinge of Coales, and

63

such lyke affaires in unseasonable weather'. In 1628 they proposed – unsuccessfully – that they should be allowed to erect gateways, one at each end of the town, 'to be cheaned and Locked upp in un-seasonable weather' to force the owners of coal carts to move them only in 'fair & houlsome weather'.[17] The 1620s were, therefore, a time of particularly vociferous complaints about the growth of traffic, which is significant because other evidence suggests that the period from about 1600 did indeed see a major expansion in the scale and range of the county's industries.

THE ROADS OF MOSSES,
COMMONS AND MOORS

In the late twentieth century the condition of the roads across Lancashire mosslands is the cause of many complaints and these routes require substantial expenditure. The combination of subsidence – as the peat shrinks during drainage and as the water table is lowered with pumping – and the softness and instability of the peat itself produces frequent collapses of road surfaces, cracking and fracturing of the metal, and deep hollows and corrugations in the road level. Despite the fact that the moss roads usually run on causeways and embankments the problem, which is shared by roads in areas such as the Fens and the Somerset Levels, shows no sign of improvement – rather the opposite, because the shrinking of the peat continues apace.

It is a problem which was noted well over three hundred years ago, when large-scale reclamation and draining of the mosses began. Much of the early evidence comes from south Lancashire, where the mosses north and west of Warrington were being drained in the early years of the seventeenth century. Once a moss was drained – or a peaty common was reclaimed from the waste – roads would be laid out across it, and what had been footpaths and bridle tracks became routes for wheeled vehicles. Unless the work was done carefully, and unless the draining of the moss itself had been successful, serious problems were likely to ensue.

In 1627, for example, the inhabitants of the townships of Bedford and Culcheth petitioned the justices, saying that 'sythence [since] a common called Fearnhead Common within the parish of Warrington hath beene improved the wayes over the said improved comon leadinge out of the said . . . townshippes to the towne of Warrington are so . . . spungie beinge a mossie soyle that the same are not passable neither for horse nor man without great danger and troble'.[18] Later in the same year the same roads were described as 'verie fowle & almost unpassable', but subsequent petitions imply that although remedial work was under-taken it had little long-term effect.[19]

A complaint was made in July 1632 that the improvers of 'markelles mosse' in Burtonwood had not done their work properly, for they had left unrepaired a lane, a 'waie or passage for cart carriage & otherwise', which was 'very dangerous in respect of broken pavementes & the fundacion beinge mosse groundes'. Here, too, the remedy ordered by the justices – that the improvers of the moss should ensure that repair work was carried out – proved ineffectual. In 1650 it was reported that the same highway was in great decay, and this time the inhabitants of the township were ordered to pay for the necessary work.[20]

Similar problems affected north Lancashire as well – at Cockerham in 1633 it was claimed that the reclamation of the moss and the removal of turf and peat, had caused havoc: 'the which mosse beinge all of late delved and digged aways, the flood and seas doe verie often breake In and . . . the Inhabittantes are . . . thereby stopped in their waie to the Church and market'.[21]

A related problem was experienced at Eccles in 1650, after the enclosure of Barton Moor. It was noted in a very lengthy and detailed petition that this land was formerly used by 'severall of the poore in habittance of the towne of Eckles that weare used to keepe 4 or 6 or 8 Shepe or A Cow or A horse'. It had since been divided up into private enclosures, yet the poor inhabitants of the town, who had once used the roads on the common to give access to their animals, were still being forced to repair the roads which were now of benefit only to the new owners. Furthermore, it was said, most of the inhabitants did not do the statute labour and carrying of material which the law required, but left these tasks to their poorer neighbours, the vicar being one of the worst offenders.[22]

High in the moorlands of Rossendale the enclosure of the great tracts of upland waste, which was proceeding rapidly in the early years of the seventeenth century, gave rise to disputes over who was respon-sible for the upkeep of the roads laid out across the new lands. It is apparent from the petitions and papers that here, in some instances at least, roads were being constructed for the first time, in areas which had hitherto had only pathways. In 1649 the copyholders (manorial tenants) of the Forest of Rossendale said that the common pasture of Henheads had recently been divided up by commissioners, who 'did leave forth the highe wayes thereuppon of a good & sufficient breadth which ought to bee repaired by the said Coppieholders'. The road from 'Staniforth to Warrneden Clough & another from that to Good-shaw yate' had subsequently been left to decay, and the petition asked that the copyholders 'within the severall Boothes within the said Forest' should fulfil their obligations and do the repair work.[23]

At Haslingden Grane the common lands on the northern slopes of the valley, leading up to Oswaldtwistle Moor, were enclosed in 1619–20. A new track was laid out along the southern edge of the enclosures, following the contours along the hillside. It was not intended primarily as a public road, but 'for the use only of those inhabitants within Graine whose lands were adioyninge'. In 1677, however, the inhabitants asked to be relieved of their obligations to maintain it, because the older road along the valley was 'in much better repair and more convenient for travellers' and the newer route was 'A very great charge . . . as well as miscevious to have two ways soe neere adioyninge to repaire'. The magistrates approved the request and after less than sixty years the enclosure route was officially abandoned – although it remained in informal use and has become accepted as a public right of way.[24]

OBSTRUCTIONS IN THE HIGHWAY

The difficulties experienced by travellers were not only the result of the poor state of the roads – the ruts, potholes, muddy pools and filthy sloughs. There were broken down hedges and fences, obstructions and impediments (such as those toll bars and locked gates put up by local communities to extract money from travellers or to prevent heavy carts and carriages passing along difficult stretches of road in bad weather). Other obstructions and hazards were the result of unauthorised and illegal encroachment upon the roadway. Mary Higham has shown how, in medieval and early modern Lancashire, a road was rarely a fixed carriageway, with a defined width, but was most likely to be a broad band of open ground edged by hedges, fences or walls. There would be wide verges, tracts of rough grassland and a meandering muddy roadway wandering across it. A road might be several hundred yards wide in places – much of it grass and bushes – yet narrow to a few feet in others.

This open land within the boundaries of the road was often used for grazing animals, as it was excellent rough pasture. Cows, horses, sheep, geese and swine would be put out on the roadside (sometimes tethered, sometimes not) and many farmers and cottagers regarded the roadside waste as a very useful, and usually completely free, extension to their own property. Other people saw the roadside verges as ideal potential building land – nobody appeared to own it (though in fact it was invariably the property of the lord of the manor) and it was easy to fence in a small patch and turn it into an allotment or an extension to a cottage garden, or even to build a rough cottage or shack on the land.[25]

The effect of such actions was to reduce the width of the roadway

Penwortham Hill looking towards Preston, in 1821. Although the road shown was part of the Preston and Liverpool turnpike the surface is clearly in a deplorable condition, with deep muddy ruts, very inadequate drainage, tumbledown fencing and – it would appear – a possible previous blockage by a fallen tree. In the background can be seen the Penwortham toll bridge built in 1758 *(Redding and Taylor,* Illustrated Itinerary of Lancashire *(1842),* p.156).

and this might, in some circumstances, cause a serious obstruction. In 1627 the constable of Sutton, near St Helens, told the justices that Richard Farehurst, a poor man, had recently built a little cottage beside 'towe Buttes Lane, which is a very large and spacious lane, and the only highway for your peticioners to church and markett'. He had been allowed to plant a quickset hedge within the curtilage of the lane itself, 'soe as hee might pasture some parte thereof in the somer tyme', on the condition that free passage was maintained for all men at all times. All was well until 5 January 1627, when the funeral party carrying the corpse of Elizabeth Woodcock was prevented from passing by George Travis, who then dwelled in the cottage and had decided to bar the public highway.[26]

Roads not only offered the possibility of cheap land or free grazing – they also provided building materials at minimum cost. There are numerous records of roadways being dug up and material carted away for other purposes, and individuals often considered that they had a right to plunder roads for their own private purposes. This was bad enough but, much more seriously, they invariably left great holes and pits in the road surface, which at best were an inconvenience to road users and at worst were, in the dark or in wet weather, a major danger to the travelling public. Long-suffering highway surveyors had to prosecute those responsible, if they could be traced, or to take action to fill in the pits and holes.

The road from Rawcliffe to St Michaels on Wyre was said in 1627 to be impassable partly because 'their bee pittes for marle dugged in or neare the said waie',[27] while a description of the main road from Liverpool to Ormskirk in 1630 claimed that 'there are severall incroach-mentes & other dangerowes places digged, cast & made, by severall of the inhabitantes of the Towneshippe of Melling . . . to the great danger of severall of his Majesties Subjectes there goodes & cattalles in travel-linge & passinge to either of the afforesaide markett townes'.[28] A particularly blatant example of this practice occurred in Preston in 1665, when Elizabeth Woodhouse, widow, was said to have 'broken the pavement in ye Streete [to] make a Sawe pit to the great prejudice of the town and a bad Example of others'. She was ordered 'to Fill upp the same sawe pitt and pave the same again' or be fined 6s. 8d.[29]

ROADS IN TOWNS

This example illustrates the way in which road maintenance even in urban areas was a major problem, one in some ways more complex than in the countryside. There were some towns – Preston, Wigan, Liverpool, Lancaster and Clitheroe – which were corporate boroughs, where the council usually played a part in the upkeep of the roads. However, in other towns – and even to some extent in the corporate boroughs – the local manorial court leet continued to exercise an authority in the management of the highway system. Most significant towns eventually obtained private Acts of Parliament, which allowed new authorities to be established with the specific tasks of improving and paving the highways and pathways, building new roads, providing street lighting and drainage, and undertaking other worthy and necessary projects. These bodies, usually known as 'improvement commissions', were able to raise rate money and to bypass the existing and inadequate local government structure.

The records of the Preston court leet give some typical examples of the working of the local system of urban highway management. The action of Elizabeth Woodhouse in digging a sawpit in the street was just one of many nuisances suffered by – and usually created by – the people of the town. Among other complaints made in that same year, 1665, were that the road between the Churchgate toll bar and the end of the town was 'much in decay and ruine'; the lane alongside the Lancaster Meadow, which was the main route north out of the town, was flooded by a ditch 'which troubleth the highway soe that people affoote cannot passe dry shodd'; the cartway from the House of Correction to the marsh was 'very ruinous and impassable, soe that neither cart nor loaded horses . . . in that place cannot passe, but are in danger of being overthrown'; a long list of people 'constantly make midden steads at theire doores in the streete belowe the Fryergate Barrs, to the great Annoyance of their neighbors and shame to the government of this Burrowe . . . and there is the like undecencie used with middings lying within the Fishergate barrs from yeare to yeare'; and that another brook, running towards Marsh Mill, did not 'keepe in it's [sic] right Course [but] overflowe the highway'.[30]

This was a typical year. The records of the court leet are full of such entries. In 1654 two men were ordered (one for the second time and one for the third), to remove 'the earth slidden downe into the high way leadinge to Swillbrooke', and were fined for not obeying previous instructions. The following year saw a characteristic problem, frequently mentioned – there was 'A great abuse in this Towne by reason of Carryon, dead Swyne, Doggs, and other noysome, filthie carryon being throwne in St John's Weende and other Weends and backe lanes'. In 1668 Nicholas Watson left timber and wood lying in the roadway outside his house 'to ye great nusance of ye Burgesses of this towne and ye hazard of theire lives and limbs by falling over or upon ye same in ye night time'. Three citizens were fined in 1679 for digging claypits in the middle of Churchgate, the main road out from the town to the east and south. In 1707 an alderman and two others were accused of blocking up the public footpaths which gave access to the Marsh Mill, and one of the three was also said to have built a wall across a sidestreet in the town centre. At the same court Widow Richardson was fined for dumping a heap of old thatch, taken from the roof of her house, in the middle of the road and leaving it there.[31]

Such problems, arising largely from a lack of consideration or common sense on the part of individual townspeople, or from the absence of a sense of communal responsibility, were found in all towns. In Liverpool, for example, John Smith and Rafe Wyggan were presented in 1623 for 'abusinge the water street with mucke and Rubbage to the annoyance of neighbors', while in the same year John Barrow was

fined because he had dug holes in the highways to take clay. In a similar case in 1611 one of the aldermen of the borough, Rafe Seacombe, was fined 3s. 4d. for 'annoying the Kinges highway and taking some marle away to carie to his own ground'. Two years before John Crosse was accused of 'plowinge up the highe way wherby the way is made upon the townes Common neare to the pinfould yate'.[32] This sort of behaviour is found throughout the period: in October 1537 the manor court of Furness ordered – in vain – that 'no clay pyttes' were to be dug in the highways at Dalton in Furness, while in the following year Thomas Cokeson was fined 3s. 4d. for obstructing 'the common rake' between Ulverston town and Swarthmore.[33]

In Liverpool and Preston, as in other towns, the supervisors of the highways regularly inspected the streets, lanes and pathways, and made presentments at each court stating that repairs or improvements were needed. The court would then order the work to be done, and would authorise the expenditure involved. This was often inadequate, and frequently the work was insufficient, so that the same streets soon needed more repair. Others might, in turn, present the supervisors for not doing the work properly, or for neglecting their duties. Thus, in 1681 the Preston court leet fined 'ye supervisors of ye highways for not doing their duty xxs.', while in May 1691 it was reported that the supervisors had not repaired 'the Causey betwixt ffishergate bars and

Market Street, Manchester, in 1826: this delightful engraving shows the typical cobbled surface of an important urban street, paving of which was one of the main tasks of the town's improvement commissioners since the 1770s. On the left is a laden stagecoach, its roof precariously piled with luggage, while other two-wheeled vehicles can also be seen (*Austin,* Lancashire Illustrated *(1829), p. 66*).

70

the Spring head, and the laine called ffryer lane and likewise the Rampier [parapet] nere the ffryergate More gate' – they were threatened with a fine of £1 6s. 8d. if they had not done the work by early August.[34]

As towns grew and became industrialised in the later eighteenth century, the need to have proper paving, as well as lighting and scavenging of the streets, became acute. The existing administration was generally (although not invariably) ineffective, and the solution found in many places was to create new bodies which were specifically charged with the task of undertaking these works. The improvement commissions, as they were usually known, had statutory powers and could levy rates for public purposes, and their work was crucial to the improvement and upgrading in the standards of urban roads between 1790 and 1850. After 1835 municipal government was reformed, and new boroughs could be created, so that the borough councils gradually took over the role of the commissions.

The new authorities did not only pave and light – they also built new streets and rebuilt existing ones. In Manchester, for example, the sprawling city of the early nineteenth century saw the laying out of new squares (of which St Ann's Square survives as an excellent example). Under an Act of 1776, which created the town's first improvement commission (known as the Police Commission), Old Millgate, Cateaton Street and St Mary's Gate, hitherto narrow medieval lanes, were widened and straightened, and Exchange Street was made to give proper access from St Ann's Square to the Market Place. Later improvements included the rebuilding of the winding Market Street during the 1820s, and the major widening and straightening of Cross Street in the 1850s.[35]

THE OWNERSHIP OF ROADS

One of the problems regularly encountered by those who had responsibility for maintaining roads was determining the ownership of a highway. Even in the 1990s disputes over these matters sometimes come to court and the status and ownership of roads and tracks is often unclear. This was much more the case in the sixteenth and seventeenth centuries, when highway law was still evolving by ad hoc case decisions based on loose interpretations of imprecise medieval statutes. Highways, and what we would call 'public rights of way', could be – and often were – the cause of irritation and annoyance to neighbouring landowners and there are many examples of attempts to close off such roads. The resultant legal cases usually centred on the question of whether or not the public did have a right of uninterrupted access.

The building of a wall across a street in central Preston has already been mentioned, but these cases tended to be found more often in rural areas, where the highway pattern was less fixed and where 'informal' access had always been common. The deliberations were often inconclusive but eventually it became usual to seek the permission of the magistrates before routes were diverted, altered or closed. This eventually led to the procedure known as the 'road order', which gave formal legal authority to such an application and is the ancestor of the public notices about highway matters which are now so frequent in local newspapers.

During the 1630s there was a lengthy case at Colne, which eventually went to the bishop's court in Chester for adjudication, concerning the route from Colne to Barnside (north-east of Laneshaw Bridge) 'both for church and market for Cart, and carriage', which went through a field called Rough Shaw and then 'to and through a gate or passage called the yate at the hole'. It was claimed that the gate had been locked by the landowner and that the alternative route was 'through and over moores & places not passable for a teame and cart laden', with a detour of 'two or three miles, at least above a mile, about, and after so much compasse, must come within xxtie [twenty] roods of the foresayd yate'. The extreme lack of precision as to the length of the detour must have made the evidence markedly less convincing.[36]

In 1684–5 much agitation resulted from the apparent misuse of a rate which had been levied for the repair of Sefton Church and churchyard. The private road to the manorial mill ran through the churchyard and the traffic was causing severe damage to the sacred ground. Thomas Harrison of Litherland testified that 'before the re-membrance of any man living' Lord Molyneux 'did enjoye a way to his mill for all Carts & Carriages', but that 'many times, especially betwixt a frost and a thawe, both Carts, and laden horses, in their passages through there, did presse and tread very deep in many graves especially such as were new'. For many years there had been talk of a diversion and eventually, in June 1684, a parish meeting agreed to levy a general rate to make good the churchyard and build a diversionary road 'all along att ye side of ye church-yard wall'.

However, William Blundell of Crosby, a landowner in Sefton parish, took the matter to the bishop's court, claiming (unsuccessfully) that the money had been put 'towards the repaire and perfectinge of a private Way' and that 'noe man of the same parish can be charged with the repaire of the said private way . . . who is not bound to make Suite to the said Milne' – that is, only those who were required by their tenancy agreement to use the mill had to pay for the private road.[37]

Crossing private land might often be an expedient measure, the result of the deterioration of an existing route. In chapter 1 Ben Edwards notes how the creation of diversions around obstacles was a very widespread phenomenon in prehistoric times and a Lancashire example can be found as late as July 1649, when John Drinkell of Wyresdale told the magistrates that 'there hath bin an usuall high way for horse and foote betwixt Abbeystead and Emotbrow . . . now spoiled and worne out by the violence of the water of wyer running through the said way By reason whereof the passengers usually passing that way doe make a high way through [his] grounds whereby he hath suffered great losse in his corne grasse & ground'.[38]

By the late seventeenth centuries major landowners were beginning to find it unacceptable for reasons of privacy and aesthetics, to have public roads such as these crossing their estates and passing close to their residences. It became increasingly common for them to seek the approval of their fellow-magistrates to have these roads diverted – often by lengthy detours – and to close the old routes to public vehicular access (although they often remained as footpaths). Examples can be found all over Lancashire.

At Lytham the public highways to Heyhouses and Blackpool, and to Ballam and Westby, ran through the park of Lytham Hall, just under the windows of the house and past the front door. After the house was rebuilt in 1754 in the most fashionable style this was socially less acceptable, and the growth in traffic as Lytham expanded into a town during the early nineteenth century exacerbated the problem. In 1832 Thomas Clifton came into his inheritance as the new squire of Lytham and he immediately began to 'improve' the park and home farm. Central to this strategy was the diversion in 1833 of the busy Blackpool road to run south of the park in a great curve which is now Church Road. The minor road to Ballam remained for a few more years, but in the early 1840s it, too, was diverted around the edge of the park. The correspondence between Clifton and his agent, James Fair, tells how gangs of Irish navvies laboured during the winter of 1844–5 breaking stones and laying the new roads. Thereafter the peace and tranquility of the house were undisturbed by the populace passing by.

At Holker the Cavendish family and their predecessors undertook extensive road diversion and improvement during the century after 1740, with the twin aims of increasing the privacy of Holker Hall and its occupants and of encouraging and promoting the better agricultural development of the estate. A new road was built from Bigland Scar across the moss to Old Park and on to the small anchorage at Park Head, to divert traffic associated with 'the Baltic Vessels [which] used to Winter there, the Captains living at Carke, Holker & Flookburgh, the only road then from it to Holker was through Holker Park, & to Carke &c over the Sands & Marshes'. East of the house, on Holker Bank, major road works were undertaken to open up the hilltop ground

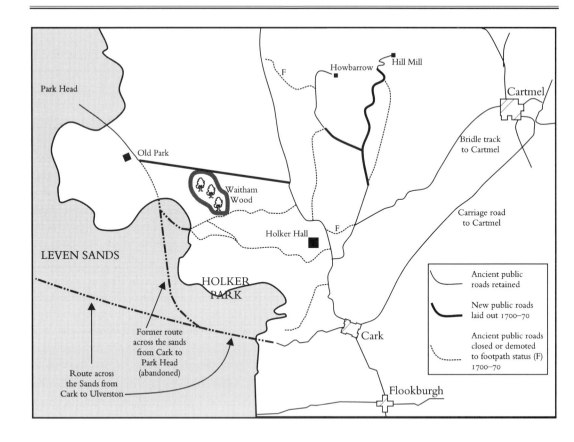

Park Head

Old Park

Waitham Wood

LEVEN SANDS

Holker Hall

HOLKER PARK

Howbarrow

Hill Mill

F

F

Cartmel

Bridle track to Cartmel

Carriage road to Cartmel

Cark

Flookburgh

Former route across the sands from Cark to Park Head (abandoned)

Route across the Sands from Cark to Ulverston

	Ancient public roads retained
	New public roads laid out 1700–70
	Ancient public roads closed or demoted to footpath status (F) 1700–70

to agricultural use and to give better access to Hill Mill and some of the outlying tenanted properties.[39] All these roads were carefully designed, with preliminary plans and sketches, and their superior alignments and gradients reveal their origins. The moss road for example, runs in two long straights across the flat lands, in contrast to the circuitous route of its predecessor.

Some of the Holker roads were associated with the enclosure of the waste and this process – affecting lowland mosses and commons, as well as extensive tracts of upland moor – had an important impact upon the road pattern of significant areas of the county. In the south and midlands of England parliamentary enclosure (that is, where a private act of parliament authorised the work) was ubiquitous, whereas in Lancashire the majority of enclosures were undertaken by private agreement among landowners and tenants. The road pattern produced was perhaps less rigid than that of typical parliamentary enclosure but by the early eighteenth century the same general characteristics were found – broad roads of regular width on long straight alignments. Such features reflected the use of professional surveyors and the preparation of an overall design for the new landscape and its pattern of farms and fields.

Alterations to the road network on the Holker estate, near Cartmel, between 1700 and 1770. Major improvements to the layout and management of the estate were made in the eighteenth century, including an extensive programme of road closures, diversions and new construction *(based on LRO DDCa 21/27)*.

In Lytham West End (the area which is now St Annes) enclosure took place in the years after 1616 and a regular network of new roads, serving evenly-spaced new farms, was laid out across the flat, sandy, grazing lands lying just inland from the dunes. Although no contemporary map survives, it is clear from later cartographical evidence that the landscape was reorganised and redesigned as a whole, and the regularity of its road and field network is apparent even today in the streets of St Annes.

Two centuries later, the moors and commons of the lower part of Quernmore were enclosed by Act of Parliament after 1811 and a wholesale replanning of the landscape followed. Existing roads were straightened, widened and fenced or hedged, while new roads were laid out cutting straight across the former waste. Littledale Road, once a rough track leading up on to the slopes of Bowland, is an example of the former. Rigg Lane, which now gives access to the Clougha car park, and Postern Gate Road running north from Quernmore village past the church, were completely new highways laid out in the 1810s, and are among Lancashire's best examples of the roads typical of parliamentary enclosure.

THE CONDITION OF LANCASHIRE BRIDGES

More highway petitions relate to bridges than to any other subject. Whereas there were usually diversionary routes and other ways of avoiding poor roads, there was little which could be done about bridges. They, with towns, were the focal points of the road network, and while fords and ferries still abounded, any traveller would prefer to cross rivers and streams dry shod and without paying. Bridges were also the part of the highway system most at risk from floods and tempests, from structural decay and from accidental damage, and hazards for travellers were many. The inhabitants of Hornby claimed in 1649 that 'three or four severall persons within the compasse of these few yeares' had lost their lives because of the decay of the town's bridge.[40] The administration of bridges was also distinctive, because for some of them, as for no other part of the highway system, special arrangements were made to try to ensure that their upkeep was the responsibility of the district rather than just the township.

Bridges were divided into four groups. Those on private roads and paths were, like the routes themselves, the responsibility of the landowner or tenant. The bridges on minor public roads, paths and tracks which seemed only of local importance were maintained by the township. A considerable number, which were deemed to be of regional significance and to benefit travellers from a wider area, were classed as 'hundred bridges', maintainable by the levying of a rate across all the townships in that hundred. Finally, there were the 'county bridges' which were looked after by the county justices using rates levied across the whole of Lancashire. Although the fewest in number, these were the most important bridges, those on the major national roads and routes connecting the chief towns of the county.

This arrangement worked with tolerable efficiency in its later years, especially after the county justices and the hundreds began to use professional staff who were much better equipped to deal with major reconstruction and maintenance work. The county bridge-masters, in particular, began a very important programme of rebuilding and widening during the early eighteenth century and many of Lancashire's finest bridges are a surviving tribute to the quality and architectural excellence of their efforts. At the more local level, however, the administration was still undertaken on a voluntary and unpaid basis. Although bridgework had to be contracted out to builders, because it was beyond the capacity of the inhabitants under statute labour, the cost and complexity of doing so deterred many surveyors from embarking upon essential tasks until the collapse of the bridge rendered the work absolutely imperative.

Even then there was often lengthy prevarication and serious financial confusion before the job was finished. All too often it was not done sufficiently well and more work was required within a few years. At Skippool, on the main road to Garstang at the northern end of Poulton-le-Fylde, a replacement wooden bridge was built in about 1612, chargeable to Amounderness hundred. By 1634 it had become dangerous and over the next seventy years a succession of renovation and restoration projects was carried out – it was the subject of major work in 1634, 1639, 1659, 1677 and 1693, but in 1702 the ratepayers of the hundred were again being required to provide funds for repairs. These were not incidental maintenance costs – on each occasion the work approached a full-scale reconstruction.[41]

The damage to bridges was, as noted above, especially the result of weather and flood. In lowland Lancashire stone was only used for the most important structures before the sixteenth century and even then

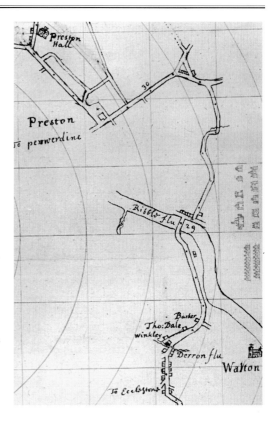

The earliest detailed road maps of Lancashire were drawn in 1684 by Dr Richard Kuerden of Preston. They cover several of the major routes within the county, and give valuable information about the alignments and the landmarks. This section shows the old winding road from Walton-le-Dale over the Ribble bridge and into Preston, a road which was superseded in the eighteenth century by the new turnpike which is the present main road (LRO DDX 194/39).

Manchester in 1728, drawn by Samuel Buck; the engraving shows the fine medieval bridge, much admired by observant travellers, across the Irwell between Manchester and Salford. Note in the foreground the chain ferry for passengers; ferries such as this represented a considerable impediment to shipping, and their replacement by bridges was often demanded by shipping interests. Some small vessels can be seen moored on the Manchester side upstream of the ferry (*LRO DP 189/11*).

the decking and parapets might well be of wood, so that only the piers were stone. In the upland areas, where stone was more abundant, it was probably used to a greater extent, but the ease and simplicity of building in wood, and the cheapness of construction, meant that it retained favour for minor bridges. Most bridges were very narrow, as the surviving examples of packhorse bridges testify. The restored bridge across the Colne Water at Wycoller is one of the best-known: it is adjacent to the ford which would have been used by wheeled vehicles and by herds of animals. Just upstream is a single stone slab, or 'clapper bridge', which although undated is an example of the most primitive form of bridge.

The larger medieval stone bridges were objects of note to travellers: for example, the Ribble Bridge at Walton-le-Dale was made of stone after 1403, when a grant of pontage was authorised for the replacement of the old wooden structure after it had been damaged by floods and ice. It was described by Leland as 'the great stone bridge of Ribyll' and by Kuerden as 'a fayr and one of the statelyst stone bridges in the north of England'.[42]

The upstream part of the fourteenth-century stone bridge over the Ribble at Edisford near Clitheroe, described in the previous chapter, still survives − it has three spans with pointed arches and three ribs, and is only eight feet wide. The original bridge apparently had six spans of 25 feet but in 1665 frost damage resulted in the collapse of the second pier from the Lancashire bank, and the second and third arches therefore fell. These arches were replaced with a single span of 60 feet.[43] At Garstang, on the Wyre, the old wooden bridge was rebuilt during the late 1490s after Thomas, 1st earl of Derby, left £20 in his will for the purpose: the result was the 'fine stone bridge' which Leland saw forty years later. Other famous stone bridges in the county included those at Warrington, Manchester and Whalley.[44]

Descriptions of damage to bridges by storm and flood are often very vivid. While, as with roads, there would have been a pardonable exaggeration of the case to impress the justices and to try to ensure that money for repairs would be authorised, the precariousness of many bridges and the destruction wrought after winter rains are quite clear. For example, at Church in 1649 the bridge over the Hyndburn was 'presented to be wholly fallen downe'.[45] The sudden floods on the tributaries of the Lune and Wyre have remained notorious right up to the present day and they regularly caused havoc in the past. In 1627 the hundred bridge over the Leck Beck at Burrow was being rebuilt at a cost of £106 13s. 4d., but when construction was well-advanced 'a suddane inundation of watter took it awaye', leaving the masons without pay and the bridge wrecked again.[46] The bridge was rebuilt, but in 1648 the inhabitants of Lonsdale petitioned the justices, saying that the bridge 'hath beene brake downe two or three severall times by the violence of the water' and was again in danger of collapse: 'much earth was worne and washed away by the force & violence of the water'.[47]

The diary of Timothy Cragg, a Quaker farmer of Ortner in Wyresdale, records many such destructive floods in the late eighteenth century. 'On Sunday the 26th of August [1792] there was a most fearful thunderstorm and a very great flood . . . Damas Gill was the greatest flood that ever I saw, and it overflowed a great extent of land and did much damage particularly to the groundwork of the bridge [which] stands in a very precarious fashion all the ground work is washed out and the bridge now stands only on two stones, one at either side, that lower down the water is near washed out only holding by one corner. Conder [river] was the greatest known in the memory of any person living. It has greatly damaged the bridge at Galgate and made it quite impassable & the bridge at the New Mills is driven down. There are also two bridges at this side of Galgate near Smith Green of which one is washed away and the other greatly damaged'.[48]

These examples concern existing bridges but of course many river crossings still had fords or ferries. On the Ribble below Clitheroe the only bridges until 1759 were at Mitton, Walton and Ribchester, but there were at least fourteen other crossing points: most of these had

The superb seven-teenth-century bridge over the Ribble at Edisford near Clitheroe, which replaced a medieval predecessor which had been badly-damaged by flooding. This was a constant problem on Lancashire rivers and much new work was undertaken in the years after 1700 to replace inadequate medieval bridges. In the background can be seen the parish church and castle at Clitheroe (From *Whitaker's* History of Whalley, vol. 1 (1818), p. 255).

both a ferry and a ford, to be used according to the type of traffic and the state of the river. The Mersey below Stockport also had only three bridges, at Cheadle, at Crossford (on the old road from Manchester to Chester via Altrincham) and at Warrington. Here, too, there were fords and ferries. The inhabitants of the parishes of Flixton, Eccles and Stretford petitioned successfully in 1628 for the construction of a bridge at Barton, because the ferry there was decrepit and the ford was very dangerous. Barton Bridge quickly became a major crossing point, of great strategic value.[49]

The main road from Whalley and Clitheroe through Accrington to Bury and Manchester crossed the Calder at Fenisford near Great Harwood (now known as Cock Bridge, on the A680). In 1632 it was said that 'when the Water is little there is Comonly 200 or 300 loaden horses every daie passe over, besides great numbers of other passengers', an unusual but – if even reasonably reliable – important illustration of the very substantial volumes of traffic which main roads in Lancashire carried as early as the reign of Charles I. However, the depth of the river was often 'especially [sic] in the winter season so great that there is no passage for man or horse, and many attemptinge at such tymes to passe have been drowned, and almost daily some persons are here put in danger of theire lives or have there Loades and Carriages drowned or lost'. The ford itself seems to have been eroding and becoming treacherous – it was 'of late yeares so worne and growne so rocky that in short tyme it is thought yt will become alltogether impassable'.

Local people asked for the construction of a strong stone bridge, estimated to cost at least £100, to be maintained by the hundred of Blackburn. Their pleas were favourably received: the justices recorded that 'yt were much pitty that such Worke should go backe for want of a tryfle or small contribucion [and] it is therefore . . . ordered by an unanimous vote of all the Justices of peace present, with consent of all the Constables and inhabitantes of the said hundred assembled at this sessions' that the work should go ahead.[50]

When a bridge was to be repaired or, as in the case of Fenisford, a new bridge was planned, there was a routine to be followed. The justices would receive a petition or a statement of the case from local people – usually the surveyors of the highways of the townships involved, or a document signed by leading inhabitants. Unless they felt that the case was completely out of the question the justices would then send men to view the site – invariably other justices, or local gentlemen appointed to act on their behalf. These people would not be able to assess the technical requirements of the project so they would take with them experts to give professional advice. In 1634, when the Douglas Bridge at Rufford was decayed, the Wigan sessions requested that 'William Mawdesley of Mawdesley, gent., Roberte Hesketh of Rufforth, gent. & Micheall Nelson of Mawdesley yeo[man]' should 'apointe some convenient tyme & take with them workemen of skill' to assess the cost of repairs. The three men duly did so, and reported that the workman estimated the cost of the work at £9.[51] When the Higher Hodder Bridge was in disrepair in 1649 the viewers were 'both of Yorkeshire & Lancashire', and they estimated the cost at no less than £230 to be divided equally between the two counties.[52]

Often the gentlemen-viewers would prepare a detailed assessment of the necessary work. In 1632 those who checked on the small Gooding Bridge, on the Liverpool–Wigan road at Windle, reported that it needed two arches, each of seventeen feet span and ten feet wide, with causeways at each end and 'battelling' or parapets two feet high. The whole, including materials and labour, was expected to cost £53.[53] At Darcy Lever Bridge, over the Croal on the main road from Bolton to Rochdale, the viewers in 1627 found that 'the said Brydge [was] of wood and standing upon three great pillares of Stone and being in Length between Landstall and Landstall about five or six and thirty yardes'. They reported that the stone piers were 'so decayed in the foundacon as wee thinke cannot be sufficiently repayred without taking to the bottom and begininge a new groundworke', which would cost at least £50 but, if the work was to be done properly, about £100.

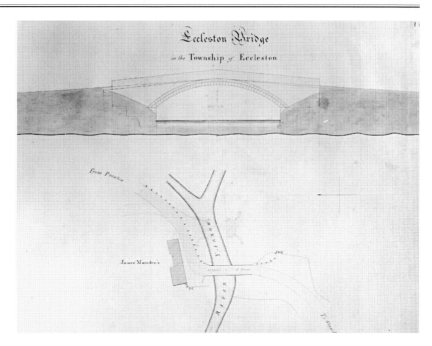

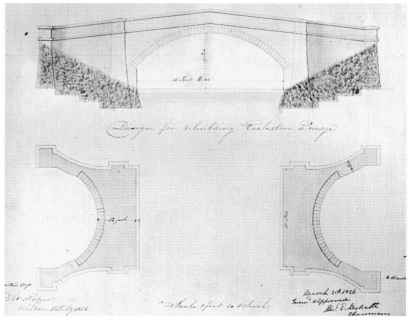

These two beautiful watercolours show the bridge over the Yarrow at the north end of the village of Eccleston, near Chorley. The one above shows a 'before' view, depicting the old bridge, and the second view of Yarrow Bridge (of 1826) shows a proposed design for its reconstruction with a higher and slightly wider arch to reduce the threat from flood damage *(LRO QAR 6/10).*

However, rebuilding three pillars in the stream was, they considered, likely to mean that eventually the bridge would become unsafe again. They therefore thought 'yt good husbandry for the Cuntry to have in place of the said wooden Brydge tow arches of Stone which will not amount to above twentie pound more in the whole'. This was agreed by the justices, the money being chargeable to Salford hundred.[54]

Viewers might also investigate the previous history of a bridge and the way in which the charges of earlier work had been borne. In July 1627 Sir George Booth of Dunham Massey wrote to the Lancashire justices to say that 'George Smyth my tenant had his mare killed upon the assention even [Ascension Eve] last with a fale' from Breton Bridge near Leigh. He claimed that Smyth 'was in greate danger to have lost his lyef there & two other of my Servantes being alltogeather upon the same bridge . . . it beinge such a longe rotten woodden bridge'.[55] Faced with such a complaint from a leading landowner the justices promptly ordered an investigation and four bridges in Leigh parish — 'Breton, Barkers, Hoareorcharde and Hyndefford' — were found to have been 'usually amended and repayred by taxacons assessed upon all the severall Townes & villages within the Hundred of West darbye'. It was agreed that the bridges, which were 'utterly decayed & Ruynated . . . they beinge bridges standinge upon Rotten groundes & upon dangerous waters', would be rebuilt in timber with stone piers and ends, at a cost to the hundred of £110.[56]

The work of reconstruction was usually supervised by the appropriate highway overseers. If a hundred or county bridge was involved the justices would normally ask the high constable of the relevant area to make sure that all went well and to deal with the collection and paying out of money. None of this guaranteed that the work would be satisfactory, or that the money was properly managed, but it was better than nothing. At the end of the work a set of accounts was supposed to be handed to the justices, with certification that the job was satisfactorily completed. A typical example is given below:

Expenses of building Cawsey bridge, Burtonwood, 1633

	£	s.	d.
To John Towers for five hundred of ashlars	3	03	00
for one hundred more at gouferdayne delfe	0	14	06
For leading the stones from the getters to the top of the Brow to John Towers	0	05	00
To the masons for the building of the bridge and searching of the stone	14	12	00
For lime for the bridge	1	18	06
For leading of stone, timber and lime	5	06	04
To Robert Wright for slate	0	12	00
For paving of the bridge	0	05	00
To a workman for filling of sand	0	02	08
For five loads of paving stones	0	03	04
To two labourers for one day	0	01	04

For making of a causey since the bridge was built in the Causey Bridge Lane for paving the same and Railing it to keep carts from it	7	19	00
For our expenses in divers journeys to the sessions and our other pains bestowed at the work of the bridge at the least 40 days	2	00	00
For our expenses to the Sessions when this account was delivered up	0	05	00
	37	07	08

John Cubbon,
Randle Barlow, overseers

This job went smoothly and does not seem to have left any residual problems, but such a happy outcome was comparatively rare. The masons who built or repaired bridges were not paid in advance, and therefore often had to find large sums of money to buy materials and equipment and to hire labour. If they then encountered problems outside their own control they might not be recompensed without a struggle. In January 1633 Barnard Wood and Francis Crompton, who had been the contractors for the new stone bridge over the Irwell at Farnworth, reported that they had spent £16 in finishing one arch and almost completing the second, but that 'it pleased god Almightie the disposer and finisher of all good workes to send a great raine upon ye earth, which caused such an extreame high flood that the same worke . . . was altogether perished, & overthrowne, for the frame was burst in pieces and almost lost'. The frame, or wooden structure which was used to support the arch during its construction, was always vulnerable – a note appended to this report says that 'ye fframe for ffarnworth Bridge was twice erected and taken away by the water'. Happily, the masons were eventually compensated for their loss.[57]

Less fortunate was Michael Thwaite, who in 1649 spent his permitted budget of £14 on rebuilding Claytonford Bridge in Bolton (which had collapsed) but was only paid £10. The work he had undertaken included raising the old stones, driving piles in the stream bed, diverting the water while work was in progress, paying wallers for sixty-six days' work, getting the moss which was used as a packing for the mortar, small sums on baskets, packthread (needed for lines) and sharpening picks and 1s. 4d. 'for Ale & tobachoe given the workmen'.[58] In her history of Barton Bridge, Diana Winterbotham shows how the masons employed there had to fight for eleven years before they received payment, by which time one of their number had died.[59]

Perhaps the most serious problems arose when individuals or townships refused to pay the rates which were levied for bridge or road repair, or when the money was collected but was then withheld and perhaps embezzled, by the official in whose custody it was placed. The work on rebuilding the four bridges in Leigh, chargeable to West Derby hundred, is referred to above. In the following year, 1628, the justices of the hundred ordered the high constable, Richard Hill of Burscough, to enforce the collection of a total of £9 11s. 9d. for this purpose from the inhabitants of North Meols, Kirkdale, Altcar, Great and Little Crosby, Ince Blundell and Lydiate, who had all refused to pay.[60] It is easy to see why: these places were all distant from Leigh and it is extremely unlikely that their inhabitants ever made use of the bridges or roads of that district, so they saw no good reason to pay money towards their upkeep. The West Derby justices heard in 1634 that Warrington, Rixton & Glazebrook, Woolston Fearnhead & Poulton, Burtonwood, Newton and Haydock had all refused or failed to pay any bridge levies during the first half of that year and that 'Leigh is behind for hurst milne bridge & will pay none'.[61]

The major and costly work of reconstructing Darcy Lever Bridge was especially unpopular. In 1628 Richard Fletcher, the constable of Pilkington, was ordered to arrest his fellow constable – possibly his brother – Roger Fletcher, who had collected and kept the money levied for the work and refused to hand it over. Richard was instructed to convey Roger to Lancaster Castle and put him in gaol there if he continued to refuse.[62] At Rivington the former constable, Roger Brown, was summoned in 1629 for refusal to hand over the money collected for Darcy Lever.[63] It appears that the inhabitants of Chadderton would not pay the sums required in the first place, for in April 1629 the constables there were ordered to collect the 35s. which was the contribution of that township and to hand it over at the dwelling of Roger Browning, innkeeper, in Manchester on Saturday 9 May before 10 p.m.[64] This was two years after the start of work on the bridge.

Reliance on these procedures for bridge construction was clearly a problem even in the seventeenth century, but by the early eighteenth century the pressures of growing traffic and the general upgrading of the road network, which produced the concept of the turnpike and its administration by a separate trust, also prompted the county justices to employ professionals for bridge management. By the 1750s the county and each of the six hundreds had paid bridgemasters, who provided expert architectural and engineering services and undertook all major projects, using contractors. This revolutionised the administration of this key area, a change further assisted by the establishment, in 1798, of a permanent session of the county justices with its own clerical staff.[65] Lancashire, well ahead of any other county, had created an efficient and effective administration which functioned in much the same way as the later county council.

In the hundred of Blackburn the first record of the appointment of a salaried official to supervise bridges appears in 1693, when Geoffrey

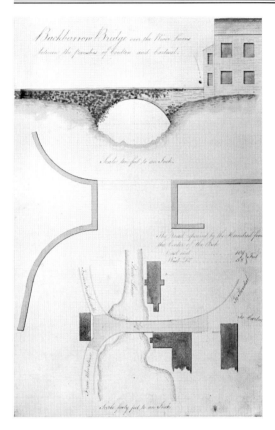

Backbarrow Bridge over the River Leven between the parishes of Coulton and Cartmel

The bridge over the river Leven at Backbarrow, on the turnpike from Kendal to Ulverston, in 1805. The drawing includes details of the adjacent Backbarrow mills, while the plan is shaded to indicate the precise stretch of road which was legally repairable not by the turnpike trustees but by the ratepayers of Lonsdale hundred (LRO QAR 6/8).

Roby, the steward at Hoghton Tower, began to manage the Ribble Bridge and Walton Cop: he seems also to have assisted on other bridge projects locally. In January 1717 the county justices authorised the appointment of two permanent salaried bridgemasters for the Blackburn hundred and thereafter the succession in this office was unbroken.[66]

With this improvement in supervision it was possible to reconstruct the important bridges throughout the county during the century after 1720 and the impressive legacy of this radical programme remains with us today. For example, Walton Bridge was rebuilt in 1779–81 by John Law, his son Samuel and his brother Robert at a cost of £4,200. John Law was the Salford bridgemaster until his death in 1781 and was succeeded in that post by Samuel. Richard Threlfall, the Amounderness bridgemaster, supervised the Walton contract and the remarkably detailed account book for the work, filling no fewer than 432 pages, still survives – the cost was £50 less than the estimate despite a one-year overrun on the construction period! At Ribchester the present bridge was constructed in 1775–6, supervised by Threlfall and with John Law as the master mason.[67]

The bridgemasters were professionals and the quality of their work is reflected in the superb and beautiful bridge-books which contain hand-coloured and engraved elevations and plans of all the bridges under their control.[68] The design of new bridges was sometimes opened to competition: at Lancaster, for example, the old medieval stone bridge was decaying and too narrow and in 1782 an Act of Parliament authorised a replacement slightly upstream at the Skerton crossing. A competition was held and the winning design, by Harrison of Chester, was constructed in 1783–8 at a cost of £14,000. All over the county palatine the bridges of the late eighteenth century survive – splendidly proportioned, built to the highest standards and almost invariably bearing, proudly and justifiably so, the date of construction and often the initials of the bridgemaster. Many were widened in later years without spoiling their elegance and grace.

In general, though and particularly where roads were concerned, the old problems of intransigent local communities, individuals who refused to pay their highway rates and the inability to see the highway network

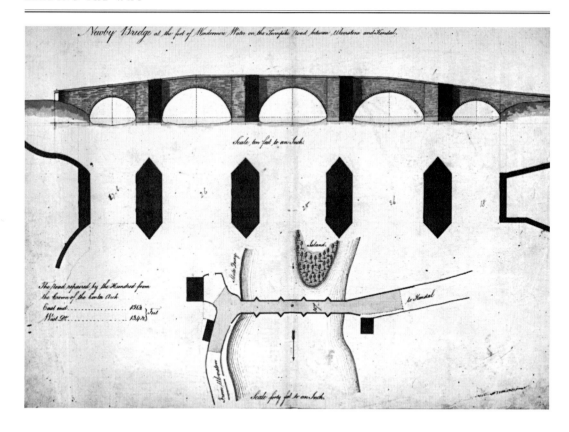

as a whole, remained. It is scarcely surprising that the system of road repair and bridge renewal was often ineffective – although everybody agreed in principle that the work should be done and although all townships welcomed and many requested help from outside to alleviate their own burdens, no individual or community was willing to pay for work further afield. Each saw itself as the only specially deserving case.

The system as a whole depended on voluntary effort, with all the inefficiencies and slownesses which that implied. At Coppull in 1630 the two supervisors of the highways could agree on nothing and, as a result, so some of the inhabitants claimed, the roads had fallen into disrepair. One of the surveyors, William Slater, produced a testimonial signed by forty householders to say that by his 'industry . . . they are nowe sufficiently repayred & Amended'.[69] At Pennington near Leigh, two years earlier, Thomas Smith, the surveyor, said that he had not been able to get anything done 'by reason of the extreame weettnes of the whether' and because of 'the Slownes of his fellowe Surveyor, whoe hath amended lyttle or nothinge'.[70]

Sometimes one pities the conscientious surveyor frustrated by the failure of the inhabitants to pay the money required: at Rainford in 1645, for example, the surveyor lamented that 'the highwayes both for Carte, horse and man, are very sore decayed & out of Raper which

Newby Bridge, over the Leven at the southern end of Windermere, is one of the finest of all Lancashire bridges. It is largely medieval, although there has been much subsequent repair and restoration. The bridge is now on a minor road, but in 1805, when this watercolour plan and elevation was made, the road was the turnpike into Furness. The bridge books from which this and the previous illustration were taken were not only working documents used by the surveyors, but were also beautiful examples of technical drawing and watercolour painting (LRO QAR 6/8).

your peticoner cannot by noe meanes gett money nor worke to make theme passable but hath laid moneys out of his owne pursse to gett some work'.[71] Other inhabitants refused to turn up for their 'community service' on the roads. In 1647 the surveyor of Eccles listed 'them that doth deny to Repeare the high way over against ther own Landes which belongeth to them to day' and also forty-nine people who 'nether Came nor payd nor sent to the Repeare of the high way', among the latter being the vicar, John Jones, who 'should have Carred 6 loades of Stone butt did none at all'.[72] He rather forlornly noted that only eleven people turned up on the appointed day or sent substitutes from among their tenants. Perhaps our sympathies might lie with Joseph Tompson of Sefton, who wrote in 1648 about the damage done by the flooding of the river Alt: 'I made soe many motions about the river Alt, that for some reasons I grew wearie, & sate down'.[73]

CONCLUSION

The road network of Lancashire was a vital aspect of the early industrial and urban development of the county. In the popular imagination, canals and then railways were the driving force which enabled the dramatic changes in the local geography and economy to take place. However, it is now increasingly accepted that the 'Industrial Revolution' was only part of a long evolutionary process – indeed, some argue that there never was a 'Revolution' – which can be traced back to the sixteenth century and perhaps even earlier. The industrialisation of Lancashire, like its urban growth, had much earlier origins than used to be supposed. The first phases of this process occurred long before the development of railways and well before canals were being built in the county. It was the road network which provided the opportunities for transport and the vivid phraseology of the petitions to the justices in the reigns of James I and Charles I make it plain that heavy industrial and commercial traffic was already commonplace and a rapid growth in the use of roads was well under way.

But there were problems: the system of highway administration was confusing, complex and fragmented. Reliance on voluntary labour and voluntary supervision, the cumbersome procedures for raising money and the inadequacy of the means to collect and account for the sums so gathered, the opportunities for embezzlement and the invariable emphasis on economy at the expense of quality made for continuous problems. Above all, the slowness of action and the impossibility of achieving any form of comprehensive solution to the needs of the traveller and the demands of industry and commerce were major deficiencies.

In the long term these inadequacies eventually led to the adoption of turnpikes, but it is striking that, despite industrial and urban growth, Lancashire was comparatively slow to make use of toll roads. It can be argued that the road network of the county was, even in its pre-turnpike state, surprisingly well able to cope with the heavier volumes and new types of traffic. We tend only to hear about the bad times and the problem areas while the routine and ordinary use of the roads receives no mention. The county justices were fully conscious of the need for road improvements, as their very early appointment of salaried officers indicates and – despite the limitations which the system imposed – the network was upgraded and made more effective. Could it be, perhaps, that the late adoption of turnpikes was a tribute to the quality of existing Lancashire roads in the late seventeenth and early eighteenth centuries?

4

On the road: traffic and travellers

I T IS COMMONLY BELIEVED that most people in the past rarely travelled and that they only occasionally moved outside the town or
village of their birth. This is only partly the case: as Mary Higham has
demonstrated in Chapter 2 of this book, there was extensive commercial
and social traffic on Lancashire's roads during the medieval period and
even quite ordinary people could and did travel for local business and
trade. The ease of twentieth-century travel has made modern Lancastrians accustomed to journeying widely and regularly within the county
and beyond and while it would be misleading to suggest that as many
people in earlier centuries travelled as much as most of us do today –
they had neither the means nor the reason to do so – a surprising
number of people did go far afield from time to time.

Some travelled regularly and many carried letters or parcels for friends,
or undertook to purchase items for them in distant places. Even in the
Middle Ages there were carriers who regularly plied between groups
of towns or commercial centres such as large monasteries and by the
eighteenth century this network had become more complex and more
sophisticated. Carriers and mail services ran regularly along a network
of long-distance routes which had London as its hub: Willan's study
of Abraham Dent, an eighteenth-century shopkeeper from Kirkby
Stephen in Westmorland, has demonstrated vividly that even this remote
country town had frequent contact with cities as far away as London,
Newcastle, Norwich, Coventry and Manchester.[1]

Within Lancashire itself, in addition to the local carriers, a very wide
variety of people were regular travellers along the county's roads: they
included vagrants and paupers, itinerant vendors and pedlars, doctors,
farmers, soldiers (serving and discharged) and the gentry, as well as the
thousands of ordinary folk going about the routine life of farm and
town. Most of them remain unsung and their journeys unrecorded –
today, when we go into Manchester on the M61, or drive to work
along a ring road, we usually leave no tangible record of that journey.
So it was in the past – the detailed evidence which we have for travel
and travellers is scanty, sporadic and often biased towards the dramatic
event or the indignant outpouring. Nonetheless, such sources are
fascinating and valuable and help to give us the 'human' picture of the
development of Lancashire's roads.

EARLY TOURISTS

From the early centuries of Lancashire's written history no detailed personal record of the experiences of travellers has survived, but from the sixteenth century onwards such accounts begin to appear. In England there was an increasing interest among leisured and educated people in observing life and industry and in investigating the past – the beginnings of antiquarian and local history can be traced to this period. Travellers came from other parts of the land and recorded what they saw in Lancashire and their often very valuable accounts are some of the first descriptions available to us.

One of the earliest of these travellers was the celebrated John Leland, the first and one of the greatest of the antiquarian historians. The Leyland family of Morleys Hall, near Leigh, were probably his relatives and he called to stay with them on his journey through Lancashire. In 1533 Leland had been granted a commission from the crown, whereby he was to make a search for English antiquities in cathedral libraries, abbeys, priories, colleges and other repositories. He undertook his antiquarian work mainly between 1534 and 1543 and his Lancashire journey probably took place in 1539. As well as recording the antiquarian information which was the main purpose of his journeyings, he was also a shrewd and observant traveller who noted many fascinating contemporary details: time and again, it is Leland who provides us with our earliest reference to a physical feature, a building or an economic activity.[2]

Although Leland did not record much about conditions for the traveller, he detailed his route through the county and described what he saw. He entered Lancashire by way of Crossford Bridge at Stretford, on one of the most important north–south routes in the region; Crossford Bridge was then, as he reports, 'a great bridge of tymbre'. At that date, as the previous chapter illustrates, many bridges were built of stone piers with a timber superstructure, but when Leland reached Manchester he remarked that 'ther be divers stone bridgis in the toune'. He thought the best of these was the three-arched Salford Bridge over the River Irwell. On it there was 'a praty litle chapel': after Leland's time this chapel was used as a town dungeon and it was only demolished in 1779 when the bridge was widened.[3]

Leland did not travel by a very direct route to Morleys when he left Manchester, but this does not mean that there was no direct route to Leigh – rather, he may have simply wanted to observe more of the country. He rode northwards out of the town along the left bank of the Irwell through Broughton and probably turned westwards to cross the river in the neighbourhood of Pilkington Park in Prestwich parish. He described a bridge which was 'veri hy and greate off tymbre in

Irwel' and this is likely to have been at Ringley – although, perhaps strangely, no bridge is shown on this stretch of the river on Saxton's map of 1577.

John Leland arrived in due course at Morleys Hall, a moated building which still stands as a farmhouse and which had 'as much pleasur of orchardes' and walks and gardens 'as ther is in any place of Lancastre-shire'. When he left there he continued northwards through Chorley, noting the millstone quarries nearby and so on to Preston and Garstang. He thus followed the approximate line of the route which became the modern A6. After Garstang he made a detour to go over the Cocker sands, which he passed 'not without sum feare of quikkesands'. He remarked on the nearby saltcotes and then saw Cockersand Abbey 'standing veri blekely and object to al wynddes' before leaving the county by way of Lancaster – those who visit the fragmentary remains of the abbey today will fully appreciate his comments on its bleak and exposed situation.

Leland's journey through Lancashire was not a direct one, but when he chose to go over Cocker sands he was taking one of the old-established north–south ways through the county. Mary Higham has shown in Chapter 2 the way in which the sands crossings and the coastal routeways were of major importance throughout the Middle Ages and this significance continued into modern times. As descriptions of journeys become more widely available it is clear that this was a main thoroughfare. Passengers travelling north from west Cheshire – indeed, from the important town of 'Westchester', as Chester was sometimes known – could save many miles and, in north Lancashire and Cumbria, much hilly country by following the coastal route.

People frequently forded the river Mersey at Hale, near Liverpool, then crossed the south-west Lancashire plain to the ford over the Ribble from Hesketh Bank to Warton. The ford at Hale was a formidably difficult crossing, even bearing in mind that the river channel has been deepened in more modern times to allow progressively larger ships to reach Manchester. There are several accounts of the ford being used during the Civil War. Edward Robinson, who took part in the war, tells how in 1643 Lord Molineux marched his troops 'over Liverpool Watter at Hales ford [and] fled into Cheshire' and how, later, Sir John Meldrum marched with troops into Ormskirk and attacked an enemy force who 'fled in a most confused manner towardes Liverpoole and Hailles ford and soe quitting the Countie into Cheshire and into Walles'. After the siege of Bolton in 1644, royalist troops marched towards Liverpool, taking prisoners with them 'tyed twoo and twoo together and forced over Liverpool Watter at Hales ford when it was too deep, almost for horses to goe. They must wade over either in their Cloathes or putting them off carry them upon their neckes'.[4]

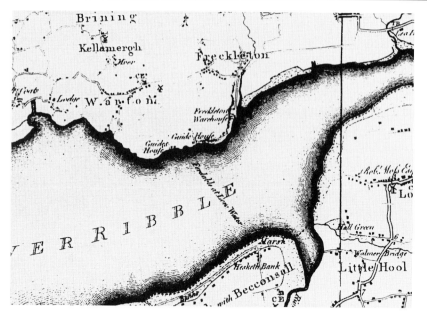

Part of William Yates' Map of Lancashire of 1786: Yates marks the sands crossings over Morecambe Bay and also shows the ford over the river Ribble at Hesketh Bank. On the northern bank he marks two guide houses, at Freckleton and Warton. The location of the ford may perhaps have shifted, or it is possible that a new house had more recently been built for the guide.

When the northbound traveller reached Hesketh Bank he could employ the services of the Warton guide to see him across the estuary. In 1655 this man was William Tomlinson, who in that year petitioned the quarter sessions for an allowance towards buying a horse, because 'the peticoner hath served the people of the Comonwealth as guide over the same River for the space of ffortie yeares and upwards and hath beene readie upon all seasonable tymes and occasions with himselfe & his horse to guide and preserve passengers from the danger of the water. In that tyme and service [he] hath lost above the number of Ten horses'. Very significantly, William Tomlinson calls the route 'the high Roade from Chester to Lancaster and into divers other parts'.[5] Local people, as well as long distance travellers, used the ford and the account books of the steward at Lytham Hall record many payments to the Ribble guide for leading passengers over the river between 1697 and 1705, sometimes with carts:

 1 Sep 1697 Paid William Jumpe for guiding cart 3 times over Ribble and me once, 3s. 6d.

 30 Oct 1697 Paid Roger what he paid for a guide over Ribble when he fetched linen cloth 6d.

 3 Jul 1698 Paid William Abram for bringing carts over Ribble with oats 1s. 0d.[6]

Having crossed the river at Warton, our traveller would then move onwards across the Fylde, crossing the Wyre by one of its fords and so towards the coast and the Cocker estuary, avoiding the wastes of

Pilling Moss. Until the Reformation the monks at Cockersand had helped to guide travellers over the sands, a vital public service. Following the dissolution of the monasteries the officials of the Duchy of Lancaster recorded the duties which had previously been performed for coastal travellers by the local religious houses and made arrangements for these to be continued. It was noted that

> it is very necessarie to have one bell at Cokersande [and] one bell at Cartemele and another bell at Conyshed to be kepte styll hangynge in the Staples [steeples] there to be ronge & used as a watche & knowledge for Guydinge of the kyngs subietts ovr the Sands & Wasshes there in tyme of mysts & other Danngerouse tempests risynge upon the same.[7]

It was recommended that at Conishead the new lessee of the demesnes should provide a fire (as a beacon) and an officer to ring a bell when necessary to guide passengers over the sands and the lessees of Cartmel and Cockersand lands were each to provide a guide over the nearby sands,[8] but the Duchy itself undertook to employ one Thomas Hogeson as guide over Kent sands on the Hest Bank to Cartmel crossing. This office and that of a guide over the Leven sands, are still supported by the Duchy today.

After continuing through Ashton to Lancaster, the traveller could follow the main road towards Kendal, although this route became hilly. In 1698 Celia Fiennes made a diversion through the park at Leighton Hall and so avoided some of the road, which she described as 'stony and steep far worse than the Peake in Darbyshire'.[9] This was certainly an exaggeration, but it is clear that many people did choose to avoid this route and went instead over the Morecambe Bay sands from Hest Bank to Cartmel thence to western Cumbria and eventually to Carlisle. Even if the route between Carnforth and Kendal was not in itself a great deterrent, the fearsome prospect of crossing Shap or Kirkstone loomed before them – and to many travellers that was most definitely to be avoided.

Celia Fiennes was already a seasoned traveller by the time her journey through Lancashire began. She was the granddaughter of the first Viscount Saye and Sele and her home was in the south of England. From there she made journeys throughout the country on horseback, recording her experiences in a journal. Her approach to Lancashire brought her across the ford over the Dee estuary from Flintshire to Burton in Wirral, then northwards to the Mersey and by ferry to Liverpool, the boat taking an hour and a half to cross the estuary. On leaving Liverpool she did not choose the coastal route but went instead through Prescot to Wigan.

Some of the streets in the towns were paved. She describes those in Liverpool, Prescot and Preston as 'well pitch'd': 'pitching' was paving with stones, especially stones set on edge. Outside the towns it was a

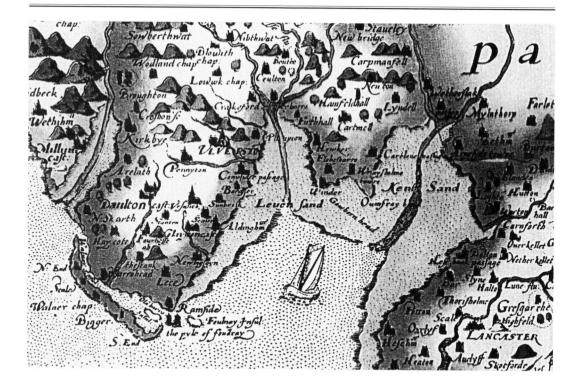

different matter and between Prescot and Wigan she went 'mostly in lanes and some hollow wayes and some pretty deep stony way so forced us upon the high Causey many [times]' – sometimes particularly steep or difficult sections of road were accompanied by a raised, paved causeway along one side, especially on routes used regularly by pack-horse traffic. She writes that fourteen miles of the journey here took her five hours and that she could have covered thirty miles near London in the same time.

After a short detour to visit the famous burning well just outside Wigan, Celia Fiennes rode north to Preston, which was reckoned, she says, 'but 12 miles from Wiggon but they exceed in length by farre those that I thought long the day before from Leverpoole'. She went out of her way to avoid the marshy places and when commenting on the high arches of the bridges she was told that the reason for their height was the need to accommodate flood water after heavy rain. She calls the bridges 'but narrow bridges for foot or horse'; where this was so, carts would have forded the streams somewhere nearby. Her way continued through Preston and Garstang to Lancaster, where she had 'a pleasing prospect of the countrys a great distance round' and saw it 'full of inclosures and some woods' and the cross roads well signed with 'Posts with Hands'. In Lancaster there were some paved streets, but her horse stumbled on some of the slippery stones by the channels in the road.

Christopher Saxton's Map of Lancashire of 1577 does not show roads, but it indicates the crossings of More-cambe Bay and the Leven estuary with the names Hest Bank passage, Cartlone pas-sage and Conyside [Conishead] passage. Saxton does not show the fords across the rivers Ribble or Cocker which are known from other contemporary sources.

Another well-known traveller was Daniel Defoe, whose account of his journeys in Lancashire first appeared in print in *A Tour Through the Whole Island of Great Britain*, published in 1724–6.[10] Although doubt has sometimes been expressed as to whether Defoe's descriptions were written entirely from his own experience, the account of his arrival in Liverpool by ferry certainly has the ring of authenticity. He writes that

> I entred Lancashire at the remotest western point of that county. Here is a ferry over the Mersee, which, at full sea, is more than two miles over. We land on the flat shore on the [Liverpool] side and are contented to ride through the water for some length, not on horseback but on the shoulders of some honest Lancashire clown, who comes knee deep to the boat side, to truss you up and then runs away with you, as nimbly as you desire to ride, unless his trot were easier; for I was shaken by him that I had the luck to be carry'd by more than I car'd for and much worse than a hard trotting horse would have shaken me.

On another day Defoe travelled from Rochdale over Blackstone Edge into Yorkshire. It was August, but they saw the hills ahead covered with snow as they began their journey. They started to climb 'and though the snow which had fallen in the night lay a little upon the ground, yet we thought it was not so much'; but as they went onwards they found it was still snowing at the highest levels.

> It is not easy to express the consternation we were in when we came up near the top of the mountain; the wind blew exceeding hard and blew the snow so directly in our faces and that so thick, that it was impossible to keep our eyes open to see our way. The ground also was so covered with snow, that we could see no track, or when we were in the way, or when out; except when we were shewed it by a frightful precipice on one hand and uneven ground on the other.

They eventually completed their journey safely, but Defoe's alarm had been very real. Bad weather could be a danger to life for the traveller.

MILITARY MANOEUVRES

Lancashire's position on one of the main routes from Scotland to England made the county particularly vulnerable when relations between the two countries descended into warfare. Occasionally the Scots, in their recurring forays into England, reached Lancashire. One of their most devastating incursions was that of 1322, when some raiders arrived by the coastal route, crossing the Duddon sands to Furness where the abbot paid a ransom to avoid destruction of abbey property – it was not the first time the abbey had received the attentions of Scottish raiders. The Scots then crossed the sands to Lancaster, where they were joined by another party which had arrived by way of Kendal. Together they moved south through Preston and Chorley, plundering adjacent areas on the way and local folk fled before their advance.

Other local people capitalised on the confusion to prey upon their fellow citizens. In subsequent tribunals John and William, the sons of Warin de Goldeburn, William Prymerole, Henry Hogg, William del Kar, Alice late the wife of Hugh le clerk, Matilda de la Halle of Longeton and John and Richard, sons of Adam de Moutheslegh, were all named as having robbed 'certain people who were fleeing before the Scots at the bridge of Loststock [sic], namely John le Tailour, Ellen de Plesington and several others, of goods and chattels, to wit, clothes, corn and sundry other goods, to the value of £10'. Another group of men was accused of having stolen 'ten oxen belonging to the abbot of Holcoltram [Holm Cultram], Patrick de Colewenne and others and cows and mares belonging to certain men who were fleeing before the Scots at Anderton near Horwych, to the value of £10'.[11]

In November 1715, when the Jacobites marched southwards, their route took them through Kirkby Lonsdale to Lancaster, where James Edward, son of James II, was proclaimed King James III. Some 4,000 Jacobites then marched through Garstang to Preston, where they were defeated by government troops. Apart from the alarm that so many rebels and soldiers must have caused in the villages as they passed, the commandeering of food and the demand for shelter would have depleted the already slender resources of many wayside cottagers. Sometimes there was violence. The Gressingham parish registers record how in 1745, when the Scots visited the county again, a Highlander stripped a man on the moors and sent him home in his clogs.[12] This second Jacobite army marched through Lancashire in November and continued as far south as Derby, passing through Manchester on the way. After their advance was abandoned, the soldiers streamed back the way they had come and must have presented a sorry spectacle compared with that of the enthusiastic troops who had marched southwards behind Bonnie Prince Charlie. Dr Richard Kay of Bury recorded in his diary on 10 December 1745 that

> Having never seen the Rebells, or any in a Highland Dress, I set out this Morning on Foot in Company with some other Friends to see them march on the Road from Manchester to Wigan, we went to a Place called four Lane Ends in Hilton [Hulton], where the Rebells marched from one o'th'Clock till betwixt four and five o'th'Clock in the Afternoon as throng as the Road cou'd well receive them. I suppose their Number may be near 10000 Men in all.[13]

A field on the outskirts of Wardley, not far south of Hulton, was known at the end of the eighteenth century as Rebel Field and a strong local tradition told how rebel soldiers had camped there overnight on their return northwards. A group of soldiers is said to have visited nearby Wardley Hall, where they forcibly commandeered carts and horses. This so impoverished the tenant family that the son started to pull down an old part of the building to make room to house some looms, so that they could earn a living. It is said that while doing this he found a box containing the famous Wardley skull, which is now thought to be that of St Ambrose Barlow, the recusant priest and is still kept beside the staircase at Wardley Hall.[14]

The very great burden on individual communities which military activity – whether by rebels or by loyal troops of the Crown – represented is well exemplified by a petition to the quarter sessions from the constables of Garstang township in July 1689. Garstang was, by virtue of its position on the great northern highway, particularly affected by the movement of troops, as the records of the '15 and the '45 indicate. In 1689 the problem was rather different. Fierce war between Protestants, under William III and Catholics under the deposed king James II, was raging in Ireland and the government was moving troops through Lancashire to embark for the short sea crossing.

The constables complained of 'the very great Burthen of Lodging the Kings soldiers who daily March through the said Townshipp', but more particularly of the fact that these soldiers requisitioned 'Horses & Carts for carrying Armes Ammonition & other necessarys'. It was claimed that no fewer than fifty-eight carts and over 270 horses had been officially commandeered, but that in addition 'many horses the Souldiers have seized of their owne accord' – footsore and weary, the common soldiers took the opportunity for a free ride! The righteously indignant case of the Garstang constables is somewhat marred by their request that, to compensate for the losses of their own township, the people of Garstang should be allowed in turn to seize the horses and carts belonging to neighbouring communities which, 'Lyeing out of the Common Road . . . are unwilling to yield your Petitioners any assistants herein'. The magistrates, in a classic prevarication, said that they would 'take this into consideration' and did no more.[15]

Although times of unrest could produce spectacular sights such as these on the roads, occasions of this sort were mercifully rare. However, individual soldiers could often be seen on their way to or from barracks or ports, or returning home injured or sick. For example, two lame soldiers were helped on their way between Chester and York by the Manchester constable in 1612–13: his accounts record payment to them of 1s. 6d. 'to goe to Yorke one horse backe and towardes theare Releeffe'.[16] The same accounts regularly show payments to soldiers travelling across country in ones and twos; those paid in 1633–5 were on their way to Hull, Cockermouth, Carlisle, Kendal (two soldiers who had come from Bath), Exeter, 'the lowe Cuntries', Durham (two soldiers from Cornwall), Gloucester, 'Hartingpoole', Richmond and two soldiers who travelled with a pass from the governor of the Tower of London. Constables' accounts for Padiham show similar payments; in January 1698 the constable there paid 'for lodgin a soueldar All night and for reliving 7 and Careing [carrying] 6 of them 4 miles with towe horses 2s. 6d.' Other instances occur in eighteenth-century Padiham accounts.[17]

Some of the military traffic was of a heavier kind. On 7 April 1639 the Manchester constables paid £3 10s. 0d. 'for hireing wagins to carie salt-peetr vessells towards York'. Earlier accounts show that the saltpetre men had been busy in Manchester since at least 1628. Saltpetre was a component of gunpowder and was derived from earth collected from old, dry stables, pigeon lofts and sheep stalls by the saltpetre men. Carriage of other heavy goods for military use is recorded in the same accounts: during the winter of 1644–5 several journeys were made to Ormskirk, such as that on 25 November 1644, when 9s. 3d. was paid for 'carryinge victualls to Ormischurch' and on 1 January the following year 10s. 0d. was expended 'for Carryinge Magazene to Ormischurch'. Ormskirk was close to Lathom House, which had been held successfully against parliamentarian troops earlier in 1644 but was to be again besieged in the summer of 1645: staunchly parliamentarian Manchester was assisting the besieging forces with supplies of food and arms.

ROGUES . . .

Soldiers did not usually pose a serious risk to the ordinary public unless a battle was taking place, although the man sent home in his clogs from the Gressingham moorland might have thought differently and an entry in the Didsbury parish register for 10 December 1745 leaves something to the imagination when it tells of 'a poor man buried at Dids: found dead in Heaton w[he]n ye Rebels past'.[18] Robbers, however, were another matter and – especially for strangers and the more prosperous-looking travellers – lonely roads were places to avoid except in cases of necessity.

In the 1630s William Tempest of Great Lever, near Bolton, was in the service of the bishop of Chester, John Bridgeman, who had a house at Great Lever. On 27 January 1634 Tempest had been travelling 'upon speciall occasion' between Blackburn and Turton when he saw ahead of him three armed men, two with swords and cudgels and one with a bastinado (a heavy stick or baton). William dallied cautiously until they were 'gotten two fields bredth from him', but then they turned and saw him. One of the men stood on top of a stone wall so that he could be sure that William was unaccompanied, then all the men ran to meet him, made ready their weapons and one tried to catch hold of his horse's bridle. William turned round and rode off quickly and escaping them he 'called for ayde in a towne called Entwisley'. Continuing on his way towards Bolton, he found two of the men by the road half a mile further on: they saw him and pulled out their swords but, doubtless to William's relief, other people came along and one of the robbers asked the way to Bolton, leaving William Tempest to finish his journey and relate his harrowing tale. It seems likely that his narrow escape took place on the old Roman road between Blackburn and Edgworth.[19]

Less fortunate than William Tempest was a man robbed of nine guineas by two footpads near Middleton in October 1770. The report in the *Manchester Mercury* for 16 October does not name him, but tells how, although he was 'much wounded in the Struggle', he followed his attackers. They, however, turned and caught him and threatened to murder him and 'upon his earnest Entreaties to spare his Life, they bound him Neck and Heels and threw him over the Pails of an adjoining Park'. The same newspaper relates other attacks. On 29 March 1774 it was reported that 'on Tuesday Morning last, James Ratcliffe, who carries this newspaper betwixt Manchester and Burnley, was attacked on the road at Cross bank, betwixt Bury and Haslingden, by two Footpads, who after knocking him down demanded his Money; and robbed him of £5 8s. 6d. with which they got off undiscovered'. The issue of 29 December 1778 reported an attack on a post-boy who was carrying mail from Manchester to Rochdale on a Sunday afternoon. He was attacked between Blakewith Bridge and Redivals, by

> two Highwaymen and a Foot Pad, who at first stopped and struck him twice, after which they pulled him off his Horse, when they robbed him of three Guineas and seven shillings and six-pence in Silver, with which they made off. After the Robbery the Foot Pad immediately got up behind one of the Highwaymen, when they both struck up on the Gallop, towards Manchester.

On 20 July 1773 the *Manchester Mercury* carried a notice that one Benjamin Thorp was being sought for highway robbery. He was quickly apprehended, for on 26 July the Manchester constables paid £2 14s. 0d. for 'conveying Ben. Thorpe to Lancas[te]r for Highway robbery'. It was eventually decided to prosecute him at Chester assizes with another local highwayman, Edward Edwards, otherwise known as 'Long Ned'. The constables had to redeem a silver watch that had been pawned 'by some of the Gang' so that it could be used in evidence.[20]

. . . AND VAGABONDS

Although they were less alarming than highwaymen, the paupers and vagabonds who wandered the roads of the county were treated at best with wariness and at worst with hostility and sometimes brutality, by the inhabitants of the places through which they passed. There were many poor, homeless people who journeyed, begging, from place to place. Others were travelling to sell goods, in an attempt to make a precarious living. No doubt local tradesmen kept a wary eye on their goods as these destitute or near-destitute wanderers passed by. Some vagrants were quite clearly more sinned against than sinning: in March 1631 the Manchester constables paid 2s. od. to Hughe Edwards 'who had his tongue cutt out by theeves and had a passe to gather the releife of well disposed people'.[21]

In 1630 two travelling stocking-sellers, Elizabeth Johnson and Jane Clarke, were put in the stocks at Poulton-le-Fylde, accused of stealing clothing which Ellen Bisbrowne of Little Poulton had left on bushes to dry in the June sunshine. Their statement to the magistrates is eloquent about the lifestyles of wanderers. Elizabeth, a native of Langtree near Wigan, claimed to have married John Johnson at Newark-upon-Trent in February 1630. They then walked back to Lancashire, hired a cottage at Langtree for a few weeks and there knitted stockings. She and her husband had then set out on the road again, to sell the stockings, '& there upon they travelled up & downe Lancashire sometymes her husband and shee together and sometimes hee through one parte & shee through other parts of the County, shee . . . sometimes begging and sometimes working to helpe her selfe withall'. They met Jane and Thomas Clarke at 'a Lodgeing house about the ffylde, but the place shee cannot name, because shee is a stranger in that part of Lancashire' [it was in fact at Garstang] and then went with them 'all beyond wyer', before the men went off to Preston and the women to Poulton – they arranged to meet at Preston market on the following Saturday, but temptation got the better of Jane and Elizabeth and they ended up in the stocks.[22]

Parish registers record many deaths of vagrants, known and unknown. At Wigan, Richard Hinde, a vagrant, was buried on 4 February 1604, followed on 5 March by 'a poore vagrant child'. On 2 July 1608, also at Wigan, there was buried 'Ann dau[ghter] to a poore traveling woman layd in [brought to childbed] at Myles Seddones Aspoll [Aspull]'. At Lancaster two beggars, Issabell Tompson and Elizabeth Wattson, were buried on the same day in July 1635. Some vagrants were crippled, unable to earn a living and forced to beg for food, like the 'cripple unknown' who was buried at Walton on the Hill in January 1631, or the 'poore woman criple died in the streete whose name is not knowne', who was buried at Manchester in February 1622.[23]

People not only died upon the road, but were also born there. The parish registers of Heaton Norris record the baptism there, on 17 November 1789, of 'John, bastard son of Uriah Thompson, formerly of Manchester and now of Huddersfield, by Ellen Lee of Bramall, late servant to Mr. Cooke of Brazen Nose Street, Manchester. He was delivered in a caravan upon the High Road and taken to Thomas Whiteleggs upon Manchester Hill'.[24]

LOST ON A STORMY NIGHT

Vagrants were not usually a danger to travellers, although they might be embarrassing and inconvenient. In contrast, bad weather and the impenetrable darkness of a night without a moon, represented a serious risk to all travellers, whether they went on foot, on horseback or in a vehicle. During the intense cold of December, 1627, there was buried at Eccles 'Randle Starkie gent perished in Broomhous lane in a frostie night'. His burial was followed later in the month by John, son of Thomas Lightbowne of Broomhouse Lane, who 'perished on Swinton More in a stormie night'.[25] Swinton Moor was a town moor on the outskirts of Worsley: it was certainly not high Pennine moorland, yet in the cold and dark of winter John Lightbowne had died, lonely and lost, as isolated as if he had been far from any habitation.

The total darkness of a moonless night is a circumstance of which modern urban dwellers have little concept. Yet the basic danger of simply not being able to see where you were going was ever-present and very real. In December 1748 Dr Richard Kay, who three years earlier had walked to see the rebels pass by at Hulton, was returning from Crawshawbooth in Rossendale – where he had been visiting a patient – to his home at Baldingstone a little to the north of Bury. He was accompanied by James Lord, of Newchurch in Rossendale and Richard Kay records in his diary that when he was riding over a stone bridge behind Mr Lord

> I said, It is very dark; he answered, So dark It is all I can do to see the Bridge; he had no sooner said so but my Horse in the highest Part of the Bridge went over the Battlement, I light flat upon my Hands and Knees in the Water with my Face down the Stream and my Horse in the Fall turned so much that he lay upon his Feet on my right Side with his Head up the Water, I immediately got upon my Feet; Mr Lord called out, How are You Doctor; I answered, All is well, God be thanked for it; he said, How is your Horse . . .

At first Dr Kay thought his horse was dead, but feeling for him in the dark ('I was in great Darkness and Confusion') the horse stirred. Richard Kay's foot was still in the stirrup. They got up and continued home. Two days later the doctor travelled the same road again and on measuring the height of the bridge above the water found it to be almost eighteen feet.[26] Darkness was indeed dangerous and plainly the guinea expended by the Manchester constables in 1631 upon '3 pound of Candles for the watch in the Darke nights when itt was not mooneshine' was money wisely spent.[27]

ROAD ACCIDENTS

Horses could themselves be a risk for road travellers. In 1738 Richard Kay's father had been pulled from his horse and slightly trampled, though fortunately not seriously hurt, when he had met some horses yoked together in a narrow road. In April 1743 William Stout of Lancaster was knocked down and trampled by a runaway horse.[28] Between the sixteenth and the eighteenth centuries local records, such as parish registers, recount the deaths of numerous people killed by horses and by carts. For example, Thomas Wilkinsone of Rusholme (Manchester) was killed in 1583 'by a falle in getting on Horsbacke', while other deaths include Richard Thomasis of Rowe Lane, buried on 18 June 1751 at North Meols, having been 'killed out of a Marl cart' and Peter Halsall, a husbandman, of Ainsdale, buried in July 1789 after he had been killed by falling from a cart.[29]

OVER THE WATER

Occasionally the traveller's journey could be enlivened by local disturbances. Symon Leake of Halton, husbandman, was travelling towards Halton from Lancaster one Sunday in January 1628/9 when 'Comeinge to Lancaster bridge end' he saw Tristram Wallis with his wife and two sons, John and William, 'Quarellinge and ffightinge w[i]th Anne Parkinson and did heare the said Tristram cale her the said Anne Arrant whore and theefe and also sayth that hee did see the said Wallis wyfe spitt in her face' and John and William beat Anne 'w[i]th their fistes'.[30]

Travellers such as Symon Leake and the quarrelling Wallises and Parkinsons used bridges whenever they could, because crossing water could be perilous. Again, the burial registers – the source of so much information about the long-forgotten local tragedies of the past – record details of drownings and other accidents at river crossings. The Ashton-under-Lyne registers record the burial on 4 October 1630 of Mrs Marie Houlcrofte

who with her brother attemptinge the ford on horse backe in the watter houses being strangers to it and the watter verie hye were bothe over-

The milestone at Cartmel which records the distances to Lancaster via the over-sands route. The savings in mileage and journey time which the sands crossings represented were so great that they far outweighed the dangers and inconvenience of the crossing itself. This remained the most important route from Lancashire to Furness until the coming of the railway in the 1840s – even the improvements in turnpikes in the early nineteenth century did not put an end to the use of the sands *(H. Hodson)*.

whelmed the 29: 7br [September] before the daie aforesaid and shee was found the daie after but her brother was not at the recording hereof found.

Some years earlier, in September 1600, Issabell Gregson, alias Parker, illegitimate daughter of Thomas Parker of Grastonlee in Bowland, had been drowned crossing the river on a 'heble' or plank bridge: she was buried at Chipping. At Ribchester 'Richard Dewhurst ye boteman was drouned y[e] 2 day of January in ye year of our Lord 1699 [1700 N.S.]' – a 'lower boat' and an 'upper boate' are referred to in seventeenth-century parish register entries at Ribchester. In the north of the county Katharine, daughter of Thomas Stackhouse of Burton, was buried at Thornton in Lonsdale in January 1714, having been drowned 'attempting to pass ye water between Gressingham and Hornby'.[31]

The ford over the Mersey estuary at Hale has already been mentioned, but there were others, including a particularly dangerous crossing from Runcorn to Widnes. There the narrowing of the river meant that the currents were stronger and to ford here was especially hazardous – but people persisted. Local records tell of a tragedy in 1654:

> Richard Jackson and Ellen his daughter were both drowned the 15 day of July, being Saturday morneing in going over The Ford att Runcorn to the Colepitt and he was found and taken up the Sunday after and buried and Ellen was found the 19 at Ditton Poole and bury[ed] at Runcorne at night.[32]

The medieval evidence recounted in Chapter 2 shows that drownings on the oversands route were frequent over the centuries and the loss of life continued until, by the mid-nineteenth century, the turnpikes and the railway offered fast and safer alternatives to the direct route. Sometimes several people were drowned at one time. In one notorious incident in June 1846, for example, nine young people, aged between 16 and 28, were drowned on Ulverston sands when the cart in which they were riding back to Flookburgh from Ulverston Fair sank into a hole called Black Scarr. Contemporary accounts tell how 'every one of them was quickly and silently engulphed without exciting the observation of others who were following in the same direction'. On another occasion, on 30 May 1857, a party of a dozen farm labourers drowned crossing the Keer estuary. There had been some drinking, so perhaps their judgment was not of the best when they reached Priest Skear, a mile off the ordinary track. There the cart was upset by being driven into a waterfilled hole and the passengers were thrown into the water and all drowned.[33] Local people might have to bury the drowned bodies of people whose identity was not known; on 3 May 1736 the Bolton-le-Sands parishioners buried 'a man drowned upon the Sands afterwards known to be Nicholas Sharp of Preston'.[34]

An early Victorian engraving of a coach crossing the sands of the Leven estuary near Ulverston; while the dramatic mountain scenery may be somewhat exaggerated the picture gives a vivid impression of the route, which had been used for thousands of years but which, very shortly after this picture was produced, would be made redundant – except for leisure and pleasure crossings – by the coming of the railway *(Redding*, An Illustrated Itinerary of the County of Lancaster, *1842).*

Sir George Head, who visited Lancashire during his tour of the manufacturing districts in 1835, gave a vivid account of his passage from Hest Bank to Cartmel. Because the regular coach now went overland along the turnpike road and had ceased to make this crossing, Sir George hired a conveyance from Lancaster. 'It resembled a baker's covered cart and was drawn by a pair of well-bred horses, one in the shafts and the other on an out-rigger'. A number of carriers and other people assembled on the shore to make the crossing and set off 'at straggling intervals' in a line 'so far extended as barely to keep each other in sight'. The oversands guide on a white mare came out to lead the party and when they reached the River Keer, which ran out across the sands, the guide led the way,

> holding the skirts of his coat together with one hand, over the pummel of his saddle, as the white mare plunged up to her girts in the water, [and] our driver kept his vehicle close to the animal's tail. The breadth of the river was about a couple of hundred yards; the tide set out exceedingly strong and the water reached above the bottom of the carriage, on which a heavy stress was laid. The horses, both active and well bred, reeled

occasionally from side to side, exerting their utmost strength to stem the torrent; in the meantime it became indispensable, in order to counteract the delusive impression on the senses caused by the motion of the water, to keep the eyes fixed on some stationary point a-head.[35]

It must always have been with very considerable relief that passengers on an oversands coach finally reached the safety of dry land.

PACKHORSE TRAFFIC

Most goods were carried by road until the coming of canals and railways. Where navigable rivers or coastal shipping routes could be used to transport heavy loads merchants took advantage of this opportunity, but for most goods water carriage was not available. In Lancashire, furthermore, until the early eighteenth century there was – with the exception of the Mersey and Irwell up to Manchester – no navigable river which penetrated far inland.

Waggons were widely used for bulk transport in the lowland areas, but in the hilly country and especially in the high Pennines, packhorses could more easily travel. Pack animals, both individually and in trains, were used extensively across the county and beyond. Packhorses carried many heavy items as well as small goods; coal and limestone, for instance, were regular cargoes.

Sometimes the probate inventories of farmers and tradesmen in the

The packhorse causeway at Tockholes: raised and paved causeways for pack animals were made in many places on heavily-used routes, but because of their subsequent abandonment, or the improvement and widening of roads, few examples now survive. The causeway at Tockholes, which became known locally as 'The Flags', lay on the route from Bolton to Blackburn, on a section now bypassed by an alternative road following more level ground to the east. It was photographed in 1981, but in 1995 it has become so overgrown that it appears only as a grassy roadside bank *(author)*.

Packhorse at Clitheroe: writing of Clitheroe, Stephen Clarke could recall a string of packhorses 'creeping up Moor Lane' as late as 1865, but by that date packhorses had been almost entirely superseded by canal and rail transport. Genuine photographs of pack animals are therefore extremely rare. This picture was taken in the Clitheroe area, showing a pony which lived until 1902, so it can be dated to the late nineteenth century. The pony and his elderly master were then one of the last survivals of what was once a very common means of transporting goods (*Lancashire County Library: Clitheroe Local Studies Collection*).

sixteenth and seventeenth centuries include furniture for pack animals, although this was usually only for one or two horses and not for a whole train. Alexander Lowe of Flixton, for example, had 'packsadles with their furniture and halters' worth £1 5s. 4d. in 1623 and Leonard Platt of the same village had 'saddles and wontales' in 1637 – a 'wantow' was a band used to tie a pack onto the back of an animal and had a variety of spellings that few words can equal! Margret Cheetome of Farnworth (Bolton) had a 'packe saddle wombtie and overlay' among her goods in January 1598 and as she also had looms, spinning wheels and yarn she probably needed the packhorse to carry her textile materials.[36]

Packhorses were not only used for local journeys. In 1571 Robert Shaw, a Colne clothier, was regularly driving packhorses loaded with cloth to London and East Anglia.[37] Even earlier in the sixteenth century there was a well-established trade carrying woollen cloth from Kendal to Southampton for export, as the port accounts of Southampton show. In 1527 fourteen Kendalmen are recorded as taking a total of thirty-four packs of cloth there and the double journey has been estimated as taking just over four weeks. This traffic would have been seen on the roads of Lancashire and the port accounts show that some Lancashire traders also sent woollen cloths to Southampton. Nicholas Howarth of Blackburn and Thomas Hardman of Bolton regularly took goods there between 1569 and 1583 and other people with Lancashire names are also recorded.[38]

In the Clitheroe area the trains of ponies carrying limestone were a familiar sight until the mid-nineteenth century. The ponies were known as 'lime gals', the word 'gal' being a common abbreviation of 'Galloway', a small, sturdy breed of pony used in coal pits as well as in the pack-horse trade. Stephen Clarke recalled packhorse trains at Clitheroe.

> The lime gals which so regularly came into the town from Sabden, Padiham, Burnley and district were a pleasing spectacle as they drowsily bore their dusty burdens along the highways ladened with coal, coke or slates and taking back lime. I can remember seeing a string of them creeping up Moor Lane past the National School, about the year 1865.[39]

Hewitson, in his *History of Preston*, records that packhorse trains regularly passed through the town *en route* between Liverpool and Lancaster in 1756 and in 1753 the Kendal carriers were operating not only in Westmorland but also as far south as Wigan with weekly packhorse trains. The service provided by them required no fewer than 354 horses, an indication of the great scale of the trade. Some eight packhorse carriers operated from Burnley in the 1820s, based at the *Old Red Lion* inn.[40]

The condition of the packhorse routes was of great importance to traders and in their wills some of them made bequests intended for the improvement of causeways or bridges. For example, John Hanworth, a chapman and clothier of Bury, died in 1570. He was a prosperous tradesman who had trading connections with London and he left money to improve local roads:[41]

> £10 to gain interest for 1 year then to maintain roads in Bury and Bolton & upon poor maids marriages.
>
> Mending of Salforde Strete, 20s.
>
> Mending of Firwoode bridge between Herwoode . . . & Bolton 20s.
>
> Mending the platting anenste Trafforde . . . 10s.★
>
> Mending the waye in Chetham lane . . .
>
> ★ a plat (see chapter 2) was a small bridge made of planks or some-times from a flat stone.

In 1607 John Barrow of Culcheth, chapman, left 6s. 8d. 'towards the making of a pavement in Fernehead Lane'. He stipulated that if the paving had not been done within a year of his death the money had to go to 'the mending of the foote waie over fearnshead Common from Culcheth to Warrington with stone flaggs'. In 1608 Edmund Tasker of Walton-le-Dale, flaxman, left 20s. 'to the pavinge of the Lane between the dwelling house of Thomas Shore in Walton and the dwelling house of William Charnley of the same towne. viz. the highe step'. The 'highe step' must surely have been a raised causeway. Edmund Tasker also left money towards 'makinge of a bridge at the maine brookes'.[42]

CATTLE DROVING

Cattle were regularly driven in large numbers along the roads of Lancashire, often for very considerable distances, for this was a traffic which was inter-regional in its scope. Stock was often fattened in upland pastures and then driven down to the lowlands for sale or consumption. In Chapter 2 Mary Higham highlights the medieval evidence for long-distance stock movements and it is apparent from the more numerous post-medieval written sources that this traffic grew in importance during the sixteenth and seventeenth centuries.

Craven and the north-east Lancashire Pennines were an important area for cattle fattening and in the eighteenth century John Aikin states that at the Monday market in Bolton 'the cattle killed by the butchers are brought chiefly from Yorkshire and mostly consist of Scotch cows, called cushes, fattened in Craven'.[43] Local markets and fairs drew in stock from surrounding areas as well as from more distant parts. Some markets were in the larger towns such as Blackburn, which had a fortnightly cattle market, but others, such as the cattle fair held at Weeton in the Fylde, were in rural areas – Richard Watson has pointed to the proximity not only of Weeton fair but also of Pilling and other local markets to the route along the Lancashire coast.[44] The growing industrial towns required increasing quantities of fresh meat and Aikin, writing in 1795, estimates that the number of animals killed weekly in Bolton was between thirty-five and seventy, whereas within living memory it had only been about two cows a week.[45] John Holt, writing at about the same date, reports that cattle for Lancashire were being supplied from Westmorland, Durham, Yorkshire, Lincolnshire, Derbyshire, Shropshire, Wales, Ireland and Scotland, with Nottinghamshire additionally supplying some animals specifically for the Manchester market.[46]

Before the coming of the railways all these animals were driven by

Weeton Cattle Fair: Weeton, between Kirkham and Blackpool, was a local trading centre from at least 1670, when the earl of Derby obtained a charter for a weekly market and annual cattle fair. The market seems to have been a non-starter, but because Weeton lay on the 'west coast route' through the county (via the various estuarine fords and sands crossings) the fairs enjoyed a modest success. The cattle fair, held on the Tuesday following Trinity Sunday, was of local importance and still took place in the early years of the twentieth century. By 1928, when the Ministry of Agriculture and Fisheries listed markets and fairs in England and Wales, it was said to be practically extinct (reproduced from a postcard; Lancashire County Library).

road and occasionally documentary references to drovers have survived. Ottes Sagar of Colne, 'drovier', who died in 1595 was quite prosperous, his household goods including 'thre table Clots and two towels', four 'quishings' (cushions), a pewter chamber pot and other pewter goods. His clothes included 'ij shirts and iiij or [quattuor] bands', two 'hatts' and two rings of gold.[47] John Lomax of Bradshaw, formerly a drover, unfortunately fell on hard times, but had evidently been prosperous in his earlier days. He claimed in 1679 that his house had been broken into some years previously and he had then had 'fourtie Pounds of readie money stollen from him and hath sustained other greate Losses by his Trade'. As a result, he lamented, he was now 'forced to wander abroade and begg, having nothing of his owne left to manteyne him w[i]th nor howse to dwell in'.[48]

One of the most remarkable records of droving dates from the last years of the trade, before it was largely destroyed by the coming of the railways. In October 1824 Robert Walker left his wife and children in Waddington while he went to Scotland to buy cattle. He wrote a letter to them when he reached Carlisle, where he stayed overnight on his way home. The letter, which is now in the Lancashire Record Office, told his wife that he was travelling

> about 12 or 14 Miles each day . . . I have Bought 82 Hiland Scots but the pricis is verry High along with all exp[en]sis all the way from falkirk we have lodged at farm Housis till we arived hear not being in a publick road or else I would have wrote sooner.

He had to find and pay for pasture every night for the animals because, as he reports, 'I cannot leave it to the Drivers that is totaly strange to me'.[49]

Cattle were, down the centuries, a familiar sight on the roads, but occasionally more unusual animals would stir great local interest as they passed by – and they were not always welcome. In January 1634 Richard Laythwait of Westhoughton petitioned the quarter sessions, saying that Alexander Ascrofte (also known as Alexander Grimshawe) of Wigan was being a nuisance with his bears. Richard complained that although there was a high road between Wigan and Manchester, there was also a

> foote waie for men and weemen ov[e]r the feilds the one waye as neighe as the other [with his house] standinge in the feildes in the foot waye and maney and dyv[e]rs tymes bellwards w[i]th theire beares Refuse the broade waye and Come w[i]th theire beares the said foote way w[hi]ch lyeth by the Cheeke of the howse [and the bears] hath some tymes broken in and frighted yo[u]r peticon[e]r['s] wiffe and famelie.

When Richard Laythwait asked Alexander Ascrofte to use the road instead of the path, 'the said Alexander lytle Regardinge in a moste vile and malice saieth he will com that waie still'.[50]

THE MAIL

Carriage of goods by wheeled vehicles can sometimes be identified in local sources; the household accounts of the Shuttleworth family of Gawthorpe and Smithills record the payment of £1 13s. 4d. on 1 July 1589 to 'Panter the carrier' as 'the reste of the monye which was unpayed for the carredge of a wane-lode of stuffe from London'.[51] Individual small parcels could be sent by carrier and in the mid-seventeenth century a postal service began to develop. A mail service for royal letters had been started by Henry VII in the early sixteenth century, with special messengers – who were members of the royal household – as carriers, but this royal mail did not at that date carry private letters for the general public.

Informal arrangements for carrying letters were therefore necessary: the sender would find someone who was travelling in the right direction, either from among his friends or by local inquiry. When Nathan Walworth sent a letter from London to Peter Seddon at Prestolee in Pilkington in 1634, he wrote: 'I have sent all about for a messinger and I heare one Francis Medowcr[o]ft goes tomorrow; by him you shall receive this l[ette]re'. The messenger was instructed to 'leave this w[i]t[h] Mr Richard Lomax in Manchester and Desyre him to hyre one to cary this, speedelye and the partye [that is Peter Seddon, the

The departure of the Liverpool, Manchester and Holyhead mail coaches from the *Angel Inn*, Islington, in 1828, shown in a colour print by James Pollard. The inn is illuminated in celebration of the birthday of King George IV – on that evening all the coaches toured the area before beginning their journeys. By this time twenty-eight mail coaches left London for the provinces each evening *(British Museum).*

recipient] shall pay ye messinger'.[52] The regular local carrier could be asked to carry letters, as he did for Benjamin Shaw's sweetheart, who left Benjamin behind in Dolphinholme when she went to find work in Preston and later sent letters to him by the Dolphinholme waggon.[53]

In 1635 Charles I issued a proclamation by which a letter office was established and a man named Thomas Withering was allowed to develop certain postal routes. This turned a system of routes previously used by the king's messengers into a public service with regular postal charges. Between 1635 and 1660 to carry a 'single letter' cost 2*d.* for up to 80 miles, 4*d.* for 80–140 miles and 6*d.* for longer distances; it cost 8*d.* to send a letter to Scotland. A 'single letter' was one piece of paper weighing less than one ounce. At first all letters were carried by horse post; mail coaches were not introduced until the 1780s.[54]

Before the first London–Manchester mail coach ran on 15 July 1785 the mail from London was carried by horse, with more local journeys often being by foot post. In the years 1666–7 the route was from London through St Albans and Coventry to Stone and Knutsford, whence the Manchester mail continued northwards, while that for Warrington and Preston took a more westerly route. At this date there were three dispatches from London to the north west each week.

D. C. Haslam has calculated that the average journey time during these two years was 41.3 hours from London to Manchester and 52.6 hours from London to Preston.[55]

Postboys were at considerable risk of attack by robbers who hoped to find money or bills of exchange among the letters. In March 1788 James Archer, a Warrington postboy, was robbed by one William Lewin alias William Clarke alias William Brown alias William Hutchinson alias William Maule alias William Hope as he carried letters between Warrington and Northwich. James had just passed Stretton when he was threatened by Lewin, who was certainly armed with a piece of rail with a nail in the end and possibly carried a pistol as well. He took letters from Archer and rode off towards Northwich on the posthorse, chased by the postboy. When the horse came to a trough at which it was normally watered it stopped and refused to move, so the robber had to dismount and escape on foot down a lane. He was subsequently apprehended after he had tendered some of the bills which had been stolen, including one for £100.[56]

The Warrington postboy, seen here crossing the old stone bridge at Warrington on his journey southwards into Cheshire. The illustration, a woodcut, was used in Eyre's *Warrington Advertiser* for 23 March 1756. It shows a bridge of four arches; the small tower over one of the central piers was a watch house *(reproduced in* T.H.S.L.C. *vol. 5, 1853, p. 70).*

The war between Catholics and Protestants in Ireland, which had indirectly imposed such a burden upon the Garstang constables in 1689, found another victim in the Warrington postmaster. Mathew Page held that position from 1676 to 1695, but as he was growing old he allowed the office to be managed by his son-in-law, Peter Naylor. Naylor fell £200 in arrears, occasioned partly 'by reason of the many horses that were killed or lamed in the latter end of the reign of the late King and in the beginning of this present reign by the great number of persons and officers that carried expresses to and from Ireland'. Elizabeth Atkinson, widow of Nicholas Atkinson of Lancaster, carried on her husband's work of deputy postmaster there after he died in 1688 and 'after King James left the kingdom . . . was put to extraordinary expense in sending out horses and servants with several expresses for public service for which she was not paid' and so fell into debt and was imprisoned in Lancaster Castle.[57]

TRAVELLING BY COACH

The use of passenger coaches for regular services between London and the provinces began in the mid-seventeenth century. These conveyances quickly became known as 'stage' coaches, because the journey was divided into regular stages, at the end of which accommodation or food was available and horses could be changed. The mail coaches, when they were introduced, were high speed coaches carrying both mail and a limited number of passengers and they also carried an armed guard as a defence against highwaymen. The average speed of the early mail coaches was eight miles an hour including stops; by the mid-nineteenth century, aided by the improved road surfaces, the fastest coaches could travel at speeds of ten to eleven miles an hour. However, not all coach services were mail coach services and many more local services were very much slower than this.[58]

As the volume of road travel steadily increased, maps and road books for travellers began to appear. As early as 1625 John Norden had produced a travellers' compendium, *An Intended Guide for English Travellers*, which included a table of distances between towns and by the late eighteenth century other guides were available. Perhaps the best-known author of maps and gazetteers in the late eighteenth and early nineteenth centuries was John Cary, who surveyed the post roads for the Postmaster General. In his guide, *Cary's New Itinerary* (1798), he listed the towns on the main routes from London to distant parts of England, giving mileages between towns and the distance from the General Post Office in London. He also listed the main inns in each town at which accommodation and fresh horses could be obtained and his gazetteer included cross-country routes as well as the main routes to London. Such books found a ready market, often running to several editions.

Travelling by coach could be very uncomfortable and sometimes dangerous. Thomas de Quincey had an alarming experience when travelling on the Manchester and Glasgow mail coach a year or two after Waterloo. The coach left Manchester, behind time, at about midnight, running in de Quincey's estimation at about eleven miles an hour. Between Manchester and Kendal it had to travel seven stages of about eleven miles each. De Quincey travelled on the box with the driver and found the latter alarmingly liable to drop off to sleep. The driver's tendency to doze grew more pronounced, until about ten miles short of Preston 'it came about that I found myself left in charge of his Majesty's London and Glasgow mail, then running at the least twelve miles an hour'. De Quincey was surprisingly unperturbed. The dawn was just beginning to break, it was misty and 'except the feet of our own horses, which running on a sandy margin of the road, made but little disturbance, there was no sound abroad'. Then, to his alarm, he heard the sound of the wheels of a vehicle coming in the opposite direction, faintly at first and then louder. The mail coach was now on the wrong side of the road and the driver was still asleep but de Quincey could not reach him. The oncoming vehicle proved to be a gig, with a young couple as passengers. They collided, with disastrous results for the gig and its occupants, but the mail coach drove on unscathed.[59]

By the time de Quincey made this journey, coach services were numerous and busy, serving the growing commercial and industrial might of England. They reigned supreme in serving the needs of those who wanted fast and efficient passenger transport. The canals had for almost half a century carried some passengers, but although canal travel was comfortable, it was slow. Railways were soon and quickly to diminish the amount of long-distance road travel, but in the meantime coach services flourished. Baines' *Lancashire Directory* of 1824–5 gives some idea of the services operating. In Manchester the *Bridgewater Arms* in High Street was one of the main coaching inns, with eleven mail coaches leaving daily for widespread destinations – Birmingham, Carlisle, Chester, Edinburgh, Glasgow, Liverpool, London, Sheffield, Doncaster, York and Hull. The mail for London left Manchester at 7.45 a.m. and arrived in London at the *Swan with two Necks* at 6.30 next morning, travelling by way of Stockport, Macclesfield, Ashbourne, Derby, Leicester and St Albans. Other Manchester coaching inns included the *Mosley Arms*, the *Palace Inn* and the *Swan*. At least fifteen coaches ran daily to Liverpool, while other regular services went to Burnley, Blackburn, Wigan, Rochdale, Southport, Preston and a host of other places in the north west. From Liverpool, services were available to all parts of the country, departing from the *Angel, Crown, Golden Lion, Saracen's Head* and *Talbot* inns, among others. If travellers were heading across the Mersey, bookings could be made in Liverpool for seats on the Cheshire coaches, whose services were timed to coincide with the arrival of the ferry on the south shore of the estuary.[60]

Lancaster was an important centre in the regional coaching network. The 'North Star' and the 'Lancaster Doctor' ran there daily from Manchester and were additional to the through coaches from Manchester to Carlisle and Glasgow, which also took this route. Other coaches ran direct to Lancaster from Liverpool. From Lancaster, too, cross-country services went to Newcastle upon Tyne and Leeds and the 'Telegraph' left the *King's Arms* daily on the over-sands journey to Ulverston, 'as the tide will permit'. A particularly unpleasant experience befell travellers on the coach to Lancaster one Sunday in early October 1826. Isaac Sandford was the coachman of the 'New Times', travelling from Liverpool. At Preston he received delivery of a box addressed to Edinburgh, which had arrived on the Manchester coach. The box, which was 'covered with a linen wrapper and corded', had 'a very offensive smell [which] proceeded from it and several passengers complained and said, that if it was not removed when the coach arrived at Lancaster they would proceed no further with the coach'. The box was accordingly taken off at Lancaster and sent to the fly-boat warehouse

WONDER & RAILWAY COACHES.

R. ROTHWELL & Co.,

Beg to inform their Friends and the Public in general, that

THE WONDER COACH
WILL LEAVE TODMORDEN

Every Morning, Sunday excepted, immediately after the arrival of the First Trains from Manchester and Leeds respectively, passing through *Burnley, Accrington, Blackburn &c.*, and arriving at *Preston* in time for Trains to *Fleetwood, Blackpool, Lancaster, &c,*

RETURNING

FROM PRESTON,

At half-past Two P. M. passes through *Blackburn* at a quarter before Four, *Accrington* at a quarter before Five, *Burnley* at half-past Five, and meets Trains at *Todmorden* by which Passengers may be forwarded to Leeds, Manchester, Liverpool, Bolton, Birmingham, and London, arriving in London at half-past Five o'clock the following Morning.

R. ROTHWELL & Co.,

Take this opportunity of informing their Friends that in connection with the above Coach, they will on *Monday* the 28th. of *October*, establish a *regular conveyance* from the

RAILWAY OFFICE, BURNLEY,
TO THE HOLE-IN-THE-WALL, COLNE,

Every Morning immediately after the arrival of the *Wonder Coach* from *Todmorden*, at which place Passengers or Parcels will arrive nearly two hours earlier than by any other conveyance; the same Coach will LEAVE COLNE at *Four o'clock* in the Afternoon, meeting the *Wonder Coach* on its way from *Preston* to *Todmorden*, and also an OMNIBUS to *Accrington, Blackburn*, and *Clitheroe* the same Evening.

ALSO A CONVEYANCE FROM

BURNLEY TO COLNE,

Every Evening, Sundays and Tuesdays excepted, immediately after the arrival of the Railway Coach leaving *Todmorden* at half-past Three o'clock and the Wonder Coach from *Preston*; to RETURN FROM COLNE at *Seven* o'clock the same Evening.

☞ Passengers can be Booked to Colne by the Trains leaving Victoria Station, Manchester at a quarter before Seven A. M. and half-past One o'clock P. M. and from COLNE to MANCHESTER by the above Four o'clock conveyance.

AN OMNIBUS

Will also *leave Burnley* immediately after the arrival of the Coach leaving Todmorden at half-past Three o'clock, for *Accrington* and *Blackburn*, meeting a Coach at Accrington for *Whalley* and *Clitheroe*.

The time of Departure for the RAILWAY COACHES therefore will be

FROM BURNLEY,

Every Monday at 8.50 A. M. 1 o'clock, 2-15 and 5-30 P. M.
— Tuesday, Wednesday, Thursday, Friday, and Saturday at 6-15 and 8-50 A. M. 1 o'clock and 5-30 P. M.
— Sunday at 8 A. M. only.

FROM TODMORDEN,

Every Monday, Tuesday, Wednesday, Thursday, Friday and Saturday at 7-50 and 10-15 A. M. 3-50 and 7 P. M. or after the arrival of the 2nd. 4th. 6th, and 9th. down, and 1st. 3rd. 7th. and 8th. up Trains and on Sundays, at 1 o'clock only.

N. B.—Passengers and Parcels are Booked for the above Coaches at the Railway Office, Burnley; Hole in the Wall, Colne; Legs of Man and Red Lion, Preston; Black Bull, Blackburn; and Bay Horse, Accrington.

PERFORMED BY THE PUBLIC'S OBEDIENT SERVANTS,

Burnley, October 14th. 1844.   *ROTHWELL, ALLEN & STUTTARD.*

T. SUTCLIFFE, PRINTER, STAMP OFFICE, &c. BURNLEY.

The opening of railways from 1830 onwards had an immediate impact upon the network of coach services, many of which were diverted to run to and from railway stations. This poster of 1844 exemplifies the new pattern – the stations at Burnley and Todmorden became, for a time, the focal points of coach routes until, as the railways extended further, these too were forced out of business *(LRO DDBd 57/5/1)*.

so that it could be sent on by water, but it smelled so much that it was sent back to the yard of the *King's Arms* and left there. The constable was summoned: he moved the box to a coachhouse and there opened it, to find that it contained the dead bodies of a woman and a baby.[61]

Shockingly unpleasant events such as the bodies in the box were exceptional, but passengers often had to endure more routine discomforts. One day in August 1823 the governess and diarist Ellen Weeton was travelling on the coach 'Eclipse' from Southport via Ormskirk to Liverpool. It was a very wet day and she travelled outside.

> The wind blew so furiously, no umbrella could be opened or carried. The coachman was very attentive and kind to me; he gave me a stout horse rug to cover my shoulders and another to cover my knees and in this elegant costume I rode through Ormskirk and Liverpool to the Inn there, as heedless and contented as possible, the rain soaking through all the way, driving in at a little crevice between my hood and my neck and trickling in little streams down my back, so that I was literally wet to the skin; and when I descended from my elevated situation, my cloaths were so entirely wet, that I found I was a woman of much greater weight in Liverpool than I had been at Southport.[62]

Sir George Head made the journey from Liverpool to Southport by coach in 1835. It was not a comfortable experience: he thought that

> the journey thither alone, without taking into consideration the salubrity of the spot, is equal to a physician's prescription. Two coaches depart from Liverpool every day. Both these vehicles are set upon extraordinary rough springs, while the road nearly all the distance is paved with large stones; so that it is reasonable to hope that the grievous jolting inflicted on a passenger during his journey, may at least be conducive to his bodily health.

Local people awaited the arrival of the coach, listening for its approach.

> As, for the last few miles before arriving at Southport, the way lies across a flat moor, the sound of the coach-wheels, on a still day, may be heard a long way off, whence people, having nothing to do and anxious for the arrival of their letters and newspapers by the said coach, stand at their doors listening to the rumbling noise which, like the roll of a drum, lasts for near a quarter of an hour.[63]

Sir George spared a thought for the Wigan to Preston coach, which he records was 'licensed to carry four inside and four outside, luggage unlimited and drawn by one unlucky horse'.[64]

Something of the bustle of a busy road in a manufacturing district is conveyed by Simeon Dyson's description of the turnpike road through Farnworth (Bolton), at a date between about 1810 and 1830.

> The cotton spinners and manufacturers of Bolton and the towns beyond, used to travel to Manchester market on Tuesdays, Thursdays and Saturdays, either by stage coaches, or they drove to town in their own gigs and on the above-named market days there was almost a continuous procession of these vehicles passing along the turnpike road through Farnworth,

betwixt the hours of 8 and 9 a.m. The Royal Mail coach, with its scarlet-coated driver on his seat in front and the guard merrily blowing his horn on the hind seat, was to be seen daily dashing through the village with four grey horses, about half an hour before the usual bustle of coaches and gigs began to pass. [65]

ALL IN A DAY'S WALK

Coach travel was not for the working class, however, who in normal circumstances still travelled on foot. Simeon Dyson tells how the handloom weavers of Farnworth would carry their completed cloth to Manchester – a distance of some eight miles – and then walk back with the warp and weft with which to weave another piece, 'unless they sometimes got a friendly lift by the way in some empty coal cart returning from Manchester'.[66] When in 1795 Benjamin Shaw left Dolphinholme to live and work in Preston, sixteen miles away, he made the journey on foot. 'This spring', he wrote later in his auto-biography, 'I suffered a great deal in one of my feet, in coming to Preston. I got the skin of by blisters, & the wether being very frosty, & not taking care of it, the frost got into it and having to stand to work constantly made it worse, so that it was nearly May before it got well'.[67] Later, when railways had spread to all parts of the county, the train would be used for longer journeys, or those where a railway route was convenient, but there was still a very great deal of local walking. And if, for any reason, the rail service failed, walking was often the only alternative for a working man who had to reach home betimes. In December 1860 John O'Neil of Clitheroe had been to Colne on trade union business and, in company with some others, was stranded in Blackburn at ten o'clock at night when the train from Colne missed the connection for Clitheroe. Some of his companions stayed in Blackburn overnight, but one man had to be at his work the following morning, so he and O'Neil set off to walk.

> I never had such a journey in all my life. We got to Clitheroe at three o'clock in the morning and had to wade all the road nearly knee deep in snow and one of the hardest and coldest frosts that ever I was out in. When I got home my shoes was frozen to my feet and I was a long time before I could get them off. My trowsers were frozen like two iron pipes. I got to bed as soon as I could. I was fairly done up.[68]

Although journeys like this might still have to be made at any time, for most Lancashire people – and especially those who lived in the urban areas – the days when long-distance walking was a necessity were almost over. In only a few years such activities would be revived, this time for pleasure and as a means of escape from dirt and noise, but for journeys to work and within and between towns there were, by the end of the nineteenth century, extensive tramway networks. In the years before the First World War the trams were widely used by people of all classes except the very poor, who still found them a rarely affordable luxury and the rich, who had their own conveyances. The bicycle, too, was becoming a useful means of local transport for people in town and country alike.

The days of hardship for travellers were largely past and the risks for the twentieth-century road user are of a different kind. Tales of highwaymen or death by drowning or exposure make it seem that travelling was always very dangerous. That belief would be a mistaken one, for disasters have always been newsworthy. Many more journeys were made in safety than ended in misfortune and, whatever the difficulties, our Lancashire forebears were regular travellers on our county's roads.

5

The Turnpike Era

Tʜᴇ turnpike network of Lancashire was of great importance between 1725 and 1870 and its development had a lasting impact
upon the modern road system. The introduction of turnpikes to
Lancashire was rather late in national terms, but once started the
network grew rapidly and was still undergoing major improvement
and extension on the eve of the railway age. Previous chapters have
shown how the system for maintaining public roads functioned and
have also highlighted its very obvious weaknesses. By the mid-seventeenth century the stirrings of economic expansion were producing an
increase in road traffic. The demand for transport from industry and
commerce was growing and main roads were subject to increasingly
heavy use. Existing administrative arrangements were correspondingly
less able to cope with the burden – the key problem was that of trying
to force or encourage townships to maintain roads which were of little
local importance but were used by great volumes of through traffic.

Toll income was one way of raising money to maintain such routes
but, although landowners could create roads over their own lands and
charge a toll, it was illegal under existing Highway Acts to charge for
passage over public roads. In 1663, however, parliament established a
precedent by passing an Act[1] which empowered the county justices to
erect three gates along a stretch of the Great North Road (A1) and
collect tolls from road users. The Act detailed the appointment of
surveyors, the methods of payment of labour for repair of the road
and the procedures for the collection of tolls. There was thus official
recognition both of the inadequacy of statute labour and of the principle
of 'user pays', but as a precedent the experiment was not a success.
Local opposition meant that one gate was never erected and another
was so easily avoided that little money was collected.

Nevertheless, the idea eventually took root, although it was not until
the 1690s that the experiment was repeated. By 1713 twenty-three
similar Acts had been passed, all to be administered by county justices.
It seemed possible that the justices of the peace would become responsible for the main highways in addition to their existing powers over

county and hundred bridges, but subsequent turnpike acts reduced the role of the justices and substituted the appointment of trustees to administer the funds and manage the roads. Although they were still subject to some control by the justices until 1750, the trusts thereafter became totally independent and answerable only to parliament under general highway acts and the individual local acts which set up or amended the trusts.

It is necessary at this point to explain the working of a trust. In Lancashire the trustees – in some instances over one hundred in number – were mainly local businessmen, landowners and clergy, who obtained a parliamentary act for the road in question. Their first expenditure, usually met by borrowing from among themselves, was on the appointment of a clerk, a treasurer and a surveyor. These posts could be combined in one person, particularly those of clerk and treasurer and they were salaried. The surveyor was required to view the road, report on its condition and provide estimates for materials, then the trustees issued directions as to the lengths to be repaired. Toll gates and cottages were built. The surveyor then supervised the repair of the road, either by direct employment of labour or by contract. Initially it was usual for toll collectors to be salaried servants but later it became common practice to farm out the tolls – that is, to let the collection to a third party after competitive tenders, in return for a fixed annual payment to the trust. These lettings were usually for a short period, often a single year. Many trusts began with precarious finances, since they had no initial capital and had to borrow all that they spent until their income from tolls had built up.

The Acts setting up the trusts were of limited duration – typically twenty-one years. Parliament naively assumed that the roads would then be in a suitable state for the parishes to resume control, but in practice this was hardly ever the case except where a road was bypassed by a new length. Even then the old road often remained part of the turnpike, to prevent toll evasion. Regular renewal of the Acts was necessary: at these times new conditions and new tolls could be imposed and diversions and relocation of gates authorised. Further powers and limitations were often included in the 'General Turnpike Acts': for example, that of 1822 forbade the combination of offices in one person. The Liverpool and Prescot Trust, first authorised in 1726, obtained further Acts in 1746, 1753, 1771, 1797, with others following after 1801 when it joined with the Prescot and Warrington Trust.

Only seven roads partly or wholly in Lancashire were turnpiked before 1750, although by that date there had been 143 Acts covering some 3,386 miles of road in England.[2] In spite of its large geographical area Lancashire, with only eighty-seven miles turnpiked, was then eighteenth in a league table of counties. Even by 1770 it was still only fifteenth and yet, by the end of the 1840s, Lancashire was second only to Yorkshire, which was three times the size.[3] The development of the relatively late but ultimately very dense network of turnpike roads in south-east Lancashire is thus of major significance. The first part of this chapter is a chronological survey of the growth of that network.

The first road in Lancashire to be turnpiked (1725) was the northern end of the Manchester and Buxton Trust, part of the trunk route to Derby and London. It crossed the Mersey at Stockport and then followed Manchester Road, rather than the present A6 Wellington Road.[4] The latter was constructed in the early 1820s as a completely new turnpike, whereas the 1725 route was an upgrading of the old highway and is the route of the Derby–Manchester road depicted by John Ogilby in 1675 as the Manchester to London road. This pattern, of the old road being turnpiked first and then a more direct and better-graded alternative being built later, was widely found throughout Lancashire.

The first turnpike road wholly within Lancashire was from Liverpool to Prescot, for which an Act was obtained in 1726. Considering that its initial length was only seven miles the petition to Parliament was grandiose. The road, it stated, 'is very much used in the carriage of coals to the towns of Wigan, Bolton, Rochdale, Warrington and Manchester and the Counties of York, Derby and other Eastern Parts of the Kingdom, in the carriage of Wool, Cotton, Malt and all other Merchants Goods whereby the Several Parts of the said Road are so very deep and other Parts so narrow that coaches, waggons and other wheeled carriages cannot pass through the same'.[5]

The Liverpool and Prescot trustees encountered several problems in the early years. One arose from the vagueness of terminal points of the road as described in its Act, a matter which came to a head in 1734 with a bitter dispute between the trustees and the township and borough of Liverpool over who should maintain the town end of the route. In February 1735 the trustees resolved to obtain counsel's opinion 'as to how far the road between Liverpool and Prescot ought to be repaired at the charge of the Turnpike whether to the Street ends of each of the Towns or only from outside bounds or extent of the Parishes of Liverpool to the boundary or extent of the Township of Prescot'.[6]

In April 1736 counsel gave his opinion, that because the Act of 1726 referred to the 'Towns of Liverpool and Prescot', if the parishes were unable to repair the road to the boundary it was not the intention of the Act to leave half a mile of unmade road at each end in a ruinous condition and that the turnpike should therefore extend to the edge of the built-up area. This had several repercussions for the precise lengths or mileage of roads controlled by the trusts. Many other Acts

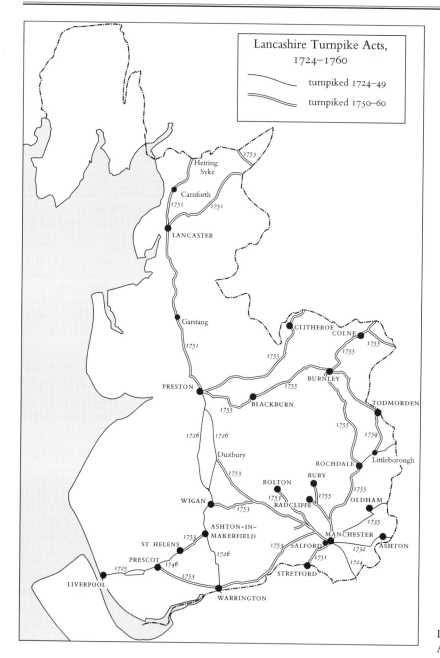

**Lancashire Turnpike Acts,
1724–1760**

———— turnpiked 1724–49

———— turnpiked 1750–60

Heiring Syke

1753

Carnforth
1751   1751

LANCASTER

Garstang

1751

CLITHEROE
COLNE
1755

1755   1755

PRESTON   BURNLEY
1755

1755   BLACKBURN   TODMORDEN

1726   1726   1755   1759

Duxbury   ROCHDALE   Littleborough

1753   BURY   1755

BOLTON

WIGAN   1753   OLDHAM
RADCLIFFE   1755

1753   1735

ASHTON-IN-
MAKERFIELD   MANCHESTER   ASHTON

1753   SALFORD   1732

ST HELENS   1753   1751

PRESCOT   1726   1724

1725   1746   STRETFORD

1753

LIVERPOOL

WARRINGTON

Lancashire Turnpike
Acts 1724–1760.

were equally vague as to the terminal points and, although some towns were already paving and maintaining their streets by earlier charters, there were numerous instances where stretches of non-urban road (which they did not want to repair) lay within their jurisdiction. In most instances the later Acts were far more specific about the stretches of road involved.

It should be noted that the creation of a turnpike trust did not exempt the township from its statutory duty on the road so turnpiked – and if the turnpike trustees proved to be ineffective or negligent in keeping the road in repair it was not they, but the local authority, which could be indicted at the quarter sessions. However, because of the inconvenience of employing statute labour on a turnpike road it became common practice for the trustees to agree a commuted sum payable by the township annually.

The Liverpool and Prescot Trust was extended to St Helens in 1746[7] and to Ashton-in-Makerfield in 1753, when an Act was also obtained to turnpike the road from Prescot to Warrington.[8] There was also a branch from Old Swan to Huyton-with-Roby. The trust was renamed the Liverpool, Prescot, Ashton and Warrington Trust: it had grown from the original seven miles to about thirty but, as will be seen, this was not always typical of the evolution of the early Lancashire trusts. Many of these, indeed, were ultimately broken up into shorter units because they were straggling and difficult to administer.

The process whereby a trust was established is well-illustrated by the Liverpool and Prescot case, because detailed minutes survive.[9] It held its first general meeting on 20 May 1726, attended by sixty-one trustees.[10] They appointed a clerk but then adjourned because of a dispute about setting up a committee. On 1 June 1726 they made provision for supply of materials and a month later appointed two surveyors to view the road. These were chosen from among the trustees so it is very doubtful if they could have cast any sort of expert eye over the problem.

The siting of two turnpike gates was also agreed and at the end of the month it was ordered that the gates be fixed immediately and the roads paved for thirty yards on each side. The dimensions of the toll cottages were carefully specified and estimates for the carriageway were obtained: a causeway six yards wide, paved with stones, would cost £1,400 per mile. This was soon considered too expensive and in July 1733 it was decided to reduce the width to three yards. A treasurer was appointed at £25 *per annum*, as were toll collectors at Prescot Road (for a £16 salary) and Roby Road. Toll collection began in February 1727, but the trust was already in deficit by nearly £3,000.

THE GROWING NETWORK, 1725–1750

The next road to be turnpiked was the south Lancashire section of the ancient highway from London to Carlisle. It was divided into three separate trusts, one covering Warrington to Wigan, another Chorley to Preston joining the Wigan Trust at Bamber Bridge. The third, the

Wigan and Preston Trust, initially had two routes, one via Euxton (A49) and another from Boars Head to Chorley via Heath Charnock. This Trust was later split into two divisions, north and south of the River Yarrow: the Chorley route was called the Higher Road and the Euxton route the Lower Road. Little change occurred to the Lower Road but more extensive alterations were made to the Higher Road at Duxbury, to the south of the Yarrow and a new section of road was later built in Whittle-le-Woods, to bypass the steep, narrow hills at Dolphin Brow and Shaw Brow.

Before 1750 there were three other significant Acts for turnpikes in south-east Lancashire and these set a pattern which was to be followed for a century – namely, that the development of cross-Pennine links was of outstanding importance. The new and improved roads linked the fast-growing industrial areas of Lancashire and Yorkshire and gave access to ports on both coasts. The first such Act, in 1732, was for the road from Manchester to Ashton-under-Lyne and then up Longdendale to a terminus high on the Yorkshire border at Saltersbrook, on the way to Sheffield and Barnsley. It was followed in 1735 by the road from Manchester to Oldham and Austerland, just across the Yorkshire boundary.

In the same year a section of the ancient road from Rochdale to Halifax and Elland was turnpiked. The Act for the last-named conveys well the flavour of contemporary attitudes to the unimproved roads: it was for 'repairing and widening the Road from the Town of Rochdale in the County Palatine of Lancashire leading over a certain craggy Mountain called Blackstone Edge in the same County and from thence to the Town of Halifax'.[11] The section between Manchester and Rochdale was not turnpiked for a further 20 years, until 1755. This crossing of the Pennines at Blackstone Edge had a long history, with its possible Roman and undoubted packhorse routes and it is described by Ogilby as the road from York to Chester. The ascent of the Edge on the Lancashire side was further reconstructed in 1815 on the line of the present day A58 and from a point on the hillside the whole history of the evolution of this route is clearly visible today.

During the period 1725–50 a total of eighty-seven miles of road was turnpiked (Appendix 1a gives a detailed list of the Acts, routes and mileages). As stated previously, this was a relatively slow and late start for a county which had a major port and fast-growing industries and a limited inland waterway network. The Lune was navigable only to Lancaster and the Ribble to Freckleton, except by very small boats at favourable tides when Preston could be reached. In 1720 the first navigation improvement was enacted, for the Douglas up to Wigan, but work was not completed until 1742. After 1736 the Mersey and Irwell Navigation enabled 'Mersey Flats', with some difficulty, to reach

Hunts Bank in Manchester.[12] The poor condition of the roads was cited in these Acts to justify the need for improved navigation – although such claims would inevitably be made by those with a vested interest – and it is perhaps surprising, therefore, that more was not done to improve the roads themselves.

THE GREATEST GROWTH, 1750–1760

Whereas the period up to 1750 saw comparatively little activity, the next decade witnessed a dramatic change. During the ten years 1751–60 the mileage of new turnpikes was more than double that for 1725–50. The momentum of commercial and demographic expansion was gaining pace and the clear success of turnpikes in Lancashire and elsewhere encouraged greater activity. Turnpikes were quicker and easier to build than canals, especially in the hilly country of the eastern part of the county and they were of great benefit to local users as well as to longer distance commercial traffic.

Manchester-with-Salford was already emerging as the focal point of regional and sub-regional routes. In 1751 the turnpiking of the very important ancient route southwards into Cheshire, through Stretford and over Crossford Bridge, was authorised. Two years later the network generally known as 'Salford Roads' received its Act. This covered a group of routes radiating north and west from the town – to Warrington via Eccles Old Road, Irlam and Hollins Green (the modern A57), to Bolton via Irlams o'th' Height and Moses Gate (A666) and from Irlams o'th' Height via Swinton and Blackrod to join the Wigan–Preston (Higher Road) Trust at Duxbury (A6). There was also a road to Wigan, which was a branch running from the last-named route at Westhoughton via Hindley (A58/A557) and a short branch from Swinton to Broad Oak near Worsley (A572).[13]

Because of the multiplicity of routes, which connected with the turnpikes of many other trusts, the administration of the 'Salford Roads' was very cumbersome. It had some fifty-two miles of route and eventually this was broken up into several smaller individual trusts of more manageable length. Although the core of the system, close to Salford, became the Pendleton Trust (P.T.) even that was eventually sub-divided. By 1845 the 'Salford Roads' were as follows:

SALFORD–WARRINGTON (A57):
  Pendleton District of the P.T. (Eccles Old Road)
  Gilda Brook and Irlam District of the P.T.
  Warrington and Lower Irlam Trust

SALFORD–BOLTON (A666):
  Irlams o'th' Height District of the P.T.
  Moses Gate Trust

SALFORD–DUXBURY (A6):
  Swinton District of the P.T.
  Little Hulton Trust
  Adlington and Westhoughton Trust

SALFORD–WIGAN (A58/A577):
  (from Westhoughton) Ince, Hindley and Westhoughton Trust

WORSLEY BRANCH to BROAD OAK:
  Included in the Swinton District of the P.T.

The link between Bolton Road (A666) and Bury Old Road (A6044) was added to the Agecroft District of the P.T.

In the same area there was another 'omnibus' Act in 1755, embracing 'the Roads from the Township of Crumpsall to the Town of Rochdale and from the said Place called the White Smithy, by a Place called Besses of the Barn, to the Town of Bury and from the said Place called Besses of the Barn, to Radcliffe Bridge'.[14] The road out of Manchester to Crumpsall was Bury Old Road, up Cheetham Hill, a route which, as Alan Crosby notes, suffered from very heavy industrial and commercial traffic as early as the 1630s. As a main route out of Manchester to the north it was a very obvious candidate for major improvement. The two legs of the trust diverged at Cheetham Hill, one going to Rochdale via Middleton and the other to Bury via Besses o' th' Barn – or Besses of the Barn, as the 1755 Act calls it – and Whitefield. As with the other collective trusts this was eventually broken down into shorter lengths or incorporated into new trusts.

The 1750s also saw much activity in the north of the county. In 1751 an Act for the very important section of the Carlisle road from Preston via Lancaster to Heiring (Heron) Syke on the Westmorland boundary was passed. In the same year the turnpiking of a further route from Lancashire to Yorkshire was enacted, to cover 'the Road from the East End of Brumpton High Lane, in the County of York to the Town of Richmond and from thence to and through the Towns of Askrigg and Ingleton in the said County to the Town of Lancaster'. It will be noted that the terminal point and route in Yorkshire were well defined but not that in Lancashire: the road was in fact via Cantsfield Bridge, Hornby and Caton, the last-named village being bypassed in the late 1830s. In 1753 the road from Keighley to Kendal (A65), of which a short length south-east of Kirkby Lonsdale was within Lancashire, was turnpiked.

Hitherto east Lancashire had not been affected by the turnpike

The old turnpike road looking towards Nab Side Farm, between Blackburn and Whalley, part of the Leeds–Skipton–Blackburn–Preston road which was turnpiked from 1755. To the north of Blackburn its route followed the ancient highway (now Whalley Old Road) over Billington Moor, with a very steep descent to Whalley Bridge shown in this view. In 1808 the road was superseded by a new route through Mellor Brook and Langho, and it was disturnpiked in 1819 (author).

boom, but in the mid-1750s the tentacles began to reach through that area too. Here, as in the south-east of the county, the links across the Pennines into Yorkshire were of crucial significance, with Colne – in its key geographical position – being a focus for much of the activity. Three of the Acts in 1755 related to roads into the town. The most important of these [15] was for the regional route from 'the Town of Leeds in the West Riding of the County of York, through Otley, Skipton, Colne, Burnley and Blackburn to Burscough Bridge in Walton in the County of Lancaster and from Skipton through Gisburn and Clitheroe to Preston in the said County of Lancaster'.

Pawson considers this, at 115 miles, to be among the longest of all turnpike trusts: of the total route about fifty miles was within Lancashire.[16] It should be noted that the approach to Colne from Skipton was very indirect, running via Carleton and not the present A56. Two other Acts in the same year helped to rectify this: one covered the road from Bradford through Haworth to 'a place called Blue Bell, near Colne', this being on the Skipton–Colne road. The other Act was for the road 'from Cocking End, near Addingham . . . through Kildwick to Black Lane End in the County Palatine of Lancaster'. Here it, too, met the Skipton–Colne road just within the county boundary, near a place known as Tom's Cross about three miles north-east of Colne. This became the more important route until the present main road to Cowling (A6068) was built after an Act of 1827. Like the 'Salford Roads' this lengthy and awkward trust was later broken up into smaller units.

Further south, the Rossendale area was also promising ground for turnpikes, with its hilly, steep and narrow roads long-overdue for improvement. In 1755 the Rochdale and Burnley Trust was authorised, to administer the road via Whitworth, Bacup and Deerplay. Although extensive alterations to this route were made north of Bacup in 1817, the original turnpike from Deerplay crossed the moors of Habergham Eaves via Crown Point and approached Burnley from the west along Cog Lane to Gannow. The amended line of 1817 involved completely new construction, so that the present A671 approaches Burnley from the east. The 1750s also saw the improvement of the road from Halifax to Todmorden and Burnley, together with the road from Todmorden to Littleborough. Both these early routes were subsequently altered: the original approach to Burnley was via Mere Clough, while at Littleborough the link with the Rochdale-Blackstone Edge turnpike was along Calderbrook Road, replaced by Todmorden Road (A6033) in 1819. Appendix 1b lists the new turnpikes for the very active decade 1751 to 1760, in which almost 230 miles were authorised in the county. The network of roads which had been developed by this date is shown on the map (p. 122).

SLOWER GROWTH, 1760–1790

For the next thirty years the system grew at a much slower rate – only 125 miles were added in the period 1761–90. This followed the national trend: in the country as whole, over the period from the 1660s to the end of the eighteenth century, the twenty years 1751–1770 produced the greatest number of Acts for new roads. No less than 54 per cent of all trusts set up before 1801 were established in those two decades. This probably reflects both the state and the changing nature of the economy. During this period there was not only a rapid increase in the demand for efficient transport, but also a greater availability of finance. From the mid-1760s, however, the development of the canal network, in Lancashire and elsewhere, may have somewhat diminished the enthusiasm for road building, while also absorbing increasing amounts of the capital which was available for investment.

Links across south Lancashire were established in the mid-1760s by the turnpiking of the roads from Bolton to Leigh, Golborne and Newton-le-Willows and from thence to Parr (St Helens). Bolton, too, was becoming a nodal point in the network. In 1763 Chorley Old Road (B6226), Horwich, was turnpiked by the Bolton and Nightingales

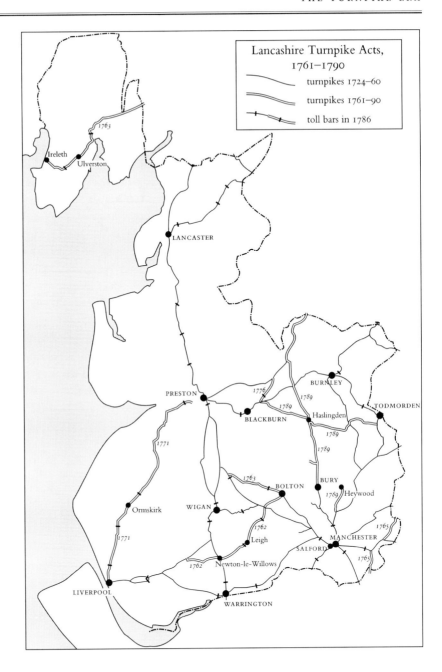

Lancashire Turnpike
Acts, 1761-1790

Trust, the curious name of which derives from a house at Heath
Charnock, where the trust had a junction with both the Wigan to
Preston road and the 'Salford Road'. The physical connection between
the three trusts here had a somewhat complicated history, the line of
the road being altered considerably over the years. The first road,
between Wigan and Preston along Wigan Lane, followed an ancient

route through Duxbury Park, close to the Hall and crossed the Yarrow ¼ mile downstream of the present bridge. The second, the 'Salford Roads' from Westhoughton, joined the former west of Nightingales, using Rawlinson Lane. The last arrival, the Bolton road, used the eastern section of Rawlinson Lane to Nightingales.

The first change arose from the construction of the Lancaster Canal in 1799 when, to economise in bridge construction, the Salford road was diverted alongside the canal's eastern bank to join the Bolton road.[17] A few years later, following an Act of 1824, the Bolton and Nightingales Trust, with the trustees of both sections of the Wigan and Preston and of the Westhoughton and Duxbury Trust (a successor to the Salford Roads), built a new road from Holes Brow to Chorley including a new Yarrow bridge and a skew bridge over the Lancaster Canal. The Westhoughton Trust was extended from Rawlinson Lane to join this new road south of Skew Bridge and the Wigan Lane diverted to join north of Skew Bridge. The ancient road through Duxbury Park was then abandoned.

In 1763 the first turnpike Act for the Furness area was passed. It covered the Kendal to Kirkby Ireleth road, which followed a devious route over hills and round estuaries from Bowland Bridge to the Leven at Newby Bridge and then via Bouth, Penny Bridge, Ulverston and Lindal in Furness to Kirkby Ireleth, where the sands route took travellers over the Duddon estuary to Cumberland. For travellers from the south the long detour via Kendal was particularly unattractive – not least because these turnpikes were notoriously ill-maintained – and so the Morecambe Bay sands crossings remained in regular use well after this date.

Despite its immense commercial importance and the early adoption of turnpiking for the Prescot road, Liverpool did not become the focus of a dense network in the way that Manchester did. Not until 1771, for example, did the road through Ormskirk to Preston become a turnpike.[18] Waterway competition and the fact that it passed through a largely rural and agricultural district, meant that this turnpike, although it was later to be a major component of the motor road network, was comparatively lightly-trafficked. It did not have the heavy industrial business of the south-east Lancashire roads, although it was a very important route for stagecoaches and mail. There was almost no new construction on the road and it meandered through the villages with a very indirect route (especially north of the Douglas) until transformed by the demands of motor traffic between the wars.

Appendix 1c lists the Acts, routes and mileages of turnpikes in the period 1761–1790. Although existing trusts obtained their necessary renewal Acts there were few additions to the system until 1789. In that year one of the last 'omnibus' Acts, that for the Haslingden roads, was passed. Its Trust initiated a new approach to layout and construction and the preamble described in detail the provision for 'amending, widening, turning, varying, altering and keeping in repair' roads from Bury to Haslingden and thence to the east end of Salford Bridge in Blackburn; from Haslingden to Cockshut Bridge in Whalley; and from Haslingden through Newchurch and Bacup to Todmorden.[19] The Trust had much wider powers to alter and amend the line of the turnpike, an important indicator of future trends.

THE CONSTRUCTION OF THE ROADS

By the late eighteenth century the science of land surveying had made great progress but, in contrast, the 'surveyors' appointed by the turnpike trusts remained largely unskilled. Their work was often inadequate and ineffective and the condition of Lancashire roads was not greatly improved by them. High, narrow causeways, typical of Lancashire and described in earlier chapters, persisted well into the turnpike era, despite attracting adverse criticism from travellers such as Celia Fiennes who, on arriving in Wigan, commented that 'we are now in a county where roads are paved with small pebbles so that we both walk and ride on their pavement which is about a yard and half broad, but the middle of the road, where carriages are obliged to go is very bad'.

The road alongside the causeway was not surfaced and in wet weather rapidly became a quagmire and virtually impassable. Although the travellers referred to the use of 'pebbles' there was much debate as to the relative effectiveness of these or paving with stone slabs or flags. In 1734 the Liverpool and Prescot trustees ordered a length of road in Prescot to be repaved 'with the best of the Great Stones that were taken out of the Old Causeway',[20] but 'paving' usually consisted of tipping lumps of stone into the worst of the slough. Without a proper foundation blocks or slabs would tip and move. The Prescot road was described as 'unworthy of the name of turnpike and a scandal to the town [Liverpool] . . . being a continued series of unequal stones piled on one another so as to form the roughest pavement in the universe' – and this the most important road leading to what had become the major port of northern England.[21] Because of the weight of traffic and the dearth of suitable stone in the locality 'slab stone' was imported into Liverpool, often from Wales. This method of construction was also favoured in the vicinity of Manchester and Wigan, because of the heavy traffic in coal. The rounded pebbles mentioned by travellers did not lock or bind together, as anyone who has walked a shingle beach will appreciate, but they remained popular: as late as 1867 the surveyor to the Clitheroe and Blackburn trust was directed to 'repave with

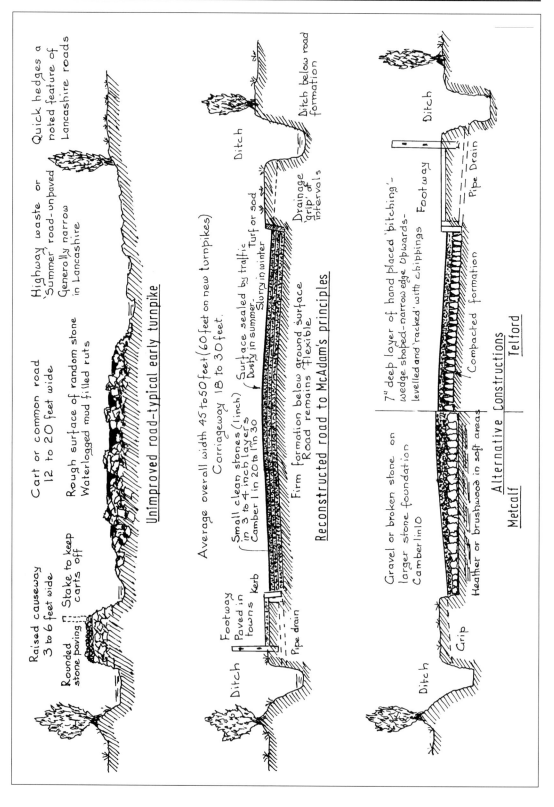

Raised causeway 3 to 6 feet wide

Rounded stone paving

Stake to keep carts off

Cart or common road 12 to 20 feet wide

Rough surface of random stone Waterlogged mud filled ruts

Highway waste or 'Summer' road-unpaved Generally narrow in Lancashire

Quick hedges a noted feature of Lancashire roads

Unimproved road-typical early turnpike

Ditch

Footway Paved in towns

kerb

Pipe drain

Small clean stones (1inch) in 3 to 4 inch layers Camber 1 in 20 to 1 in 30

Surface sealed by traffic Dusty in summer. Slurry in winter

Turf or sod

Drainage 'grip' of intervals

Ditch

Ditch below road formation

Average overall width 45 to 50 feet (60 feet on new turnpikes) Carriageway 18 to 30 feet.

Firm formation below ground surface Road remains flexible

Reconstructed road to McAdam's principles

Ditch

Grip

Gravel or broken stone on larger stone foundation Camber 1 in 10

Heather or brushwood in soft areas

Compacted formation

7" deep layer of hand placed 'pitching'- wedge shaped-narrow edge upwards- levelled and racked with chippings

Footway

Pipe Drain

Ditch

Metcalf

Telford

Alternative Constructions

pebbles six hundred square yards of road within the village of Whalley'. It is possible that the pebbled area resembled a cobblestone pavement – but even so it was not a good material for a roadway.[22] Local materials were used if available, quarried if possible but often dug from adjacent fields. One more unusual material employed with some success in south Lancashire was copper slag, but some of this proved too hard to break down and it would not lock together properly.

Because of these deficiencies the condition of Lancashire turnpikes in the late eighteenth century was usually only marginally better than that of other roads, despite the administration by trusts and the availability of toll money. At this point, however, three men appear to whom is attributed a revolution in road construction: John Metcalf (1717–1810), Thomas Telford (1757–1835) and James Loudon McAdam (1756–1836).

Metcalf, nicknamed 'Blind Jack of Knaresborough', was blinded at the age of six but led a very varied existence as a musician, coach proprietor, fishdealer, army recruiting sergeant, horse dealer and waggoner, until quite late in life he began working as a road contractor in Yorkshire. Most of his road-building was in the Pennines and in Lancashire he is thought to have worked on the Burnley–Skipton and Stockport–Ashton-under-Lyne roads and most notably on a considerable length of the Bury, Blackburn and Whalley Trust, building in 1790–1 the new road through what is now Accrington. The old road wound along the valley sides, but Metcalf's new road is represented by the direct alignment of Whalley Road, Abbey Street and Manchester Road. The construction of a completely new route over this difficult terrain was a fine achievement: although blind, Metcalf possessed an almost uncanny 'feel' for topography and ground conditions.

Previous page: Eighteenth-nineteenth-century road construction.

Whalley Bridge, at a very ancient crossing point over the river Calder on the old road from Skipton to Blackburn. Viewed from beneath, the oldest arch is formed of stone ribs supporting flat slabs, and dates from the twelfth or thirteenth centuries. The road was turnpiked in 1755 and the bridge widened on the downstream side. It was widened again in 1914 on both sides, with the provision of footways and new parapets *(author)*.

He is often credited with developing a more scientific method of road building, whereby the ground was first levelled and made firm with adequate drainage ditches on either side at a lower level – the so-called 'formation'. On this he placed a layer of stone blocks as a foundation and then covered the whole with a layer of gravel or broken small stones, with a curve across the road profile for drainage purposes. This camber was rather excessive, its rise of 1 in 10 to the crown giving the road a distinct barrel shape and it was criticised because carts tended to use only the middle of the road. This accentuated wear, but although later road surveyors modified the degree of camber the Metcalf principles were retained. The extent to which Metcalf was truly original is questionable – General Wade, for example, had constructed many miles of excellent military roads in Scotland in the mid-eighteenth century and in 1765 the trustees of the Rochdale to Burnley road instructed their labourers to build a section of road with features such as drainage ditches, foundations and a covering of good gravel. Co-incidentally, it will be noted that Metcalf's design amounted to a rediscovery of the long-lost Roman methods.

The second of the new generation of road surveyors, Thomas Telford, was recognisably a civil engineer with many roads, bridges

The Lower Hodder Packhorse Bridge, on the county boundary between Lancashire and Yorkshire. This stone-arched bridge, only seven feet wide, was built in 1561 to replace an earlier structure. In 1818 it was superseded by the present main road bridge which was designed by Bernard Hartley, the Bridge Surveyor to the West Riding, to coincide with the construction of McAdam's new road to Hurst Green *(author)*.

and other constructions to his credit – in fact he was the first president of the Institute of Civil Engineers. His road-making did not differ greatly from that of Metcalf but was more thorough in its preparation of the formation and foundation layer and in defining the size of the broken stone for the surface. Although it is not known whether Telford was personally retained by any Lancashire trusts, his method of construction was most certainly used. His procedures – with only a change to tarmac for surfacing – persisted on many classes of roads well into the motor age. The foundation stones were to be of seven-inch depth and carefully set by hand with the broadest ends downward. All were cross-bonded and no stone was to be more than three inches wide on top. Any protuberances were levelled with a sledgehammer and the interfaces filled, or 'racked', with small stones. The process, described as hand 'pitching', was very labour intensive even after the mid-nineteenth century when steam rollers were used to assist compaction.

McAdam's method was completely different from those of Metcalf and Telford. The initial work on preparing and draining the formation was similar but the road was built entirely of layers of relatively small stones (almost walnut size – they 'could be comfortably held in the mouth') to a depth of some twelve inches. The success of this method was almost fortuitous: traffic ground the top layer of stones together producing a dust which sealed the surface, making it virtually waterproof and thus protecting the formation. This process is described as 'water-bound macadam': binding with tar was a much later development, but McAdam's name is perpetuated in the term 'tarmac'.

He criticised the use of large stones in the repair of highways because their irregularity produced holes and ruts as wheels crashed over them. His method was cheaper than Telford's – he claimed that there was

Ewood Bridge, over the Irwell on the road between Haslingden and Edenfield which was turnpiked in 1789. The surveyor was said to be the celebrated John Metcalf, 'Blind Jack of Knaresborough' and the inner (lower) arches of the bridge seen in this photograph may be his work. The later bridge has been super-imposed on the earlier structure.
(*John Priestley*).

usually enough stone in an ill-repaired highway to build a new road, provided that the material was broken down to the specified size. This led to the familiar illustrations of stone breakers seated beside the road: the later turnpikes provided small embayments to accommodate the roadman and his heaps of raw and prepared stone.

McAdam was eventually advisor to no fewer than thirty-four trusts in thirteen counties. He not only had a fresh approach to construction but was also very scathing about the administration of many of the trusts and about the so-called 'surveyors'. In evidence to a parliamentary committee in 1819 he listed his predecessors in six trusts: 'four were old men, one bedridden, two carpenters, two publicans, a baker, a coal merchant and a former underwriter at Lloyds'. If this was typical it is not surprising that the trusts had made little impression on the roads in their care!

The introduction of the new methods to the improvement of individual existing roads is difficult to date but most of the later new roads in Lancashire used McAdam's principles. His name is definitely associated with at least two schemes in the county. One was the major new turnpike for the Haslingden and Todmorden Trust along the Irwell Valley from Haslingden to Stacksteads, constructed about 1815. The other, rather oddly, was not a turnpike but a diversion of the old road past Stonyhurst College near Hurst Green, described at the end of this chapter.

THE FASHION FOR NEW
CONSTRUCTION, 1790–1820

The map on page 129 shows the routes which had been turnpiked by 1790. There were still considerable areas of the county served only by township roads – for example, with the exception of the private toll roads to Kirkham and Freckleton, there were no turnpikes in the Fylde and nor were any created subsequently. However, south of the Ribble and east of the Warrington–Preston axis the picture was very different. Almost all the larger towns were interconnected by trusts, although there were a few gaps and most of the trusts were for the old roads which were often devious and inconvenient. Manchester was, as always, the hub of communications but there had been a very considerable emphasis on attempts to improve the trans-Pennine routes: no fewer than eleven trusts now crossed into Yorkshire and during the 1790s the turnpiking of a second route eastwards from Oldham to Saddleworth (A669) and of a longer route to the north east from Oldham to Ripponden (A672) added to this list.

The considerable programme of canal construction in the county improved the skills of local surveyors and contractors, including bridge-

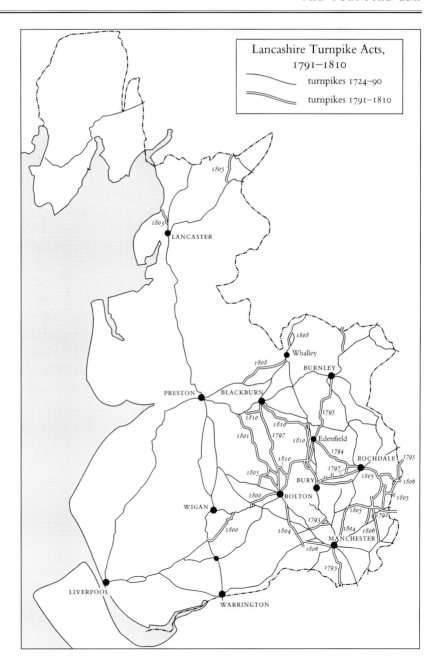

Lancashire Turnpike Acts, 1791–1810

Lancashire Turnpike
Acts, 1791-1810

builders – although bridges were often designed or built by masons rather than engineers. The major earthworks which were necessary to maintain a canal's level showed road surveyors the techniques of planning and designing more ambitious alignments which, by excavation, allowed easier and more regular gradients. This not only benefited the horsedrawn carts and carriages but often permitted the line of a road to be substantially straightened and shortened. During the twenty years from 1790 some new trusts still followed the line of older roads but many others began to undertake large-scale diversions, as Metcalf had already done at Accrington, or to start from scratch. Existing trusts could also contemplate significant changes in alignment or gradient and the result was a large-scale programme of extension and improvement.

During the decade to 1800 the large gap in the existing network between Burnley, Rochdale and Bolton was closed, with the authorisation of several trusts converging on Edenfield, previously an insignificant hamlet on the Bury–Haslingden road (A676). These further Acts were for the Rochdale–Edenfield road (A680) in 1794, Burnley–Edenfield in 1795 and Little Bolton–Edenfield in 1797. Thus Edenfield was, because of its geographical position at the 'throat' of the Rossendale valley system, the meeting place of no fewer than five turnpikes crossing over the surrounding moors and dales.

Bolton's centrality was further improved when the Bolton–Blackburn road via Darwen (A666) and the Bolton–Westhoughton road (A58) were turnpiked in 1797 and 1800 respectively. The latter connected not only with the Manchester–Chorley road but also with the already-turnpiked route from Westhoughton to Wigan via Hindley. From Hindley, too, the turnpike was extended to Ashton-in-Makerfield via Platt Bridge (A58). It is apparent that the development of a true network, with a variety of interconnections and alternative routes, was by this time well under way, but that – like the later growth of the railway network – the process was without an overall plan and lacking in any coordinated or systematic approach.

Between Rochdale and Bury a new situation arose in 1797, when two roughly parallel routes were both turnpiked. The first, now known as Rochdale and Bury Old Road (B6222), included a branch from Bamford to the Edenfield Road and, more curiously, two dead-end branches to Birtle and Woodgate Hill. This road was operated by the Rochdale, Bamford and Bury Trust. The second, parallel, road left the Manchester and Rochdale Trust at Sudden Bridge and reached Bury via Heywood and Heap Bridge (A58). The western half of this road was completely new construction and it thus became Bury New Road – bypassing yet another Bury Old Road, between the latter two villages. It becomes quite confusing!

Lancashire turnpike mileage by decade, 1721–1800

	New	Total		New	Total
1721–1730	59.00	59.00	1761–1770	50.25	364.00
1731–1740	24.25	83.25	1771–1780	33.50	397.50
1741–1750	3.75	87.00	1781–1790	41.00	438.50
1751–1760	226.75	313.75	1791–1800	72.25	510.75

In the decade to 1800, when just over seventy miles were turnpiked, over 40 per cent of the work involved major diversions or completely new alignments (for more detail see Appendix 1d) and it is clear that the fashion was swinging very strongly in favour of building new roads rather than merely upgrading existing ones. This trend continued in the next decade, as shown in Appendix 1e.

The physical intrusion which such new roads represented resembled that of the railways which were to follow and, of course, of new roads in the twentieth century: they sliced ruthlessly across the pre-existing landscapes. This is typified by the results of the 1801 Act for the road from Sharples (near Bolton) to Brindle Lane Ends (near Hoghton), now the A675 Belmont Road. The majority of this road was built across moorland on a new alignment and it is typical of new turnpike construction. There are long straight sections quite separate from old roads and no account was taken of the existing routeways or field patterns. The remaining sections of an older road can be seen in places, such as Roddlesworth Lane which is now mostly a farm track.

The turnpiking of all the important roads in the Manchester area continued. Another route south from the city was provided by Ardwick Green and Wilmslow Road (A34), authorised in 1793 with a new crossing of the Mersey at Didsbury. This road filled the sector between the Stockport and Stretford roads. The first completely new road in the Manchester area was built by the Hulme to Eccles Trust under its Act of 1806. It began at Great Bridgewater Street, crossed the Irwell and then followed a virtually straight course through Salford and Eccles to rejoin the old road to Irlam. It is now Eccles New Road (A57),

The Bolton and Hoghton turnpike (now the A675) looking north towards Riley Green from the junction with Pennington Lane. The road was turnpiked in 1801, almost entirely on new alignments. This view emphasises the long straights – not since the Roman period had such care been taken in the planning and construction of roads *(author)*.

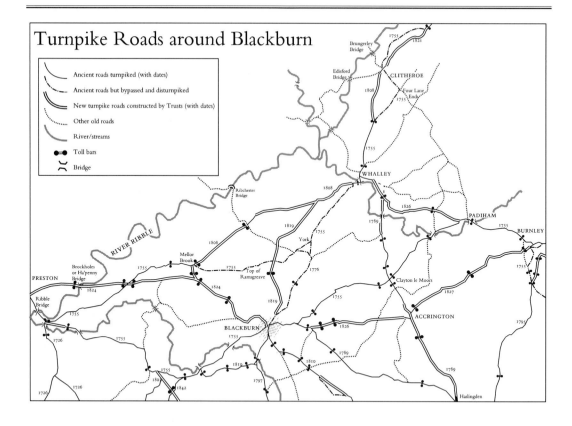

Turnpike Roads around Blackburn

the former route being renamed Eccles Old Road but remaining a turnpike as a division of the Pendleton Trust (A576).

A comparable example of 'Old' and 'New' roads, but in a rural area, is found in the Ribble valley between Preston, Blackburn and Clitheroe. Here the first totally new road was built in 1808 from Whalley Bridge to Balderstone, where it rejoined the old road to Walton-le-Dale. It avoided the long climbs to the summit at Ramsgreave and York which had been a major drawback to the older route, However, the latter remained as a turnpike until Whalley New Road (A666) was constructed in 1819, when it became Whalley Old Road from Blackburn and, together with the section of the original Preston to Whalley road from Mellor Brook over Ramsgreave to York, was disturnpiked. These sections had formed part of the original Skipton and Walton-le-Dale Trust of 1755.

In this area the new routes crossed low ground instead of following the ridgetops as favoured by their predecessors, which had been built on the alignments of country lanes and farm tracks. The new roads were designed for heavy modern traffic from the outset, with much easier and safer gradients and improved alignments using long straights and easy curves. Nevertheless, because speeds remained those of the

Turnpike roads around Blackburn, showing the extensive construction on completely new alignments which superseded the earlier routes.

horse the odd 'blind spot' could be tolerated. One of the most notorious was at the junction of the old Ramsgreave – Salmesbury road with the new Whalley–Balderstone road at Mellor Brook. This problem junction was made worse when a link road was added in 1819 by the Blackburn–Clitheroe Trust. The black spot here, a legacy of turnpike expansion, was not improved until the Mellor Brook bypass opened in 1992.

The first decade of the new century saw major improvements in the district between Rochdale, Oldham, Ashton and Manchester as well as more cross-Pennine roads. In 1804 the Manchester and Rochdale Trust obtained powers to construct the direct road into Manchester from Middleton (A664), largely on a new alignment. Two years later the Manchester, Oldham and Austerland Trust created in 1735 was authorised to create or improve the direct road (A627) between Oldham and Ashton-under-Lyne and to extend it northwards to Royton, although its logical extension, from Royton to Rochdale, was not authorised until a further Act in 1825. After that date the undertaking was burdened with the clumsy title of the Manchester, Oldham, Austerlands, Ashton-under-Lyne and Rochdale Trust. The route from Ashton to Rochdale required extensive new construction and diversion of country lanes and was virtually a new road throughout.

In contrast to the success of many south Lancashire turnpikes, the history of the Hollinwood and Featherstall Trust is a sorry tale of delay, financial mismanagement and failure. It was authorised in 1805, with powers for a new road to pass west of Oldham to Dry Clough near Royton and on to Shaw thence by existing roads to New Hey, Milnrow and Rochdale.[23] There was also to be a new branch road from New Hey to Featherstall, a hamlet west of Littleborough. At this date the direct road between Oldham and Rochdale had only been turnpiked as far as Royton and the new Hollinwood–Featherstall road was intended to provide a route which, by skirting Oldham town centre and bypassing Rochdale, would link the Manchester–Oldham and Rochdale–Halifax turnpikes and give a very direct Manchester–Yorkshire road avoiding congested towns. The trust also had powers for a new road from the west of Oldham to Middleton and for a branch from an existing road from Crompton, north east of Shaw, to Grains Bar on the Ripponden Turnpike in Yorkshire.

Despite this initial promise the trust suffered serious financial troubles from the start and little construction was undertaken. Twenty years later, in 1827, a renewal Act permitted an increase in tolls and, although it was claimed that progress had been made, a subsequent Act cast doubt on this. The 1827 Act amended the line of the Hollinwood–Royton road which, as Featherstall North and South Roads, was eventually built from Werneth almost to Dry Clough. The proposed

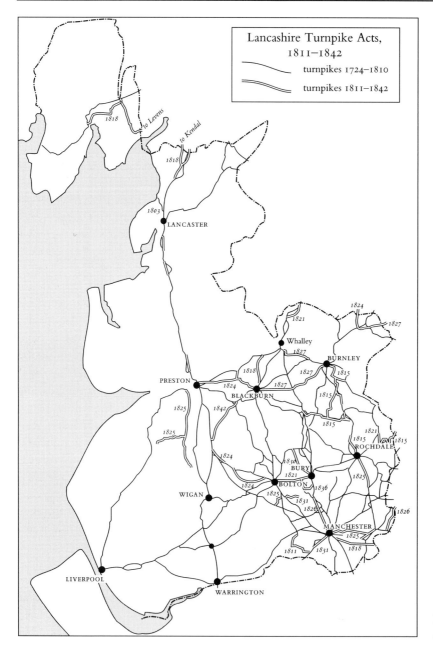

Lancashire Turnpike
Acts, 1811–1842

New Hey–Featherstall link was also to be realigned, to terminate (more logically) in Littleborough. It would appear the Dry Clough–Shaw and Oldham–Middleton roads had at least been started.

In 1830 a further Act was required, again stating that progress had been made but that further finance was required to continue with the improvements and meet interest charges, and tolls were again increased.

By 1837 the situation was desperate: the previous Acts were repealed
and the New Hey–Littleborough link was abandoned. Under a new
name – the Dry Clough, Shaw and Rochdale Trust – work on the
Crompton–Grains Branch (B6197) and the detached Oldham–Middleton road (A669) continued but the Featherstall roads in Oldham were
absorbed by the Manchester, Oldham and Austerlands Trust. Tolls were
reduced but the Act limited further borrowing to a sum not exceeding
£4,000 and required that the monies were to be spent on building the
new lengths of road between Mills Hill and Middleton, Dry Clough
and Shaw and Two Bridges to New Hey.

Thus, thirty-two years after the first Act, these roads were still
apparently unfinished, even though most of them are shown on Green-
wood's Map of 1818. The 1837 Act forbade the trust from repairing
the road through Shaw itself – it was to revert to an ordinary highway
– and required that any available money was to be used in paying
interest and capital debt. In this too, it was unsuccessful, as an Act as
late as 1866 stated that some part of the debt had not received interest
payment for 20 years! The problems of the Hollinwood and Featherstall
Trust seem to have stemmed from an excess of optimism and also of
financial incompetence but were greatly exacerbated by the turnpiking
and improvement of the direct road between Royton and Rochdale
after 1826. This reduced the through traffic on the Dry Clough loop,
rendering it an uneconomical 'white elephant'.

In north Lancashire the long detours around Morecambe Bay continued to exercise the minds of turnpike promoters. A short spur from
Slyne to Hest Bank was added to the Garstang–Heiring Syke road in
1803, to give turnpike traffic direct access to the sands route to Grange.
Even by modern 'A' roads the distance from Lancaster to Ulverston is
36 miles and to follow the turnpike in 1803 involved a detour as far
north as Kendal, a distance no less than 41 miles. It is no wonder that,
tides permitting, the much shorter sands route was preferred. The old
turnpike was in any case in a deplorable condition – a journey from
Cark to Ulverston by turnpike was described as being 'of some fifteen
miles . . . over narrow and rough roads, wooden bridges and precipitous hills, occupying about three and a half hours in performance'.[24]
With reclamation projects planned or in progress on the shores of the
Bay the possibility of providing more direct roads across former inlets
was coming to the fore and in the following decade some of these
schemes came to fruition.[25]

Other major projects undertaken in the early years of the century
included the link from Marsden (Nelson) to Gisburn (A682) and the
turnpiking of the road from Moses Gate through Worsley to Barton
Bridge (A575) in 1804. An additional alternative route between Bury
and Blackburn was turnpiked by the Elton and Blackburn Trust in

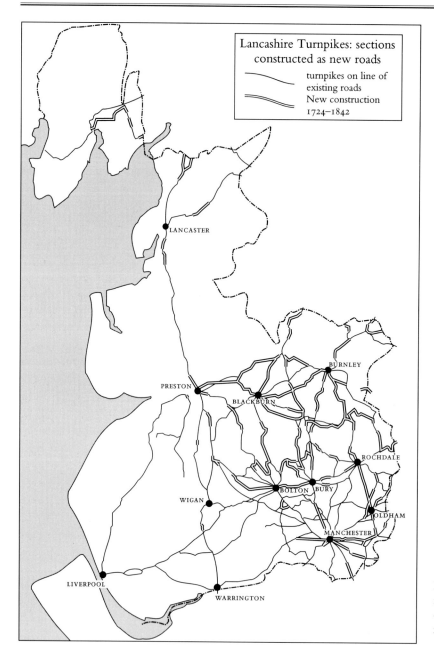

Lancashire turnpike roads: summary map of the construction of new alignments, 1724–1842.

1810. This ran from Elton Bridge, west of Bury and then turned west up Haslingden Grane (B6232). Although there were earlier tracks over the moor this scheme included some major reconstruction and a bypass of Belthorn village. The trust also managed the Holden Hall and Dearden Gate branch which gave a direct link into Haslingden.

By the 1810s the proportion of newly authorised routes which involved either substantial reconstruction or totally new build had increased to approximately 69 per cent (see Appendixes 1e and 1f). New construction, even if lagging behind the date of the Act, required loan capital in advance of any income and it is possible that the newer trusts were more business-like in their approach to such matters. Increasingly, too, the trusts were catering for heavy industrial traffic and this represented a potential source of capital. In the same way that manufacturers were prepared to invest in canals and railways to serve their businesses, so they would promote turnpikes.

An Act of 1811, turnpiking the road from Barton Bridge to Stretford (A575) as a logical extension of the existing turnpike route from Moses Gate, was of the traditional type whereby an existing road was improved. However, most legislation in the 1810s dealt with new construction. The existing network was becoming very intricate, but in the more heavily populated areas, or where older roads were indirect, there was a pressing need to duplicate the first-generation turnpike roads. Often the new alignments were in close proximity to the old, but whereas in some cases – as in the Whalley area – the older route was disturnpiked, in the south of the county both roads usually remained subject to trust control as operating turnpikes.

One of the best examples was the new road (A681) from Haslingden to Stacksteads in the Irwell valley, already mentioned in connection with McAdam's activities. Authorised in 1815, it is often only ½ mile from the parallel old road, but the latter remained a turnpike. They were both part of the Haslingden and Todmorden Trust and both had toll gates – there were nine in this short stretch of the valley. A new spur (A6066) was built to the Rochdale road south of Bacup and a much longer branch from Waterfoot to the Bacup–Burnley road at Deerplay (B6238). Also in 1815, the Halifax road at Blackstone Edge was reconstructed to its present alignment (A58). Where the old and new turnpikes intersected halfway up the hill a single toll bar was erected to cover both roads. At the same time the Mytholmroyd Bridge Trust was created from the top of Blackstone Edge. All but a very short section of this road (B6138) was in Yorkshire but it formed yet another cross-Pennine link.

In Furness a new or improved road was constructed after 1818 by the Ulverston and Carnforth Trust from Levens Bridge through Lindale to Newby Bridge and then on to join the older Kendal to Kirkby Ireleth Trust at Greenodd. The old winding road through Bouth to Newby Bridge and Kendal remained a turnpike under the original Trust but since, at least in Lancashire, there were no toll gates one wonders how much maintenance it received. The old Trust also remained responsible for the road from Greenodd to Kirkby Ireleth.

The same 1818 Act provided for the building, in conjunction with the Garstang and Heiring Syke Trust, of a completely new road from Milnthorpe to Carnforth (the present A6) with a branch (A6070) from Dock Acres to join the old Heiring Syke road north of Tewitfield near the county boundary. The lengths of new road south of the Westmorland boundary became the responsibility of the Garstang Trust and those to its north of the Ulverston Trust, while the old route from Carnforth to Burton was disturnpiked. About the same time the two Trusts for the Preston-Lancaster Road north and south of Garstang built new diversions. In Preston, Garstang Road was laid out as far as the *Black Bull* in Fulwood, it being noted in 1817 that in easing the gradient over Gallows Hill the burials of executed Jacobites were revealed.[26] Further north the roads from Forton to Hampson Green and from Galgate to Scotforth were built as completely new alignments.

Also in 1818 powers were obtained for what became one of the major routes to the east from Manchester, with the Act for the Manchester, Hyde and Mottram Trust which began at the eastern end of Ardwick Green and ran through Gorton and Denton to Hyde. The greater part of this road was of totally new construction, characterised by the long straight stretches from Ardwick to Gorton and from Gorton to Denton. The 'kink' at Gorton, which until recently formed a very awkward junction, resulted from the incorporation of a short length of old village street in the alignment of the new road. This route (A57) became the main Sheffield road, bypassing the earlier route through Ashton and Stalybridge. It was the last major road to the east from the Manchester area to be improved and constructed by a turnpike trust.

THE FINAL PERIOD OF
TURNPIKE EXPANSION, 1821–1842

The building of new turnpiked roads virtually ceased from the early 1830s and only two new trusts were set up after that time, both applying to existing roads. Major new construction in the 1820s began with the building of Bury to Bolton New Road (A58) following an Act of 1821. The existing route, Bury Old Road (B6169) through Ainsworth, was said to be 'very hilly, circuitous and inconvenient' and had never been turnpiked despite the importance of the towns it connected. The Bolton-Nightingales Trust obtained an Act in 1824 for Chorley New Road, paralleling the old road as far as Scholes Brow to the west of Horwich (A673) where it rejoined the original turnpike: both routes remained under the Trust's control. This Act also contained the provision for the changes at Yarrow and Duxbury affecting the Wigan–Preston and Westhoughton–Adlington Trusts, as described previously.

Also authorised in 1824 was the construction of the Preston–

Blackburn New Road, from New Hall Lane in Preston over a new Ribble bridge at Brockholes to an intersection with the old Preston–Clitheroe turnpike at what used to be called the *Five Barred Gate* (now the *Trafalgar Hotel*) and thence by the direct road to Blackburn, ending in a sweeping curve to avoid Beardwood and Dukes Brows. The 1824 Act defined the dimensions for a stone bridge at Brockholes, but a timber bridge was built as a temporary economy measure. In 1852 another Act authorised a permanent replacement but no action was taken until a further Act of 1859 stated that 'the temporary wooden bridge having collapsed it is now expedient to build a more substantial and permanent bridge'. The present stone bridge was then constructed. Normally on a turnpike road foot travellers were exempt from paying any toll at the gates, but the 1824 and 1859 Acts specifically permitted tolls on pedestrians at the new bridge. From 1859 the toll was a halfpenny and for many years after the gate had gone the bridge was known as Ha'penny Bridge.[27]

In the Blackburn area, the Bury, Haslingden and Whalley Trust obtained an Act in 1826 for the construction of a new road from Blackburn to 'New' Accrington, beginning at Furthergate in Blackburn and passing Church to join Metcalf's road (A679). This Act also included a branch from Portfield near Whalley to Padiham (A671) joining the older Blackburn-Burnley road. In the next year, 1827, the Blackburn, Addingham and Cocking End Trust obtained powers for another new road continuing the Blackburn-Accrington road from 'Old' Accrington to Burnley (A679). The Act included powers to extend to the Rochdale turnpike at Habergham Eaves but this project does not appear to have been implemented. A further section of this Act authorised a diversion from Colne to Cocking End, the present A6068 crossing into Yorkshire near Cowling. This bypassed both the original Skipton Old Road from Colne to Toms Cross and a short length of the Keighley and Haworth Trust to the Blue Bell and these were disturnpiked. The Skipton Old Road was further made redundant by the turnpiking in 1824 of the Colne–Broughton road through Foulridge (A56).

The network in Greater Manchester was further developed in the 1820s. An Act of 1825 authorised an addition to the Manchester and Salters Brook Trust of 1732 as a new road from Great Ancoats Street, Manchester to Audenshaw (A662) and on to Ashton-under-Lyne (A635). Inevitably this became Ashton New Road and the former turnpike Ashton Old Road: these parallel routes were close together but both remained turnpikes with several toll gates. North-west of the city the Manchester and Bury New Road Trust was established in 1826 to build on a new alignment from 'the Top of Hunts Bank in the Town of Manchester to join the present Manchester to Bury Turnpike at Pilkington'. The original Manchester–Bury route remained a turnpike road under the Cheetham Hill Trust (A665) and the Bury and Prest-wich Trust.

The new road reconstructed the line of Ducie Street, described as a footpath on William Green's plan of Manchester and Salford of 1794 and continued by a new road to Besses. Early maps show no previous road over this length but it would appear, whether by coincidence or the logical adaptation of the footway, to have recovered the line of the Roman road to Ribchester and is so marked by the Ordnance Survey. A similar coincidence applies to the Manchester, Hyde and Mottram Trust which appears to be on, or very close to, the line of the Roman road to Melandra (Glossop) although, with minor excep-tions, no road existed prior to the construction of the turnpike.

The remaining new trusts created in this last period of growth returned to the earlier pattern of applying toll collection to existing roads. The first (1825) was for the road from Penwortham (Old Bridge) to Wrightington and Shevington (B5250), with a branch to Little Hanging Bridge (A581). The former skirted Leyland and passed through Eccleston, to a point in the middle of nowhere on the township boundary south of Wrightington Bar. The branch passed through Croston – the road through the village and the alternative route on Barbers Moor Lane (B5249) were controlled by the toll gate. This route also ended at a curious place, as Little Hanging Bridge is only half a mile short of the junction with the Liverpool–Preston turnpike – but it, too, is the township boundary. The other 'traditional' trust covered the road from Ashton-under-Lyne to Ridge Hill Lane and Hole House (via Mossley) and received its Act in 1826. This, the modern A635, was the final cross-Pennine route into Yorkshire.

The last two Acts were very late. One, in 1836, was for the Radcliffe Trust which included a small network of roads from Radcliffe Bridge to the Manchester–Bury and Bury–Bolton turnpikes and other branches, with a total length of about six miles and with five toll gates. A branch from Radcliffe to Whitefield was added as late as 1857, replacing the Besses–Radcliffe Bridge spur of the Bury and Prestwich Trust. The final Act, in 1842, covered the road from Chorley to Finnington Bar (A674) on the Preston–Blackburn Old Road. It is perhaps surprising that this important road was not turnpiked sooner and it is unclear why it was felt necessary to do so at such a late date. The text of the Act is much shorter and simpler than those of the heyday of turnpiking, when solicitors and parliamentary draughtsmen had a field day with convoluted phraseology. The preamble is only a few lines and boldly states that 'it would be of public utility if powers were given to Divert and Improve and to make up and maintain a Turnpike Road leading from the Preston to Blackburn Turnpike Road at Finnington to Chorley'.[28] Nevertheless, the powers were similar to preceding Acts with nomination of Trustees to set up and collect tolls. Appendix 1g lists the turnpikes of the period 1821–42.

LENGTH OF TURNPIKED ROADS

The appendices include a series of tables which list chronologically the turnpike trusts and the lengths of road which they controlled. Most of the trusts which crossed into Yorkshire and other counties were much longer than these figures suggest, since only the lengths within Lancashire are given – for example, the Sedbergh Trust was approximately fourteen miles long with three miles in Lancashire and the Mytholmroyd Bridge Trust, with only mile in Lancashire, was about six miles long. Nonetheless there were considerable variations within Lancashire itself, from the tiny Little Lever Trust of less than one mile to major undertakings such as the Bury, Haslingden, Blackburn and Whalley Trust, with over thirty miles of road.

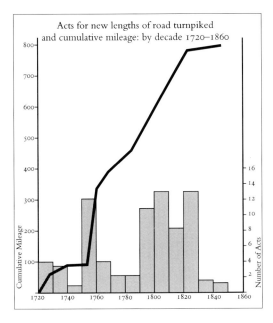

Lancashire turnpikes: cumulative mileage for turnpiked roads, and the length authorised in each decade, 1720-1860.

Because many of the big trusts were broken up into smaller units and not all roads were built immediately after authorisation, the exact length of turnpike road at any one time is difficult to determine. New diversions meant that some lengths were disturnpiked and it is in any case difficult to pinpoint the exact limit of many trusts in the larger towns. The boundaries between roads maintained by the town authorities and those which were turnpiked often changed, particularly in the nineteenth century. For example, in 1830 the Manchester and Wilmslow Trust returned the road from Ardwick Green in Chorlton Row to the surveyor of highways for that township.[29]

A further uncertainty regarding length is that, on existing roads which were turnpiked, the surface over any county or hundred bridge was the responsibility of the bridgemaster and not of the trust. Although in most cases the lengths were short, in others causeway approaches were included. To define jurisdiction the bridgemasters produced 'bridge books', with a plan of each. These books give little or no detail of the superstructures, being only concerned with the waterway span and lengths of road that were their responsibility. On new roads, bridges were maintained by the trust until disturnpiked, when generally they became county bridges. Bridges over canals and, later, railways were the responsibility of the company: railway undertakings often tried to avoid this by providing level crossings. In 1847 the Bury, Haslingden, Blackburn and Whalley Trust went so far as to offer the East Lancashire Railway £600 towards the cost of building a bridge over the turnpike at Alleytroyds, but it was later reported that the railway company had refused.

A maximum figure of 744 miles has been quoted by Tupling but such precision is suspect. The best that can be said is that, at one time or another, slightly in excess of 750 miles of road were subject to trust control. By the mid-nineteenth century, when the six-inch Ordnance Survey maps allow greater accuracy of route measurement and a clearer indication of termini, the length still turnpiked had fallen back to less than 710 miles. At this time the roads were controlled by some seventy-two trusts, some of them being divisions of the original bodies such as Preston–Heron Syke north and south of Garstang and Wigan–Preston north and south of the Yarrow. The Pendleton Trust had five major districts and some others were subdivided for administration and maintenance, particularly those with substantial branches.

TOLL GATES AND KEEPERS' COTTAGES

As every turnpike was based on the principle that the user should pay for the upkeep of the road, it was inevitable that the first directions of trustees to their surveyors usually concerned the erection of gates and toll keepers' cottages. The word 'turnpike' is derived from an early form of bar or pivoted pole resembling a pike – many placenames and documentary sources use the word 'bar' to indicate the location of a turnpike gate. A typical gate resembled a substantial field gate attached to stout posts, the footway alongside being obstructed by posts or bollards.

As traffic increased near busy towns, such as Manchester, paired gates were built on wider sections of road for two-way traffic, often with a traffic island between. Examples of double gates were at Pendleton on Eccles Old Road, at Swinton and at Newton Heath on Oldham Road. Similar pairs of gates were provided where turnpikes branched, as at Old Trafford where Chester Road and Stretford Road diverged and at Heaton Norris where the new Wellington Road to Stockport branched from the old turnpike down Lancashire Hill. In such cases the keeper's cottage was sited in the apex of the junction, to control both roads.[30]

Many gates were sited next to important side roads, even if these

Opposite: Ladies Lane, Hindley, near Wigan: the Penny Gate tollbar was situated just north of Hindley railway station. Although it was a private gate on the road past Hindley Hall it was very typical of the smaller turnpike gates and side-gates, which were usually attached to the front of an existing cottage. Note the wall lanterns and the small gap for pedestrians, and also the change in the carriageway where the private road begins (Wigan Heritage Service Archives).

The toll house at Barrowford, on the Marsden, Gisburn and Long Preston Trust which was formed in 1803. This substantial two-storeyed building was erected at the junction of Gisburn Road (now the A682) and Colne Road (B6247) in the centre of Barrowford. It has recently been renovated, but retains a rare example of an original board which displays the toll charges *(author)*.

were not in themselves turnpikes, to ensure maximisation of revenue. Both turnpike and side road could be gated, although sometimes gates were placed only on the side road, or locked chains were used. Where such side roads were adjacent to a gate the keeper could be called to unlock the obstruction, on payment or proof of payment of the toll. Some side gates, sited away from a main gate, had their own keeper's

cottage. Examples of side gates included those at the junctions of Mill Lane, Wrightington with the Wigan road and of Brindle Lane with Preston Old Road.

Most cottages controlled single gates and, to reduce the width, the cottage projected into the highway. As a result all but a few have since been demolished for road widening or junction improvements. Initially the cottages were very simple: the first two on the Liverpool and Prescot Trust were to be built 'of brick or stone whichever is the cheaper no more than four yards broad and five yards long and have no upper storey' – they cost £140 the pair.[31] In the early years most were single-storey but in later years bay windows or projecting porches were added to enable the keeper to view the road. Later Acts laid down the need for 'facilities and gardens' and many were built with two storeys: it became fashionable for the road frontage to have a hexagonal plan. A few examples have survived although these have usually been altered to increase the accommodation. A simple single-storey type survives near Hoole at Carr House and, although added to, at Oakes Bar near Copster Green. North of Garstang a transitional cottage survives with a flat front but small upper storey. Its twin at Scotforth was demolished as recently as 1953 and its site commemorated in the name of a filling station. A few examples of the two-storey houses with multi-angular frontage have survived, the best known being at Barrowford, which is complete with its toll board. There is also one in Whittle-le-Woods, at the

The Henley Wood Tollhouse, on the Burnley and Todmorden turnpike (photographed 8 June 1927). This house, at the junction of Rock Lane (extreme left) with the Todmorden road, was shortly afterwards demolished to make way for the construction of Glen View Road. It was originally a typical octagonal building, dating from the initial turnpiking, but a substantial house was added subsequently. The tollhouse was situated on the boundary of Burnley county borough: note that the road within the borough is paved with setts, whereas the county road (left) is unsurfaced *(Lancashire County Library: Burnley Local Studies Collection).*

junction with Sandy Lane north of Chorley and – converted into a shop – in Chatburn village.[32]

The most reliable evidence for the location of gates, albeit for the later period 1845–50, is provided by the six-inch maps, on which some 300 toll gate sites can be identified. Many are named and a handful of 'side gates' are shown. Several other sites, abandoned by the 1840s, can be identified from earlier maps or turnpike records. Gates were moved or erected even after the 1850s, when the turnpikes were in financial decline. The Bury, Haslingden, Blackburn and Whalley Trust resited a gate in Church to Old Accrington in 1848 and in 1863 the Clitheroe and Blackburn Trust gave notice of intention to erect two gates between Whalley and the *Petre Arms*.[33] The usual justification for new or relocated gates was to prevent evasion, particularly as suburban housing areas developed. A good example comes from the old turnpike from Burnley to Padiham. The first gate was located at the bottom of Sandygate on Westgate; it was then moved to the *Mitre* at the junction of Westgate and Trafalgar Street, as the construction of the latter had bypassed the first site. A third move, to Padiham Road a little north of Gannow Top, was eventually necessary.[34]

The distribution of the gates is very uneven, the great majority obviously being in the south-east of the county with its very dense network of turnpike roads. Nevertheless, their incidence is not proportional to the length of the turnpikes. Between Preston and Heron Syke there were only seven gates – three north of Preston, one at either end of Garstang and one on each approach to Lancaster. The gap between the Garstang and Scotforth gates was nearly eight miles. John Holt, in his 1795 survey of Lancashire agriculture, called Liverpool 'a great enemy to turnpikes', claiming there were only three gates within eight miles and none within four miles of the port.[35] This implies that most of the short-distance traffic in the area used the turnpikes free of toll. By 1845 there were at least eleven gates within eight miles, nine of them were on the extremely busy roads to Prescot and Roby. However, Liverpool does seem to have got off lightly: there were no fewer than seventy-two gates within eight miles of Manchester – but then Liverpool does have the sea on one side!

The main Lancashire towns were ringed with gates. By the late 1840s there were, within a two-mile radius of the centre, eight at Burnley, twelve at Rochdale and Bolton and no fewer than thirteen at Blackburn. Nor were such densities confined to the perimeter of the main towns. The Manchester to Oldham road had five gates in seven miles, Rochdale to Edenfield seven in only seven miles and the twin roads through Rossendale from Haslingden to Bacup nine in five miles. The number of gates per trust also varied, from the Heywood Trust with one and the Radcliffe Trust with five, to the Bury,

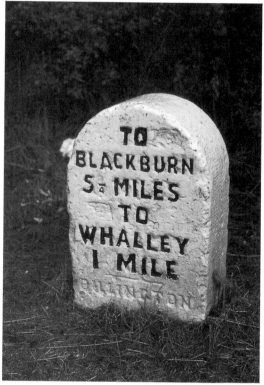

Examples of milestones on turnpike roads.

Clockwise from top left:

Milestone on the Haslingden and Todmorden Turnpike (A631) at Hollin Gate between Bacup and Todmorden. This stone is of the older 'pointing finger' design which in the nineteenth century fell out of favour. The road was turnpiked in 1789 *(John Priestley)*.

The milestone on the Whalley New Road, the Blackburn and Clitheroe turnpike of 1819, near Billington. This stone is of an old-fashioned design for the period; it has a pointing finger and also gives the name of the township, Billington, but these have not been highlighted by the black paint *(author)*.

Milestone on the new section of the Bolton and Nightingales Trust, which was laid out on realignment in 1824. The design of this stone, close to Skew Bridge at Adlington, is more modern and the lettering tablet is raised proud of the surface of the stone itself *(John Priestley)*.

Haslingden, Blackburn and Whalley Trust which had seventeen. On these three trusts the gates were, on average, every 1½ miles, while for the county as a whole they were roughly every 2½ miles.

The General Turnpike Act of 1733 required that trustees should erect milestones along all turnpike roads. This would, in theory, have implied a total of over 700 stones in Lancashire, but today fewer than 250 can be located. Many have been lost through road widening, accidental damage, or deliberate destruction. The older stones are generally roughly-hewn stone shafts, carved with lettering on one or two faces. By the later eighteenth century dressed stone slabs with tapered faces were usual and these were sometimes given attractive embellishments. The milestones on the turnpikes from Todmorden to Burnley and Bacup, for example, were replaced in 1826 with stone slabs incorporating a direction hand giving destination and mileage. Cast-iron plates were also found and some trusts eventually used iron milestones – those on the A49 and A5106 in the Standish area were made at Haig Foundry in Wigan in 1837. The naming of the parish or township on a stone was not usual until the beginning of the nineteenth century and was never a legal requirement.[36]

TOLLS AND TRUST FINANCE

With so many gates in close proximity it was not always necessary to pay at each: the production of a ticket or receipt at one could provide free passage to the next. In some cases the Act, which laid down the maximum tolls, also stipulated the limitation on the numbers of tolls to be paid – the Radcliffe Trust with its five gates could only charge for passage through two. A return trip through a gate at which a toll had been paid was usually free of toll on the same day, although some trusts would charge a laden waggon on each trip. The scales of charges were often very involved, because then as now vehicles were divided into different classes: there were four-wheeled coaches or waggons, two-wheeled light vehicles or carts and further subdivisions defined by the number of horses needed to draw the vehicle and the widths of its wheels. This condition was enforced by the General Turnpike Acts, as were conditions relating to weight. The object was to avoid damage to the road surface, it being considered that narrow wheels did more damage than broad ones. The width was defined by the 'felloes', the wooden segments forming the rim of the wheel and held by the tyre.

As virtually all Acts contained lists of permitted tolls and these became very repetitive, it is sufficient to simplify the wording and quote examples from differing periods. The tolls for Liverpool–Prescot Trust,[37] set out in 1725, were:

For every Horse, Ass, Mule carrying coals	½*d.*
For every Horse, Ass, Mule otherwise	1*d.*
For every wagon carrying coals only	6*d.*
Every other wagon	1*s.*
For every cart or carriage with coals only	
Drawn by 1 or 2 horses	2*d.*
With 3 horses	3*d.*
With 4 horses	4*d.*
For every other cart or carriage	6*d.*
For every other cart or carriage with earthenware	8*d.*
For every Coach, Berlin etc.	1*s.*
For every Chaise, Chair or Calash	6*d.*
Every cow or bullock	½*d.*
Every score of sheep, lambs or swine	5*d.*

The favoured rate for the carriage of coals is not surprising considering the emphasis placed on this trade in the preamble to the Act but other trusts were similarly well-disposed to the coal trade. The Lancaster and Richmond Trust levied no toll on vehicles carrying coal and the Rochdale and Halifax Trust exempted waggons entering Lancashire from Yorkshire if they were coming empty and returning laden with Lancashire coal. The Liverpool–Prescot surcharge on 'earthenware' is less explicable, since these more fragile loads cannot have caused as much damage, but it may have been an attempt to capitalise on the captive market represented by the flourishing Prescot potteries.

Later lists of tolls were much more involved, sometimes occupying two closely-printed pages of the Act. The following table is a simplification in tabular form of a very repetitive description of tolls from the Blackburn and Preston New Road in 1824.[38]

For wagons or wains with four wheels as follows:

No. of horses drawing	Breadth of felloes: Less than 4½″	4½–6″	6″	9″	Rolling 16″
8				3*s.* 0*d.*	2*s.* 0*d.*
7				2*s.* 9*d.*	2*s.* 0*d.*
6			4*s.* 0*d.*	2*s.* 6*d.*	2*s.* 0*d.*
5			3*s.* 6*d.*	2*s.* 3*d.*	2*s.* 0*d.*
4	4*s* 0*d.*	3*s.* 4*d.*	3*s.* 0*d.*	2*s.* 0*d.*	2*s.* 0*d.*
3	3*s.* 6*d.*	2*s.* 11*d.*	2*s.* 6*d.*	1*s.* 6*d.*	1*s.* 0*d.*
2	2*s.* 0*d.*	1*s.* 8*d.*	2*s.* 0*d.*	1*s.* 0*d.*	1*s.* 0*d.*
1	1*s.* 0*d.*	10*d.*	1*s.* 0*d.*	1*s.* 0*d.*	1*s.* 0*d.*

For cart or carriage with two wheels:

4			2s. 6d.	2s. 0d.
3	3s. 0d.	2s. 6d.	2s. 0d.	1s. 9d.
2	2s. 0d.	1s. 8d.	1s. 0d.	1s. 0d.
1	1s. 0d.	10d.	9d.	9d.

Coaches, by comparison were only charged according to the number of horses drawing:

5–6 or more	3s.
3–4 horses	2s.
2 horses	1s. 6d.
chaise etc. with 1 horse	9d.
Every Horse, Mule, etc. not drawing	2d.
Score of cattle, etc.	1s. 8d.
Score of sheep, swine, etc.	1s.
lesser numbers pro rata	

These high tolls must reflect the very great cost of constructing the new road and the Ribble Bridge. In contrast, the tolls on the cheaply-built Penwortham and Wrightington Turnpike of 1825 were much simpler and lower: a waggon with six horses on six-inch wheels was tolled at 3s. here, compared with 4s. on the Blackburn to Preston road:[39]

Every Horse etc. drawing a coach etc.	6d.
Every Horse drawing a wagon with felloes 6″ upward	6d.
Every Horse drawing a wagon with felloes 4½–6″	7d.
Every Horse drawing a wagon less than 4½″	9d.
Every Horse, Mule, etc. laden or unladen	2d.
Every Ass	1d.
Score of Oxen	10d.
Score of Calves, sheep, etc.	5d.

By 1842, when the Finnington–Chorley Act was passed, the rates were lower still[40] and the wheel width requirements had been dropped:

For Every Horse, Mule or Beast drawing a carriage	3d.
For Every Horse, Mule or Beast not drawing, laden or unladen	1d.
Score of Oxen, etc.	10d.
Score of Calves, etc.	5d.
For every carriage propelled or drawn by steam or other Power than Animal Power	2s.

The problem of steam on the roads is discussed below. The Radcliffe Trust in 1836 was empowered to charge 3d. 'for each wheel on which the same shall run', a procedure very different from that governing tolls on other vehicles. In 1831 the Liverpool and Prescot Trust proposed to charge a staggering 48s. for a mechanically propelled vehicle compared with 4s. for a coach.

Toll keepers were not well paid – the post was often said to be suitable for a retired soldier or sailor – and the duties were onerous. It was a 24-hour job, although at least in the early years night travel was infrequent due to the road condition and risk of robbery. Not only had the keeper to assess the type of vehicle and issue a ticket, but there was also a bewildering maze of exemptions from toll to consider. It is not altogether surprising that the honesty of the keepers were sometimes doubted. When trusts began to farm out the collection of tolls, advertisements gave an indication of the previous year's takings as guidance. Thereafter the trust was not responsible for the keeper's wages and was instead guaranteed a fixed income, although a curious clause entitled the lessee to recover from the trust any shortfall should his takings be less than his bid – a rather one sided deal! In 1781 the clerk and treasurer of the Preston and Garstang Trust surveyed the major users of the road to find out what they had paid in tolls. They then compared this with the sum which the lessee claimed to have received and found that the latter had under-declared by at least £51 – he had doubtless hoped to extract this from the trust.[41]

The Heywood Trust let its single gate for £16 per month in 1798, but in 1810 the income was only £126 5s. 7d. over an eight-month period. In its accounts for 1793 is the entry: 'Paid for Drinks for Bidders on Letting Tolls 2s. 6d'.[42] By contrast, the money received from toll lettings by the Bury, Haslingden, Blackburn and Whalley Trust was £6335 in 1831, rising to £8065 in 1836.[43] In 1846 the clerk to the Clitheroe and Blackburn Trust reported that the tolls had been advertised but not let, because the bids were too low: he was empowered to let by private treaty. The surveyor to the same trust had his salary increased from £25 to £40 in 1863 'as a consequence of diminution of his income occasioned by his being obliged to relinquish the collection of Tolls at the Lobley Gate and that he be precluded from undertaking the collection of Tolls for the future or from accepting any other employment which would interfere with his duties as Surveyor'.[44]

There is a general belief that toll gates were unpopular and there was indeed resistance in the early days. This led to government action in 1728 and 1738, making damage to turnpike gates a major criminal offence. The South Wales 'Rebecca Riots' of 1842–3 are often quoted, but these were due in large part to a particularly iniquitous system of toll collection and also had a strong political element. As Lancashire was a 'lagging' county the worst of the opposition was over and the penalties severe, before trusts were widespread in the area. The trustees were invariably people with local interests and land and property owners exerted influence over their tenants. Wide-ranging exemptions from

TURNPIKE ROAD
FROM
BLACKBURN TO WALTON COP.
LETTING OF TOLLS.
NOTICE IS HEREBY GIVEN,

That a Meeting of the Trustees of the Turnpike Road from Blackburn to Walton Cop, in the County of Lancaster, will be **HOLDEN** at the **TOWN HALL**, in Preston, in the County aforesaid, on **FRIDAY**, the 1st day of **DECEMBER** next, at twelve o'clock at Noon, on the General Business of the Trust; and, that at such Meeting the Tolls arising at the several Toll Gates and Side Gates upon the said Road, called or known by the names of the **Knot Lane End Toll Gate**, the **Brindle Lane End Toll Gate**, and the **Blackburn Toll Gate**; and also the several Side Gates at **Knot Lane End, Kitlingburne, Duxon Hill, and Brindle Lane End, WILL BE LET BY AUCTION**, to the best bidder, in the manner directed by the Acts passed in the Third and Fourth years of the Reign of his Majesty King George the Fourth, for regulating Turnpike Roads, which Tolls produced in the last year, the sum of £681. 13s. 7d., above the expenses of collecting the same, and will be put up at that sum; and if not let together and in one lot, the said Tolls will be put up in Parcels, and in several Lots, each at such sum as the Trustees shall think fit.

Whoever happens to be the best Bidder or Bidders, must give security with sufficient Sureties, to the Satisfaction of the Trustees of the said Turnpike Road, for payment Monthly of the Rent at which the said Tolls, or any Parcel thereof, shall be Let, and (if required) must pay one Month's Rent in advance.

PAUL CATTERALL, JUN.,
Clerk to the said Trustees.

Preston, October 2nd, 1854.

A. V. MYERS, PRINTER, 28, CHURCH-STREET, PRESTON.

Blackburn and Walton Cop Trust: notice announcing the forthcoming letting of the tolls on the turnpike. The leasing-out of the tolls was a very common practice on turnpikes from the mid-eighteenth century onwards, since it ensured a regular income and prevented the losses by fraud which had been a major problem when salaried toll collectors were employed (*Lancashire County Library: Harris Library, Preston, Local Studies Collection*).

tolls helped to ameliorate their disadvantages and, for the poor, who walked everywhere anyway, the turnpikes had little impact.

Local agriculture was usually given some protection, as the following typical quotation, from the Wigan and Westhoughton Act of 1825, illustrates: 'No toll shall be demanded or taken for any Horse, Beast or Cattle or Carriage carrying . . . Wood, Frith or Furze for Fuel not sold or disposed of or passing to be sold or disposed of, but laid up in the Houses, Outhouses or Yards or in the lands of Grower thereof; or of carrying or conveying Draining stone, Dung, Lime or other Manure to be used only for improving or manuring lands adjoining to or returning empty in that employment nor for any Horse Beast or Cattle . . . employed for . . . conveying Gravel, Stones, Sand, Bricks, Tiles, Wood or other material for the repairing or improving the said Road . . . or for building rebuilding or repairing any present or future public Bridge or Bridges on the said road nor for carrying or conveying potatoes grown in any Parish or Township aforesaid to be laid up or deposited in the Warehouse Barns or Bartons of or belonging to the Owners of such Potatoes and not for sale'.[45]

There was also the question of weight. Under a General Act of 1741 trustees were empowered to erect weighing machines to ensure that vehicles laden in excess of the permitted levels were charged accordingly. Several 'machines' were set up in Lancashire, although certainly not at every toll gate. In pursuance of this, the Preston and Garstang and Garstang and Heron Syke Trusts agreed to share the cost of £67 7s. for a weighing machine at Claughton toll bar, south of Garstang.[46] The Bury, Haslingden, Blackburn and Whalley Trust had four weighing machines, one with a separate machine house. In cases of damage to the roads the Radcliffe Trust had the power to weigh any one-horse cart in the same manner that carts drawn by two or more horses were liable to be weighed.[47]

In addition to the general exemptions from tolls there were many other local variations. The Liverpool and Prescot Trust exempted milk, butter or cheese if carried by a horse but not if loaded on a waggon. Manure, straw, hay and agricultural implements such as ploughs and harrows were free of toll, as were posthorses, but the trustees were less generous with regard to corpses. In February 1726 they resolved that corpses carried through a turnpike and those attending the funeral should all be tolled. This was modified in 1730 by the exclusion of those corpses from the parish in which the gate was erected who were to be buried within that parish. Residents travelling to church by coach on Sundays were also exempt. The trustees were generous to a Prescot butcher who complained at being charged 1d. when riding a horse with a calf in his arms: he had been tolled both for the horse and the calf, but it was ordered he should only be charged for the horse – perhaps they admired his feat of horsemanship![48]

Trusts sometimes engaged in disputes with local tenants and landowners who still claimed rights of passage. There was a fear that where individuals controlled land adjacent to a gate a bypass might be opened up over the fields – this was countered by the erection of fences, side gates and chains. Evasion of tolls was an offence under national statutes.

A doctor wishing to visit a patient who lived just through the toll bar at Strangeways in Manchester parked his gig by the road and walked through the gate. He was seen by the gatekeeper, summoned before the magistrates and ordered to pay the toll.[49] On one occasion the clerk to the Blackburn and Preston Trust was instructed to support the conviction of Jake Sellers for evading payment of tolls at the Lane Side branch gate near Bury — and Sellers was superintendent of police in the town![50]

Although tolls were the main income for a turnpike trust there were usually some lesser sources of revenue. Like all public roads the turnpikes were subject to statute labour but it quickly became apparent that to attempt to employ statute labour within the repair programme of the surveyors was both inefficient and uneconomic. As a result trustees normally negotiated with the township to compound a payment in lieu of statute labour. The Liverpool and Prescot Trustees opened negotiations within the first year of their existence. Eventually most trusts had similar arrangements with the townships on the line of their road, just as, in their turn, the townships were increasingly accepting payment in cash from those who were due to perform statute labour.

Faced with the need for substantial sums of money — whether at the outset, or when making major improvements or building new roads — a trust would usually borrow money, either from its own trustees or on the commercial market. Tolls were frequently mortgaged as a guarantee and interest was, of course, payable. In the early nineteenth century these debts grew to a considerable size and many trusts were burdened with heavy interest payments which had to be met from the current toll income. Where this fell short the interest due was covered by further bond issues, which in effect increased the interest payable. These large and growing debts could be managed in the short-term but nationally the problem became acute once railway competition resulted in a fall in toll income.

The Liverpool and Prescot Trust (1725) had taken up loans of about £2,000 by the beginning of 1727. Its wage bill was relatively low, but some other trusts paid their employees what seem to be inflated salaries. Below are given some samples of the income and expenditure of the Blackburn and Burscough Bridge Trust (Preston Old Road) which had two gates, at Walton-le-Dale and Moulden Water:[51]

1756–7	Burscough Bridge	£182 17s. 11¼d.
	Moulden Water	£ 79 8s. 9 d.
	Total income	£262 6s. 8¼d.
	Total expenditure	£262 3s. 4 d.
1774	Income	£378 11s. 6 d.
	Expenditure	£286 17s. 8 d.

Jan 1790–Oct 1793
  Income   £2632 14s. 5 d.   Average £693 p.a.
  Expenditure   £2055 7s. 4 d.   Average £541 p.a.

Dec 1801–Nov 1802
  Income   £ 981 19s. 5½d.
  Expenditure   £ 869 8s. 8 d.

These figures show a steady increase in profit, a situation which
continued for the first forty years of the nineteenth century. In 1829
the Bury, Haslingden, Blackburn and Whalley Trust had an income
from tolls of £5,950 and money granted by the townships amounted
to £174 14s. 1d., a total of £6,124 14s. 1d.[52] The expenditure of the
trust was:

  Repairs   £2,021 9s. 0d.
  Interest   £1,850 0s. 0d.
  Salaries   £ 300 0s. 0d.
  Contingencies   £ 500 0s. 0d.
  TOTAL   £4,671 9s. 0d.
  Balance   £1,453 5s. 1d.

While this is a favourable balance, the repairs amount to only 33
per cent of income and interest payments to 30 per cent – the repayment
burden was clearly very considerable even for this large and efficient
trust. The income from tolls continued to increase, the following sums
being received from lessees:

  1831   £6,335   1834   £6,905
  1832   £6,332 10s.   1835   £7,335
  1833   £6,647 10s.   1836   £8,065

Although this trust made a profit over a long period it continued to
draw computed payments from the townships or their successors long
after statute labour was abolished in 1835 – and it was not the only
trust to do so: a parliamentary return of 1850 records that trusts in
Lancashire had received £2,227 16s. 0d. as 'parish composition' in 1847.

Typical accounts for 1832 for Wigan and Preston (North of the
Yarrow) Trust[53] reveal much of interest:

Expenditure	£	s.	d.
Balance owing to surveyor as for last years account	290	9s.	1½d.
Balance owing to late surveyors –do–	36	9s.	10 d.
To Surveyor's account of day labour for maintenance	314	4s.	9½d.
–do– for team labour	196	17s.	1 d.
–do– for materials	623	4s.	11 d.
–do– for tools	8	7s.	7 d.
–do– repairs to tollbars, fences, &c	34	8s.	4½d.

Allowance to Townships for keeping Roads in Repair	152	10s.	0 d.
Paid interest for money owing	1,862	1s.	6 d.
Surveyor's & late Surveyor's salaries	59	1s.	6 d.
Principal money paid off	630	0s.	0 d.
Commission to banker	8	19s.	7 d.
Incidental expenses	25	19s.	5 d.
TOTAL EXPENDITURE	4,242	13s.	8½d.

Income

To balance in Treasurer's hand	493	10s.	8 d.
Cash from Tolls	3,168	3s.	6 d.
Cash from Townships	190	0s.	0 d.
Incidental receipts	2	10s.	0 d.
Interest allowed by Bank	5	14s.	2 d.
Balance owing to Surveyors	187	10s.	1½d.
Balance owing to Treasurer	195	5s.	3 d.
TOTAL INCOME	4,242	13s.	8½d.

This account shows that the surveyors were carrying out maintenance by employing direct day labour and by 'team' contract; they were also purchasing the materials. To do this they appeared to carry an appreciable 'float' of cash or debt, for the actual cash income was only £3,366 7s. 8d.

			as % of the cash income of £3,366 7s. 8d.
Expenditure on interest	£1,871 1s. 1d.		55.6
Current repairs & materials	£1,295 1s. 4d.		38.5
Capital repayment	£ 630 0s. 0d.		18.7
Salaries, commission, incidentals	£ 94 0s. 6d.		2.8
TOTAL	£3,890 2s. 11d.		115.6

The expenditure on repairs has, in this case, fallen well below interest repayments and the capital repayment must have been met by adjustment of balances. Only five years earlier the Bolton and Nightingales Trust, with a toll income of £2007 16s. 4d. and no call on statute labour, was forced to borrow a further £7712 10s. with its tolls as security.[54] Tolls, the only major source of income apart from the expedient of borrowing, were of course instantly vulnerable to changes in traffic. Many Lancashire turnpikes saw increasing toll income up to the late 1830s, reflecting a growth in traffic, but nonetheless there were signs that the debt burden was beginning to overshadow the finances of even the more prosperous trusts. It is possible to speculate that, even if there had been no competition from the railways, the financial instability of many trusts would have resulted in wholesale changes in the organisation and management of the turnpike network.

TURNPIKE TRAFFIC AND COMPETITION

The growth in toll receipts not only reflected periodic increases in the tolls themselves but also the fast-expanding economic activity of the late eighteenth and early nineteenth centuries. Traffic was growing and its character was changing because of improved road surfaces. These allowed speeds to be increased up to the limit of horse power – and so permitted shorter journey times. During the early years of the turnpikes packhorses were still widespread and although waggons had been used for hundreds of years their basic design had remained largely unchanged.

The carriage of freight by waggons over longer distances was comparatively slow to take hold in the north-west. The stage waggon, the vehicle which evolved from the basic cart, was for a long time cumbersome with a bulky body, the goods carried being protected from the weather by a hooped canvas cover. They had broad wheels, as required by various Acts of Parliament and loads were – at least in theory – regulated from 1741 onwards, being restricted to three tons in summer and two in winter. In 1765 permitted loads on wide wheels were increased to six tons. Notwithstanding all these restrictions, the imposition of tolls and the need for between four and eight horses to haul the waggons, they eventually became more effective than packhorses, which normally carried only 2–3 cwt. By the mid-eighteenth century they were widely used and regular waggon services were developing.

The best known regular carrier was Pickfords, which traces its origins back to 1649. In 1776 it still took ten days for a waggon to travel from London to Manchester but, as the surfacing of roads improved, Pickfords developed a lighter vehicle, the 'Fly Waggon' and with this reduced the journey time between Manchester and the capital to four days. By 1814 the light well-sprung Pickford vans had reduced the journey time from Manchester to London to thirty-six hours, but the charges were commensurately high – 23s. 4d. per cwt.[55] The Manchester carrier John Johnson & Sons of Oak Street ran regular waggon services to Chester, Sheffield, Nottingham, Leicester, Birmingham and London and in 1804 the *Manchester Guide* listed 120 land carriers to all parts of the kingdom, claiming that there were more waggons and carts used in Lancashire than in any other part of the country.[56] This claim may be treated with some scepticism, in view of the size of London and its use as a port, but it is indicative of the scale of these operations.

Pickfords' records give an example of the waggon service operating in 1835 over the forty-one miles of steep hilly terrain between Manchester and Sheffield. In the Pennine sections six horses were required for each vehicle, but even so speeds were as low as 2 m.p.h. The trip involved several changes of horses, for which horsekeepers were employed at suitable intervals and sixty-six horses were required to keep one waggon on the road. The route passed through eleven turnpike gates, of which three were in Lancashire and the tolls amounted to £21 12s. per waggon per week, or £1,123 4s. a year. The total annual expenses were as follows – the waggon itself was hired:

Waggoners' Wages	£ 650	0s.
Horsekeepers' Wages	£ 293	16s.
Mileage of Waggon (on hire)	£ 319	16s.
Rent (stabling etc)	£ 69	12s.
Tolls	£1,123	4s.
Total for Sheffield–Manchester service	£2,456	8s.[57]

It will be seen that the tolls were a very significant proportion of the costs of inland transport – about 46 per cent in this instance. The maximum charges for freight carriage were, from 1691 until 1827, fixed by the justices of peace, each county deciding on its own rate. These charges were assessed according to weight and distance but there were considerable variations for the type, bulk and packaging of the load. Examples of Pickfords' charges from Liverpool to the Nottingham depot in 1830 were as follows:

	per ton
Flour sacks or casks, grain in bags, meal, nails, vinegar or such like goods not very bulky or hazardous	24s.
Ashes, hardware, seeds	27s.
Bark in bags, yarn	29s.
Empties	30s.
Cheese, large wt, cotton, hops, leather, paper, wine, wool	31s.
Furniture, gentlemen's goods	55s.[58]

The carriage of passengers – other than on horseback or stage waggon – was also slow to develop in Lancashire. Although coaches first appeared in small numbers in the first half of the seventeenth century they were not popular, being heavy and unsprung. In Liverpool as late as 1741 there were said to be only two closed carriages, the use of which was confined to the town streets because of the state of roads beyond.[59] The first regular public service was that from London to Manchester via Buxton, started in 1754. The trip took four and a half days for the 185 miles. Improved timings followed improved road surfaces and in 1811 the journey time was down to twenty-seven hours. In 1834 the Manchester day coach completed the trip in eighteen hours, which was the physical limit for horses – or perhaps beyond it, since even though the animals were changed at roughly ten mile intervals and the coaches weighed less than three tons, the life of a horse on the road was no more then three years.

The carriage of mail by coach began with John Palmer's service from London to Bristol in 1784. The vehicle was a normal stagecoach but no outside passengers were carried – only an armed guard and the mail box. By the following year mail coaches were running to several other destinations including Manchester and Liverpool. The acme of the mail service came as late as 1836, when the Liverpool *New London Mail* ran at 11 m.p.h. Nationally, by 1835 there were 700 mail coaches running regularly and 3,300 stagecoaches directly employing 35,000 men and requiring 150,000 horses: a few years later the great industry had almost vanished. As the turnpikes were improved the Lancashire coach network grew rapidly. The first Liverpool service was in 1761, taking four days from London via Warrington. In 1766 the time was down to three days in winter and two in summer with two coaches running. There were also regular services once a week to Lancaster and Kendal and three times weekly to Manchester.[60] From Manchester coach services radiated out to Middleton (1804), Eccles New Road (1806), Hyde, Mottram, Glossop and Sheffield (1825) and Bury (1827) among many other destinations. The turnpikes were essential for the effective operation of these fast and expensive services.

Competition between operators and drivers led to racing, which was punished by magistrates if a case was proved. The lucrative Liverpool to Manchester service appears to have been particularly prone to this activity – the newspapers in 1814 were full of complaints about it and a report of 1817 recounted three coaches racing from Manchester: 'there were ladies of great respectability in the middle of the coach, who were under the most painful apprehension of being exposed to this sort of danger all the way to Liverpool. Happily their fears terminated at Warrington for it happened that a worthy magistrate saw the whole affair and he convicted the coachman of 'The Defiance', on his own view, in the penal sum of £10 which was paid in Liverpool' – on the spot fines for driving offences are not new![61]

The speeding-up of 'quality' road travel by, on average, 20–30 per cent between 1750 and 1830 is a measurable demonstration of the improvements brought about by the turnpike trusts but the economic effects of their work were, of course, much wider. The postal service was vastly upgraded and it was no longer necessary for merchants personally to accompany their goods in pack trains to the great markets – as, for instance, when clothiers from Bury and Rochdale together with some from Yorkshire used 1,000 packhorses to attend Sturbridge Fair near Cambridge. By the nineteenth century they could employ commercial travellers, armed only with an order book and samples, send or receive the order by post and have the goods delivered by stage waggon as and when required.

The physical growth of towns – particularly Manchester and Liverpool but also other centres in south Lancashire – was encouraged not just by a rapid increase in population but also by better roads, which fostered the trend towards commuting. Merchants and manufacturers no longer needed to live 'over the shop' in often insalubrious areas but could move to the new suburbs and travel daily two or three miles to their workplace. The development in Manchester of such fashionable and exclusive suburbs as Ardwick Green and London Road, with large villas set in extensive gardens, can be clearly seen on Thornton's map of 1831. A comparable expansion was taking place in West Derby and Fazakerley on the edge of Liverpool. Although many non-turnpike roads played their part in this pattern the quality of the turnpikes made them particularly attractive – they offered a fast and comfortable drive to work. Ribbon development began and property sale notices made frequent references to adjacent turnpikes as they do to roads and railways today. Suburbanisation thus pre-dated the coming of the railways and was in origin, in the bigger towns and cities, a road-based development.

The first competition experienced by the turnpikes came from the improvement to river navigations, soon to be followed in Lancashire by the construction of the canals. It is outside the scope of this book to detail the development of the canal network, although the county had the earliest true canals – the Sankey Navigation from Warrington to St Helens, opened in 1757 and the more famous Bridgewater Canal from Worsley to Manchester, opened in 1765. Both were primarily for the movement of coal: its price in Manchester was virtually halved when the Bridgewater opened. The canals had been preceded by navigation works for the Douglas and the Irwell.[62]

The effect of the canal system upon the turnpikes is a debatable issue. As far as the trans-Pennine routes were concerned the canals came very much later than the improvements to the roads – the Leeds and Liverpool Canal was completed in 1816, the Rochdale Canal in 1804 and Huddersfield Canal in 1811. No doubt the turnpike trusts benefited from the increased experience of contractors and although at the height of the canal mania investment funds may have been diverted away from the road schemes this was not a long-term problem.

The early nineteenth century was a period of such considerable overall growth in commerce and industry that the total increase in the movement of freight fully outweighed any loss of income to the turnpikes. In any case, most canal freight consisted of heavy bulk loads such as coal, which were the cause of damage to the turnpikes and for which road transport was arguably less appropriate. When the Glasson Dock branch of the Lancaster Canal opened in 1825 it was cheaper for seaborne coal, slate and timber traffic trade to use that port and then the canal down to Preston, rather than continue with transshipment to road vehicles at Freckleton. The topography of Lancashire meant that its canals often had devious and indirect routes and they could only penetrate parts of the industrialised south-east by heavy lockage, which made journeys slow – problems of water supply and the freezing of canals in winter adding to this problem. Many growing urban and industrial centres were not on the canal network at all – Rossendale is the best example – and there is a good deal of evidence to suggest that in many areas the roles of the canals and the turnpikes were actually complementary rather than competitive.

However, while the effect of canals on turnpike fortunes was probably only marginal, there is no doubt that the next transport revolution was catastrophic in its consequences. The forerunners of railways can be seen in Lancashire from the early eighteenth century, with the construction of tramway feeders to the canals from quarries and, particularly, collieries. With the opening of the Liverpool and Manchester Railway (L.M.R.) in 1830 Lancashire was placed in the forefront of the revolution and over the next twenty years the expansion of the network was rapid. Railways reached Bolton and Warrington in 1831, Wigan in 1832, Preston in 1838 and Lancaster in 1840. In that year also the Preston and Wyre Railway was opened to Fleetwood, connecting there with a steamer service to Scotland. Even the difficult trans-Pennine routes were soon constructed, the Manchester–Leeds line opening in 1839 and that from Sheffield to Manchester in 1841.

The Post Office was quick to use the new facilities, employing the L.M.R. within a year of its opening: a travelling post office ran between London and Preston by 1840. As fast as the rail network expanded mail and parcels were transferred to the trains and mail coaches discontinued. Stagecoach networks also declined after a brief period when they acted as feeders to the railways or closed gaps in the system until lines were complete. Compared with the money available for turnpikes the magnitude and rate of capital investment in railways was huge. Competing companies duplicated many routes and whereas many turnpikes were not paralleled by a canal, none was able to avoid the competition presented by a rail route.

DECLINE OF TURNPIKES

Since much local movement was exempt from turnpike tolls and gates were so positioned that short movements in and around most towns usually avoided them, the transfer of so much longer-distance traffic to the railways was predictably devastating. Most trusts had relied on non-local traffic and had nothing to cushion their finances when that traffic waned. The decline in revenue, which was not of course peculiar to Lancashire, came just after the major investment in new works on the turnpike roads which had been financed by borrowing against anticipated toll income.

Between 1837 and 1854 turnpike toll receipts in England as a whole fell by £470,041: the figures for Lancashire for the same period show a decline from £139,852 (1837) to £96,227 (1854), or more than 31 per cent. However this decline was by no means uniform. Those routes directly affected by parallel main line railways suffered the most – the Warrington and Lower Irlam Trust raised £1,680 in tolls in 1829, the last full year before opening of the Liverpool and Manchester Railway, but by 1834 the income had fallen to £332. On the Bolton to Blackburn road the toll income was £3,998 in 1846, but in the following year the railway between these towns opened. Income immediately fell to £3,077; three years later, in 1849, it was down to £1,185.[63]

On the other hand, a few trusts, which at first were not directly affected by railways, actually increased their income. The annual receipts of the Rochdale and Edenfield Trust ranged from £350 to £440 during 1847–57, rising to £765 in 1862–3. The Haslingden and Todmorden Trust more than doubled its income between 1834 to 1881. In the first instance there was never a parallel railway and in the second the railway came late. Both trusts probably benefited from feeder traffic heading to or from the nearest railheads.[64]

In addition to the falling traffic levels which were a major problem after 1830, the trusts lost other income. The Highway Act of 1835 not only abolished the legislation on weights and wheel widths – and so led to a reduction in tolls – but it also finally abolished statute labour. The commuted sums paid to the trusts by adjacent townships were usually the only regular source of income apart from tolls and, small though the sums may have seemed, the abolition of this principle was estimated nationally to have cost some £200,000 per year. In Lancashire trust income from this source fell from over £7,000 in 1834 to less than £700 in 1837.[65]

As already noted, all this came on top of existing financial insecurities. Many trusts had converted unpaid interest payments to capital by the issuing of bonds, which merely had the effect of increasing the yearly charge as well as the outstanding capital. For example, the Elton and Blackburn Trust (1810) had initially borrowed £14,830, but between 1816 and 1838 this total increased to £22,545 by the issue of bonds and by 1859 a further £12,635 in unpaid interest had accrued. With toll income having fallen from £900 to less than £600 a year there was absolutely no chance of repayment.[66]

The minute book of the Wigan to Preston (North of the Yarrow)

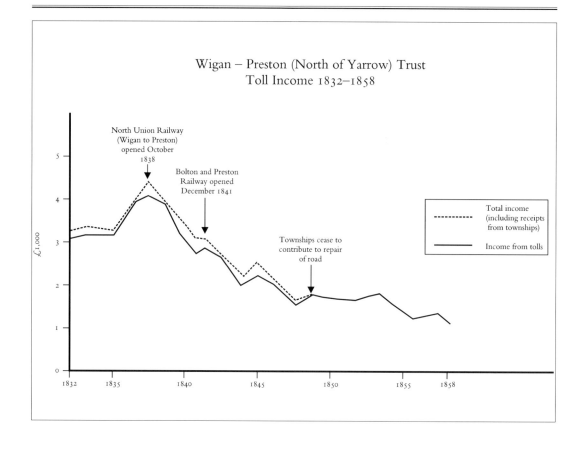

Wigan – Preston (North of Yarrow) Trust
Toll Income 1832–1858

Trust illustrates the problem in detail. From 1832 to 1835 toll income averaged around £3,200 and this increased sharply to a peak of £4,195 in 1838 – a growth accounted for by construction traffic associated with the building of the parallel North Union Railway from Wigan to Preston. After 1838, when the line opened, income fell just as sharply, to £2,799 in 1841 and, after a slight recovery in 1845, a more gradual decline continued until 1858, by which time the toll income was a mere £835. In addition the townships contributed between £50 and £298 per year from 1832 until 1847 with a final figure of £22 in 1848. In that year the Trustees stated that 'in consequence of the great fall off of the Tolls the Trustees have been under necessity of giving up to the different Townships the Repair of the Roads'.

In the following year, 1849, it was recorded that 'there is no revenue sufficient for the regular repair of the Roads and the surplus revenue, if any often paying interest and expenses will be divided between the different Townships'. The Trust had given up all attempts to repair the road – the bulk of its receipts was being swallowed up in interest payments, which in 1849 amounted to about £1,215 – and instead was paying the residue to the townships to do the work. In 1850 the

The Wigan and Preston (North of Yarrow) Trust: graph showing the toll income of the trust between 1832 and 1858.

townships received £244 and in 1854 £171. By 1856 the mortgage still stood at £26,655, the interest rate was reduced to £3 p.a. and no further payments for repairs were made to the townships.

The trustees attempted to recover some income. Following a further Act in 1855 they resited the toll house in Walton-le-Dale from near School Lane to the corner of Hennel Lane, with side bar and chains there and built a new toll house and gate with side bars and chains in Euxton. In 1858 a new gate was erected at Duxbury. It was all to no avail: the trust was terminated on 1 November 1877.[67]

The Clitheroe and Blackburn Trust was slightly better placed when wound up in 1881. Although the trustees never owned the road and any land acquired for improvement became public highway, they did own the gates and toll houses. These were therefore sold by tender: the house at Brownhills realised £272 10s. and the gates £4 10s. but most gates fetched less than £1 and houses less than £50 – the total realised was only £722. Nonetheless Thomas Hargreaves, the surveyor, received £120 in consideration of his faithful performance of his duties for over fifty years and as compensation for loss of office. A final balance of £62 9s. 0d. was distributed among all the townships except Blackburn, Little Harwood and Clitheroe.[68]

These winding-up procedures took place under the terms of an Act of 1867, which started the process whereby the turnpike system was dismantled. In Lancashire, the Hulme and Eccles Trust and the Western District of the Richmond and Lancaster were among the first to go. Continuation Acts were only granted subject to strict conditions and for a very short period. For example, the Ashton New Road Continuation Act of 1874 required that no less than £200 p.a. be used in discharge of debt and salaries, with other expenses not to exceed £60. The expiry date was 1 November 1884 but a further Act in 1875 brought the expiry date forward to 1879 and reduced tolls by a quarter. The Rochdale and Burnley Continuation Act of 1875 limited salaries to £145 *per annum* and reduced interest to 3 per cent. The Trust expired on 1 November 1880. By 1878 only twenty-four trusts remained in Lancashire and in 1884 there were six. The last to be dissolved was that for Preston to Blackburn New Road in 1890 and with it 165 years of Lancashire turnpikes came to an end.

THE AFTERMATH OF THE TURNPIKES

The Highway Act of 1835 abolished statute labour but still left townships responsible for the maintenance of the roads, to be financed by highway rates. Further Acts of 1862 and 1864 permitted townships to combine into highway districts controlled by boards. In their final years most

trusts, even when spending money on the repair of their roads, had
endeavoured to economise by such methods as reducing the width of
the metalled surface from thirty feet to fifteen feet or even less. As
each trust was terminated the responsibility for the roads reverted to
the township or highway district and – especially in south-east Lancashire with its close network of turnpikes – this increased mileage of
neglected roads was very burdensome. The government had been
encouraging the dissolution of the trusts and it gave some relief to the
townships after 1876 by grants in aid of the highway rate and by
directing the justices to contribute from county funds half the cost of
repairing roads disturnpiked since 1870. These were designated 'main
roads'.

ROAD DEVELOPMENT,
OTHER THAN TURNPIKES, UP TO 1888

In the growing urban areas roads were often laid out with little control
or thought, to serve new housing and industry. If in public use these
became maintainable by the township and for some places this represented a serious problem. In 1795 Holt instanced the case of Manchester,
not then a borough, 'which includes a great extent of country and an
immense population, faced with the intolerable burden to repair ways,
hitherto little known or used but now become public streets in the
town itself'.[69] In boroughs the local authority had greater powers over
roads but, in the rest of the county, standards remained low and the
system disorganised.

However, certain roads – as well as the public turnpikes – were
improved or constructed as new, one group being the private toll roads.
A landowner could, for his own use, create a new road over his land
and charge the general public a toll for using it. A good example was
the road from Preston to Kirkham and Freckleton. The ancient public
highway was very winding and narrow, through Lea and Clifton and
the public began to take short cuts over the Clifton and Freckleton
Marshes. The landowners, the de Hoghton and Clifton families, charged
for this access and after an agreement in 1781 they jointly constructed
proper roads, complete with toll bars. It is no coincidence that this
was the time when the growth of Blackpool was starting to increase
road traffic across the Fylde – and equally significant is the fact that
the following year saw the first long-distance stagecoach services to the
infant resort.[70] Not being a turnpike the road remained a toll road until
1902, when it was acquired by Lancashire County Council and Fylde
Rural District.

South of Rochdale, Thornham Old Road – between the A664 at

Slattocks and the A627 through Thornham Fold – was a private toll road, while slightly further north a roughly parallel Thornham New Road, also subject to toll, was laid out in the mid-nineteenth century. Both remained as such until the 1930s and the former still has public rights of way only as a bridleway. In the same area the road from Hopwood, south of Heywood, as far as Hollin Lane, Middleton, was a private toll route, Heywood New Road: it is now the A6046.

There are other lesser examples, such as the road from Portfield (Whalley) towards Sabden. In 1812, on the Long Causeway which crosses the moors from Burnley to Heptonstall, a diversion was constructed at Stiperden to avoid steep gradients into the valley: a toll gate was erected just on the Lancashire side of the county boundary. An example of road construction for a private estate development is the laying out of Chorlton Road in Whalley Range, Manchester, by Samuel Brooks in 1836. He erected a toll gate, Brooks Bar, at the junction of Moss Lane East and Withington Road.[71]

Not all new roads were tolled or turnpiked. The two miles of new road from east of Hurst Green to the 'new' Lower Hodder Bridge, bypassing the ancient route through the grounds of Stonyhurst College, has been mentioned in connection with the activities of McAdam. This new road resulted from the enclosure of much of Hurst Green and from the wish to exclude the public from the Stonyhurst estate. In south-east Lancashire, apart from the growth of streets, some new roads were constructed in the mid-nineteenth century. One, which is well used today, was Lees New Road, following a straight line from just south of Lees to Rowton Clough, then turning abruptly south to head for Ashton-under-Lyne, with an alignment typical of a late turnpike even though it was not subject to toll. The road was built as an unemployment relief scheme during the Cotton Famine of the 1860s, although the connection between Rowton Clough and Oldham via Abbey Hills Road, now the more important, was not made until the 1930s.

APPENDIX IA

TURNPIKE ACTS, ROUTES AND MILEAGES

1725–1750

Date	Act	Route	Mileage
1724/5	11 Geo I c.xiii	Buxton–Chapel en le Frith–Manchester	6½
1725/6	12 Geo I c.xxi	Liverpool–Prescot and Roby	9½
1726	13 Geo I c.ix	Wigan-Preston via Chorley (Higher Road)	13½ *
		Wigan-Preston via Euxton (Lower Road)	17¼
1726	13 Geo I c.x	Warrington–Winwick–Wigan	12¼
1732	5 Geo II c.x	Manchester–Ashton–Saltersbrook	8½
1735	8 Geo II c.iii	Manchester–Oldham–Austerlands	9½
1735	8 Geo II c.viii	Rochdale–Blackstone Edge–Elland	6¼
1746	19 Geo II c.xix	Prescot–St Helens Chapel	
		(Liverpool–Prescot)	3¾

Only mileages within Lancashire are shown
* mileage from Boar's Head to Bamber Bridge
Total mileage of road turnpiked by 1750: 87 miles

APPENDIX I B

ACTS, ROUTES AND MILEAGES

1751–1760

Date	Act	Route	Mileage A	B
1751	24 Geo II c.xiii	Manchester–Stretford–Crossford Bridge		4
1751	24 Geo II c.xvii	Richmond–Lancaster		14
1751	24 Geo II c.xx	Preston–Lancaster–Heiring Syke		32¾
1753	26 Geo II c.lxiii	Salford Roads		
		Warrington	18	
		Bolton	10	
		Duxbury	17	
		Westhoughton–Wigan	5½	
		Broad Oak Branch	1½	52
1753	26 Geo II c.lxv	(Liverpool)–Prescot–Warrington	10	
		St Helens–Ashton-in-Makerfield	5¾	15¾
1753	26 Geo II c.lxxxvi	Keighley–Kendal		3
1755	28 Geo II c.l	Bradford–Haworth–Blue Bell, Colne		4½
1755	28 Geo II c.liii	Rochdale–Burnley		14¾
1755	28 Geo II c.lviii	Manchester–Crumpsall–Rochdale	11½	
		(Manchester)–Crumpsall–Bury	6	
		Besses o'th' Barn–Radcliffe Bridge	2	19½
1755	28 Geo II c.lix	Cocking End, Aldingham–Black Lane End (Colne)		½
1755	28 Geo II c.lx	Leeds–Skipton–Colne–Burnley–Blackburn	21	
		Blackburn–Walton-le-Dale	9	
		Skipton–Gisburn–Clitheroe–Preston	20½	50½
1759	33 Geo II c.xlviii	Halifax–Todmorden–Burnley	9½	
		Todmorden–Littleborough	6	15½

Only mileages within Lancashire are shown

Mileage of road turnpiked 1751–1760   226¾

Total mileage of road turnpiked 1725–1760   313¾

Notes

A   Subdivisions of the Act

B   Total for the Act

APPENDIX IC

ACTS, ROUTES AND MILEAGES

1761–1790

Date	Act	Route	Mileage A	B
1762	2 Geo III c.xliv	Bolton–Leigh–Newton	12	
		Branch to Winwick (not implemented)		
		Newton–Parr (St Helens)	4½	16½
1763	3 Geo III c.xxxi	Bolton–Nightingales (Heath Charnock)		8¼
1763	3 Geo III c.xxxiii	Kendal–Kirkby Ireleth		19
1765	5 Geo III c.c	Stockport-Ashton-under-Lyne–Mossley		6½
		Mileage in 1761–1770		50¼
1771	11 Geo III c.xciii	Liverpool–Preston	30½	
1776	16 Geo III c.lxxv	Clitheroe–Blackburn		
		(additional mileage)	3½	
		Mileage in 1771–1780		33½
1789	29 Geo III c.cvii	Bury-Haslingden–Blackburn	16¾	
		Haslingden–Whalley	9½	
		Haslingden–Todmorden	10¾	
		Walmersley–River Irwell	¾	
		(implemented later)		37¾
1789	29 Geo III c.cx	Heywood–The Lands End (Prestwich)		4

Only mileages in Lancashire are shown
Mileage in 1781–1790   41¾
Mileage of road turnpiked 1761–1790   125½
Mileage of road turnpiked 1725–1790   438½

Notes
A   Subdivisions of the Act
B   Total for the Act

APPENDIX I D

ADDITIONAL AND NEW TURNPIKE ACTS

1791–1800

In the following tables an estimate has been made as to the relative lengths of retained, improved or new roads but it must be emphasised that there was often a substantial time lag between obtaining the Acts and constructing the new works, even though toll gates were erected as soon as possible to produce income which would help to pay for the expensive construction.

Date	Act	Route	A	B	C	D
			A	B	C	D
1792	31 Geo III c.cxxxix	Saddleworth–Oldham Mumps	1½			1½
1793	33 Geo III c.clxx	Manchester–Wilmslow	5			5
1794	34 Geo III c.cxxxiv	Rochdale–Edenfield			5½ 2	7½
1795	35 Geo III c.cxxxvii	Oldham–Ripponden (Yorks)	3		1	4
1795	35 Geo III c.cxlvi	Bury–Edenfield		2½	6½	9
1797	37 Geo III c.cxiv	Rochdale–Bamford–Bury	2½		3	
		and branches	2½			8
1797	37 Geo III c.cxlvi	Sudden Bridge–Bury		2¾	2¼	5
1797	37 Geo III c.clxxiii	Bolton–Blackburn		3	9	12½
1797	37 Geo III c.clxxiv	Edenfield–Bolton and		4¼	5	
		branch Booth Pits–Elton	1		2	12¼
1800	40 Geo III c.lxxiii	Platt Bridge–Ashton-in-Makerfield	4			4
1800	40 Geo III c.lxxiv	Bolton–Westhoughton	3½			3½

Only mileages in Lancashire are shown.

Notes
A Old roads with minor improvements or none   23 miles
B Old roads with significant improvements   18½ miles
C Major diversions or new alignments   30¾ miles
D Total lengths of new trust roads 1791–1800   72½ miles
   Aggregate length turnpiked 1725–1800   510¾ miles

APPENDIX IE

ADDITIONAL AND NEW TURNPIKE ACTS

1801–1810

Date	Act	Route	A	B	C	D
1801	41 Geo III c.cxxiii	Sharples–Houghton (Belmont Road)		2½	8	10½
1803	43 Geo III c.liv	Garstang–Heron Syke Trust: Hest Bank branch	1			1
1803	43 Geo III c.lxix	Marsden–Gisburn–Long Preston	1½			1½
1804	44 Geo III c.xxvi	Barton Bridge–Moses Gate	6			6
1804	44 Geo III c.xlix	Rochdale–Manchester Trust Middleton–Manchester		1	4	5
1805	45 Geo III c.vii	Hollinwood–Featherstall Trust				
		Featherstall Roads, Oldham			1	
		Dry Clough–Shaw New Road			3	
		Shaw–New Hay–Middleton–Rochdale	3¼			
		New Hey–Featherstall (Littleborough) not built				
		Crompton–Grains Branch	2¼			
		Oldham–Middleton New Road			3	12½
1805	45 Geo III c.xxvii	Sedbergh Trust–Greta Bridge	3½			3½
1805	45 Geo III c.xxiv	Bolton–Nightingale Trust Halliwell–Little Bolton Branch	3		1½	4½
1806	46 Geo III c.ii	Hulme–Eccles New Road			3¼	3¼
1806	46 Geo III c.lxiii	Manchester–Oldham–Austerlands Trust				
		Oldham–Ashton-under-Lyne		½	3½	
		Oldham–Royton			1¼	5¼
1806	46 Geo III c.xiii	Huddersfield–New Hey	2½			2½
1808	48 Geo III c.xxxiii	Whalley Bridge–Balderstone New Road			6½	
		Diversion Pendleton–Clitheroe			1¼	7¾
1810	50 Geo III c.c	Bolton–Blackburn Trust, Branches				
		Mather Fold–Hadleigh	1½			
		to Blackburn–Preston TP (Livesey Branch)	2			3½
1810	50 Geo III c.xxxcii	Elton–Blackburn–Haslingden Grane		6¾	9	
		Holden Hall–Dearden Gate Branch			1	16¾

Only mileages in Lancashire are shown.

Notes

A	Old roads with minor improvements	26½ miles
B	Old roads but with significant improvements	10¾ miles
C	Major diversion or new alignments	46¼ miles
D	Total length of new turnpikes 1801–1810	83½ miles
	Aggregate mileage turnpiked 1725–1810	594¼ miles

APPENDIX IF

ADDITIONAL AND NEW TURNPIKE ACTS

1811–1820

Date	Act	Route	A	B	C	D
					Mileage in Lancs	
1811	51 Geo III c.xxxi	Barton Bridge–Stretford	4			4
1815	55 Geo III c.xiv	Haslingden–Stacksteads		1	4½	
		Branch to Rochdale Road			1½	
		Branch Waterfoot–Deerplay		2	2½	11½
1815	55 Geo III c.xxxii	Mytholmroyd Bridge Trust			¼	¼
1815	55 Geo III c.xxxvi	Rochdale–Elland				
		(Blackstone Edge)			2½	2½
1817	57 Geo III c.l	Rochdale–Burnley Trust			2½	
		Rochdale–Whitworth				
		South of Bacup			2½	
		Bacup–Deerplay			3	
		Deerplay–Burnley		½	3	
c.1818		Union Branch			1½	13
1818	58 Geo III c.lxx	Ulverston–Carnforth				
		Levens–Greenodd		3	8	
		Carnforth–Milnthorpe			2	13
		Garstang–Heron Syke				
		Carnforth–Heron Syke		4		
		Improvements				
		Garstang–Lancaster			4½	8½
		Improvements				
		Preston–Garstang			1½	1½
1818	58 Geo III c.vi	Manchester–Denton–				
		Hyde Bridge		1	4½	5½
1819	59 Geo III c.l	Blackburn–Clitheroe				
		(*Petre Arms*)			4½	4½

Only mileages in Lancashire are shown.

Notes

A	Old roads with minor improvements	4 miles
B	Old roads but with significant improvements	7½ miles
C	Major diversion or new alignments	52¾ miles
D	Total length of new trust roads 1811–1820	64¼ miles
	Aggregate mileage turnpiked 1725–1820	658½ miles

APPENDIX IG

ADDITIONAL AND NEW TURNPIKE ACTS

1821–1842

Date	Act	Route	Mileage in Lancs A	B	C	D
1821	1/2 Geo IV c.cxxxi	Skipton–Clitheroe–Chatburn New Road			2	2
1821	1/2 Geo IV c.xl	Bolton–Bury New Road			4¾	4¾
1821	1/2 Geo IV c.cxi	Todmorden–Littleborough New Road			3	3
1824	5 Geo IV c.xliv	Colne–Broughton (Skipton)		1	1¾	2¾
1824	5 Geo IV c.lv	Preston–Blackburn New Road		1	9	10
1824	5 Geo IV c.cv	Little Bolton–Horwich (Duxbury)			5½	
		Changes at Duxbury–Yarrow Bridge			2½	8
1825	6 Geo IV c.ii	Penwortham–Wrightington–Shevington	12		¼	
		Little Lane–Little Hanging Bridge branch	4			16¼
1825	6 Geo IV c.li	Manchester–Ashton New Road			4	
		Branch Audenshaw–Ashton			1½	5½
1825	6 Geo IV c.lxxxiii	Oldham (Royton)–Rochdale		1	2¾	3¾
1826	7 Geo IV c.xii	Ridge Hill Lane (Ashton)–Hole House	3¼			3¼
1826	7 Geo IV c.lxxxi	Manchester–Bury New Road		1	3½	4½
1827	7/8 Geo IV c.xxxiii	Bury-Haslingden–Blackburn and Whalley Trust				
		Blackburn–Old Accrington New Road			3¾	
		Portfield-Padiham New Road			3	6¾
1827	7/8 Geo IV c.lix	Blackburn–Addingham–Cocking End Trust				
		New Accrington-Burnley New Road			5	
		Colne–Cocking End Diversion			3	8
1830	11 Geo IV c.xxxi	Edenfield–Bolton Trust				
		Branch *Bulls Head* PH–Elton		1½	2½	4
1831	1 Wm IV c.vii	Manchester–Crossford Bridge Trust				
		Old Trafford and Oxford Road Diversions			1	1
1836	6/7 Wm IV c.x	Radcliffe Trust	5		1	6
1842	5/6 Vic c.c	Finnington–Chorley	6			6

Notes

A	Old roads with minor improvements and widenings	30¼ miles
B	Old roads with significant improvements	5½ miles
C	Major diversion or new alignments	59¾ miles
D	Total length of new trust Roads 1821–1842	95½ miles
	Aggregate mileage turnpiked 1725–1842	754 miles

1821–1842 TURNPIKE ACTS

TOTAL MILEAGES AND PERCENTAGES

		Miles	Per cent
A	Old roads with minor improvements and widenings	522¼	69.2
B	Old roads with significant improvements	42¼	5.6
C	Major diversions or new alignments	189½	25.2
D	Total Turnpike mileage	754	100

6

The Beginning of the
Motor Age, 1880–1940

INTRODUCTION

THIS CHAPTER takes the story of Lancashire's highways forward from the decline of the turnpike trusts to the early years of World War II, a period which saw profound changes because of the impact of the motor vehicle. The bankruptcy and then the dissolution of the turnpike trusts left a vacuum in the management of the main roads – few townships relished the expense and nuisance of resuming maintenance work on the major highways which, despite the railways, were still busy with local traffic. The first crucial changes, towards the end of the century, were administrative – a new local government system was created, with highways among its restructured powers and this made possible the start of serious improvement work on the roads of the county.

These administrative changes coincided with the revival of road transport following the invention of the bicycle[1] and, of course, the internal combustion engine. By the first decade of the twentieth century the new traffic was having a disastrous effect on the traditional 'macadam' surfacing, so local authorities were forced to seek new approaches to road design, construction and maintenance. Before the First World War, within twenty years of the development of the motor car, some authorities were speculating about the necessity for new road-building and from the early 1920s at least some of these plans came to fruition. Between the wars leisure and commercial use of the roads grew apace and extensive construction of new and improved routes to coastal resorts and industrial centres began to change the map of Lancashire. In the urban areas ring roads and arterial roads were designed with the aim of removing traffic from congested town centres.

ADMINISTRATIVE CHANGES BEFORE 1914

The Highway Act of 1835 abolished statute labour and substituted highway rates as the main source of road funding, changes which had been widely but unofficially practised for many years. Townships and boroughs remained responsible for highway maintenance and although the 1835 Act gave the former the option to combine into highway boards few availed themselves of the opportunity.

The extreme fragmentation of administration therefore persisted. An Act of 1862 gave justices powers to order groups of townships to combine as highway districts, but there was a loophole – any township which became a sanitary district was entitled to claim exemption from a compulsory order. Many tiny places therefore became separate sanitary districts – with dire consequences for other aspects of local administration – until a further Act restricted this freedom to districts with a population exceeding 3,000.

The Public Health Act of 1872 created the Local Government Board which, although primarily concerned with the administration of legislation relating to the poor and to sanitation, was almost by default the only government body concerned with highways. From 1873 it began to oversee the winding-up of the turnpike trusts. In south Lancashire many townships were large enough to become urban sanitary authorities with their own highway powers, but in the rural areas highway districts were formed by the grouping of townships. Some districts varied widely in size – there were four in Furness, whereas the whole of Leyland hundred became one very large district. The wide-ranging Highways and Locomotive Act of 1878 required the boundaries of highway districts to coincide with those of sanitary districts, to avoid the confusion of overlapping jurisdictions.

LOCAL GOVERNMENT ACTS OF 1888 AND 1894

As turnpike trusts expired, the highways in rural areas, generally designated as 'main roads', became the responsibility of the highway districts (if these had been established) but the Local Government Board could make grants to help with maintenance and to pay off the bonded debt and it began to take action to ensure that the transition from turnpike trust to local authority went smoothly. The major administrative change came with the 1888 Act, which created the democratically-elected county councils and also designated many of the larger towns as county boroughs, equivalent to counties in status. County boroughs were the only highway authorities within their boundaries, but the county councils shared responsibility with other, lower-ranking, authorities. Only the 'main' roads and former county and hundred bridges were specifically vested in the county councils.

A further Act, in 1894, created urban districts and reconstituted those boroughs which had not been granted 'county' status as municipal boroughs. These authorities were responsible for all high-ways except the main roads but the larger districts and boroughs were entitled to 'claim' responsibility for the main roads as well. They were largely reliant on funds supplied by the county councils and this produced considerable friction. In rural areas the highway boards continued to control the non-main roads until they were replaced by rural district councils in 1897 but they had already given up all claims to repair main roads except by delegation or by contract with county councils.

Lancashire County Council was apparently suspicious of the new rural district councils and in April 1897 requested that the life of the highway boards be extended beyond 28 December 1897, the date scheduled for their abolition, on the grounds 'that the new Districts are unwieldy and extensive while the Boards have been effective'. Its request was granted by the Local Government Board and, with the exception of the Childwall and Prescot Highway Boards, their lives were extended to 31 March 1899. The four North Lonsdale highway boards were then superseded by Ulverston R.D.C., while in contrast the Leyland Hundred Highway Board, with forty-one miles of main road, was broken up between Preston, Chorley, West Lancashire and Wigan R.D.C.s. Ironically, when in 1929 the rural district councils finally lost control even of the unclassified roads (their residual highway function) these powers were delegated back to them by the county council for as long as the relevant district surveyor remained in office – in the case of Whiston R.D.C. this arrangement lasted into the 1950s.

The road across Fearns Moss, Stack-steads (undated; about 1910). This road, from Booth Road to Tunstead Lane, was reconstructed in water-bound macadam in the late nineteenth century. Although not a main road it formed a useful link to Lumb and Burnley *(Lancashire County Library: Rossendale Local Studies Collection).*

"Fearns Moss."

HIGHWAY MANAGEMENT TO 1914

To administer highway matters the new Lancashire County Council
which took office in 1889 established a Main Road and Bridges
Committee, which was required to 'consider all questions relating to
Main Roads and the provisions of the Highways and Locomotive
Amendment Act 1878; also to have charge of the County and Hundred
Bridges and the lengths of roadways attached thereto'. The posts of
county surveyor and county bridgemaster remained separate for several
years. The former had virtually no staff, but the latter inherited, in
each of the constituent hundreds, a surveyor of bridges, a bridgemaster
and a main road surveyor. All these officers, twenty-two in total, had
previously been responsible to the county justices. There was also an
additional officer to manage the Ribble Bridge and Walton Cop.

Because of lack of staff there was no easy means for the county to
undertake repair work itself so one of the first tasks of the county surveyor
was to write to all districts and boards, inquiring about the length of
main road in their areas and whether they would be willing to continue
the repairs under contract. The length of main road varied from year
to year as new stretches were designated and as other lengths passed to
the numerous county boroughs as result of boundary extensions.[2]

The chief qualifications for a road to be classified as 'main' were
that it served a town with a population of more than 25,000 or gave
access to a railway station. This meant that not all former turnpikes
were eligible, while some roads which had never been turnpikes were
deemed suitable. In November 1890 a special county council committee
was formed to consider additional main roads or the 'dismaining' of
existing ones. Many of the early proposals involved short lengths which
closed gaps in the network or which served stations – for example,
the route from Whittington to Arkholme railway station – but others,
such as the road from the Widnes boundary to St Helens (A568), were
more substantial. In May 1892 the county accepted responsibility for
a long list of routes and from this date onwards a full network of main
roads managed by the county evolved.

Those taken on in 1892 included the roads from Lancaster to
Cantsfield via Hornby (13 miles), Blackpool to Garstang railway station
via Poulton (18 miles), Wigan to Chorley (4 miles), the Preston and
Southport road at Tarleton and Mere Brow (nearly 4 miles), various
roads in Southport town (4 miles), Southport to Bootle via Formby (16
miles), the road from Rainford to Ormskirk (5 miles), Toxteth Park to
Garston (3 miles), Leigh to Wigan and to Warrington (10½ miles) and
several shorter stretches of road in Golborne and Platt Bridge (7 miles).

Ninety-one miles were added to the main road schedule between
November 1892 and February 1893.[3] 'Maining' also affected Furness,

with the busy routes into Barrow being given special attention. In January 1896 the key road from Duddon Bridge to the Barrow–Dalton road was taken over because it was 'the principal arterial high road between large towns in Cumberland and Lancashire and a thorough-fare to various Railway Stations and [because] the continuation in Cumberland is already a Main Road'. The road from Lindale to Grange station was also declared a main road in 1900.

The adoption and improvement of roads serving the heavy industrial areas of south Lancashire and Furness (with its iron and steel and ship-building industries) and those to Southport and Blackpool – which had never had any turnpike access – were seen by the county as being particularly important. It was prepared to be flexible in its approach, ignoring the official criteria where necessary. The road from Liverpool to Garston dock and railway station, for example, did not serve the 'threshold' population but was of great commercial importance: a two-week survey revealed that the road had been used by 1,149 local vehicles but over 3,500 from outside the area, reflecting its economic significance. Thus this period saw the beginning of changes in the pattern of main roads, as the geography of the turnpike network was superseded and a network more appropriate for the early twentieth century began to emerge, with new traffic destinations becoming important.

By 1893 the county surveyor was able to report that the 'reputed' mileage of main road was 666 miles 5 furlongs 17 yards – these traditional units of measure survived for many years, as did the allocation of funds according to the boundaries of the old hundreds. On this occasion he requested authority to purchase 667 new milestones, to replace those dating from the turnpike era, on the grounds that the existing stones were inaccurate. Fortunately this plan was not implemented and thus the county retains many fine examples of the handiwork of the trusts.

The lengths of main road under county control and the number of its bridges, were regularly assessed. In 1903 it was calculated that there were 113½ county and 422 hundred bridges, making a total of 535½ in the administrative county: this included fifty-seven half-bridges, two halves counting as one. This apparently bizarre number arose because long stretches of the county boundary lay in the centre of streams and rivers – half a bridge was vested in each riparian authority. The typical example of Blackburn hundred (1903) illustrates this:

Hundred bridges and associated road approaches

Total formerly repaired by Hundred	71	7,305	yards of road
Minus number now in county boroughs:			
Blackburn 7 and 2 halves			
Burnley 3	11	1,705	yards of road
Therefore remaining in Hundred	60	5,600	yards of road

These now divided into:

Bridges on main roads	25	2,632	yards of road
Bridges on non-main roads	35	2,968	yards of road

County bridges and associated road approaches

Total formerly repaired by County	38★	958	yards of road

Minus number now in county boroughs:

Blackburn	½	8½	yards of road
Therefore remaining in the County	37	949½	yards of road

These now divided into:

Bridges on main roads	4½	150½	yards of road
Bridges on non-main roads	33	799	yards of road
Total of county and hundred bridges	97½	6,549½	yards of road★

In November 1889 three county district surveyors were appointed, from among 265 applicants. Their duties were defined in February 1891 – to 'inspect the whole of the Main Roads in his District monthly . . . keep a diary and make a monthly report to the County Road Surveyor and a copy of his report and diary to the Main Road and Bridges Committee . . . [he] shall survey the Main Roads in his District distinguishing the various materials forming the surface and prepare estimates for repair . . . report at once any encroachment or obstruction, defects or damage to the Main Roads Bridges or Culverts'.[4] This looks a tall order, for the three areas (described only as 'North West, South and East') were extensive. The men travelled widely to carry out their duties, by rail, hired dog-cart or hansom – for which expenses were claimable – or by walking, for which they were not.

Difficulties increased over the next few years as further main roads were taken over and after August 1892 when 766 miles of secondary road were scheduled. Although the latter were vested in the districts the county council made grants towards their upkeep and improvement. The increased workload was such that in November 1892 the number of county district surveyors was increased to four and their areas defined respectively as North and South Lonsdale and Amounderness Hundreds, Blackburn and Leyland Hundreds, Salford Hundred and West Derby Hundred. By January 1903 the county main roads totalled 674 miles, with a budget of £149,249 and in that month a further tranche of secondary roads was adopted, giving a total mileage of 1,840. The workload of the surveyors increased accordingly but not until 1913

★ Historically there were twelve county bridges in Blackburn hundred, but twenty-six more passed to the county on disturnpiking. This illustrates an administrative problem: not only did the county have to agree maintenance and repair of boundary bridges with other authorities, but it also retained – in this hundred – 3,767 yards of isolated lengths of non-main roads in the districts.

was a fifth district surveyor deemed necessary and the divisions redrawn once more. By 1913 the district surveyors had been provided with 'cycle cars' and in 1915 these were replaced by motor cars.

For most of these early years the role of the county council was financial and supervisory. There was no 'direct labour' organisation and any work not carried out by district councils went to outside contract. The county surveyor therefore spent most of his time negotiating and agreeing estimates and payments to the local authorities, particularly those 'claiming' to retain the repair of the main roads in their district. By 1905 seventeen of the nineteen municipal boroughs and fifty-four of the ninety-three urban districts 'claimed' powers over main roads and each of these had to have a series of separate agreements and financial transactions.

In the late 1890s the county council began to raise loans for highway work, instead of relying on special grants from the Local Government Board. This allowed work to proceed at a much faster rate – in 1900 the county surveyor reported that to convert worn-out sett paving to macadam on the Preston to Southport road would take no less than nineteen years if paid for by special grants, while the Manchester to Warrington road would take fifteen years. However, the work of county and districts alike was rarely ambitious. A typical annual work schedule might include only such modest items as reducing gradients (which might mean no more than taking six feet off the top of a hill), easing corners, flagging footpaths, repairing retaining walls, converting boulder paving and taking up setts for macadam. The county estimates for materials in 1905 were:

Granite setts	3,019 Tons
Grit and 'Lonkey' setts	10,370 Tons
Granite macadam	42,118 Tons
Limestone macadam	7,692 Tons
Copper Slag	3,133 Tons
Pitch (for jointing setts)	1,439 Tons
Kerbs	16,206 yards
Flags	19,365 yards

Although there is perhaps a greater emphasis on setts and granite, these materials typify those used by the turnpike trusts a century before in the era of Macadam – a reflection of the conservatism which prevailed at this period.

Disputes between the county and the districts mainly resulted from the insistence of the latter that, because the ownership of main roads was not vested in 'claiming' authorities, the county should bear the whole cost of repair. The county maintained that the Local Government Act of 1888 only required it to make a contribution towards the cost of repair and that it was not bound to make such payments until after the year end. As early as 1889 Burnley Corporation served a writ on the county council claiming £4,360 for costs up to March 1889: the county Main Road and Bridges Committee had authorised only £2,377 and had paid just £1,188. The case did not reach the Manchester assizes until 1898, by which time Burnley had abandoned much of its claim which was finally settled by compromise.

This was perhaps a special case, as Burnley became a county borough, but more typical was the instance in 1891 when the Fulwood, Horwich and Levenshulme Local Boards, supported by other small authorities, disputed the county's interpretation of the legislation. The inspector from the Local Government Board allowed £218 of the £300 which Fulwood had claimed (the county had offered £208 anyway) and Horwich, Radcliffe and Padiham also reached agreement. Middleton Corporation went to arbitration, but finished up with much the same result as Fulwood. Nelson defiantly refused to accept the county terms. The disputes carried on for some time – in 1893 the county council decided to defer payments to claiming authorities which had not accepted or refused its offer – but eventually an uneasy peace was established.

THE LAST OF THE TOLLS
AND NEW MAIN ROADS

In October 1890 the age of public turnpikes came to an end with the extinguishing of the Blackburn to Preston (New Road) Trust. The county council then began a concerted effort to purchase and abolish the remaining private tolls, noted in the previous chapter. The first to go was a gate at Irlam, on the road from Salford to Warrington, owned by Sir Humphrey de Trafford. In February 1890 the Main Road and Bridges Committee negotiated with de Trafford's agent to buy the tolls for £1,000, together with the toll house, which partially obstructed the road. A compensatory payment of £25 was made to the toll keeper. It then was discovered that the council had no power to make such a purchase, which required either an order from the Local Government Board or the grant of parliamentary powers.[5] A clause was therefore inserted in the Lancashire County Council (Lunatic Asylums and Other Powers) Act of 1891 and the purchase was completed on 29 December 1891. A special ceremony took place on 1 January 1892, when Arthur Harding paid the last twopenny toll and the chairman of the Main Road and Bridges Committee removed the gate 'in the presence of a large concourse of people' and declared the main road continuous between Manchester and Warrington.

On 28 July 1902 the private toll bar at the Lea Gate, between Preston and Kirkham, was closed and demolished when the road was taken over by Lancashire County Council. Here a group of dignitaries, including Lord Derby, assembles to watch the proceedings *(LRO QAR 5/51)*.

The section of the Preston to Blackpool road from Lea to Kirkham was still private and subject to tolls in 1889. The other routes to Blackpool, Lytham and St Annes could only be considered as secondary roads, because of their inadequate width and condition and the local authorities were anxious that the Preston to Blackpool route should become a main road. However, despite protracted negotiations between 1893 and 1899, little progress was made, either with improving the road or abolishing the tolls. In March 1899 broad agreement was finally reached between Blackpool Corporation, Lancashire County Council, Kirkham U.D.C. and Fylde R.D.C., together with representatives of the Clifton and de Hoghton estates.[6] Fylde agreed to construct a new 45-foot wide road from Marton to the Blackpool boundary: it contributed £1,200 and the county council made a secondary road grant of £550. Blackpool completed the section within its boundaries. All this road is now within Blackpool, forming part of Preston New Road.

The Blackpool road was also widened at Five Lane Ends and Clifton and private sections were transferred to the district councils as public roads. In July 1902 the county surveyor was able to report that 'the new road at New House Farm having been built and the private Road at Five Lane Ends and Clifton now declared public by agreement and adopted by Preston and Fylde Rural District Councils on 28 July and the toll bar at Lea demolished before a concourse of people, the road throughout from Preston Borough Boundary to Blackpool Borough Boundary of 13 miles, 2 furlongs and 212 yards [is] declared to be a Main Road'. The road surface and several acute bends now required urgent attention and application was made for a loan for improvement work, which was undertaken by the district councils.[7] The Lytham road from Three Nooks at Clifton to Marsh Gate at Freckleton remained private – the toll section was claimed in 1913 to be in good condition but the rest of the Lytham road was in disrepair and had to be reconstructed from Freckleton to the Lytham boundary.

GROWTH AND CHARACTER
OF ROAD TRAFFIC UP TO 1914

As noted above, the roads into the Fylde had been receiving considerable attention since the late 1880s. In 1909 Blackpool organised a pioneering 'Aviation Week' and, in anticipation of the heavy traffic which would result, the whole of the road from Preston was put into good order. Yet in February 1910 an emergency grant had to be made for urgent repairs, as the road was almost impassable. How had the road, so recently repaired and improved at considerable expense, deteriorated so quickly? One major reason was the very great increase in the weight of road vehicles, which quickly destroyed the surfaces and caused considerable damage. Another was the use of rubber tyres on motor cars.

In the later nineteenth century highway authorities were increasingly perturbed by the development of steam-hauled traction engines, or road locomotives as they were more often called. These engines evolved after the mid-1860s from so-called portable engines, which were simply a locomotive-type boiler carrying a cylinder and flywheels mounted on cart wheels. Portable engines were drawn from farm to farm by horses and used for threshing. It was a logical step to make these agricultural engines self-moving – by the 1880s they were large and powerful and were widely used by haulage firms, particularly those specialising in moving heavy loads. One firm of hauliers associated with Lancashire was Norman Box, a family business which started in 1884 with a brickworks at Aintree, but then shifted to Manchester and specialised in hauling boilers of up to forty tons. The firm undertook tar-spraying work for the highway authorities well into the 1950s.[8]

These developments provoked government legislation. An Act of 1865 introduced the famous 'red flag', whereby every mechanical road vehicle was to have a crew of three, one of whom went ahead on foot carrying a red warning flag. Speeds were restricted to 4 m.p.h. in open country and 2 m.p.h. in towns. For road locomotives, which in any case travelled at about this speed and needed a crew of at least two, the restrictions were not irksome. A further Act in 1878 gave discretion to local authorities to prohibit the passage of such vehicles through towns by day, while the Locomotive and Highway Act of 1881 protected mechanical haulage against the excess tolls charged by some turnpikes.

The damage caused by road locomotives and their 'trains' was considerable. Although their weight was limited by law to fourteen tons, they could tow four or five waggons. Macadamised roads were not designed for such loads, and the disintegration of the surface and the development of large ruts was inevitable since the surface crust of many roads was as little as three inches thick. Local authorities usually attempted to claim the cost of repair from the engine owners – for example, in July 1896 the county took legal proceedings to recover £500 for damage to the highway in Belmont by Messrs Dealy's traction engine. In the longer term, though, it was recognised that many main roads needed to be repaved to take the weight of traction engines, with the possibility of recovering some of the cost by agreement with individual local operators who made heavy use of specific roads. Thus in 1903, under a 'ton per mile' agreement, money was obtained for repairing damage caused by traction engines at Walton-le-Dale owned by Star Paper Mill.

Although nominally limited to fourteen tons weight, many vehicles were substantially in excess of this. One of Norman Box's engines, now preserved, weighs 16½ tons, while in April 1906 Derbyshire County Council reported that a traction engine registered in Lancashire at a nominal 10 tons 15 cwt was considerably in excess of the permitted weight. The Lancashire county surveyor ordered the four engines of that firm to be weighed and found them to be seventeen tons light and no less than twenty tons with fuel and water. An application for their continued use under a general licence was refused and the surveyor then arranged for all forty-three engines licensed in the county to be weighed, together with twelve others which regularly operated here. Of these fifty-five vehicles, fifteen exceeded the limit. The licences of overweight engines were forfeited, but it was accepted that special sanction could to be given for individual loads.[9]

In April 1909 the county surveyor again reported on the use of traction engines, stating that there were 158 agricultural locomotives and thirty-two general haulage engines licensed. In the previous twelve months 222 daily permits had been issued and by special permission from 31 March 1906 to 28 February 1909 three firms had together moved 350 boilers weighing between twenty and thirty-nine tons. On these occasions the total weight of the 'trains' of locomotives and boilers had ranged from forty-eight to sixty-seven tons, hauled over an average distance of 9¾ miles. It is hardly surprising that damage occurred – no less than £692 had been collected in levies to pay for repairs.

The cracking of road surfaces because of excessive weight was the major problem associated with steam locomotives, but the motor car created a totally new set of difficulties. The Highway Act of 1896 permitted light mechanical vehicles to travel at 14 m.p.h. and removed the 'red flag' requirement: in 1903 the Motor Car Act raised the speed limit to 20 m.p.h. This Act also introduced the offences of reckless driving and driving at excessive speed and permitted local authorities to impose a speed limit of 10 m.p.h. in their area. Fourteen urban district councils requested Lancashire County Council to apply to the Local Government Board for 10 m.p.h. limits but this was opposed by the Main Road and Bridges Committee, which preferred to rely on the reckless or negligent driving clauses and on the erection of warning signs, which was also permitted by the Act. After negotiations all but Radcliffe and Urmston U.D.C.s withdrew their requests and these two authorities were not supported by the county council.[10]

The county surveyor identified the need for 615 warning signs, to be placed at dangerous corners, crossroads and 'precipitous places', but the committee drastically reduced this to 362 for reasons of economy. Wrought iron posts and signs were obtained at 6s. 11d. each (with 13s. per sign for erection) but the committee's economy was short-lived, for an additional estimate of £100 for this purpose was found annually for several years thereafter. The blossoming bureaucracy of the motor age continued, with the 1903 Act also requiring county and county borough councils to register motor cars and motorcycles and to issue driving licenses. By April 1904, a year after the scheme came into operation, the county council had registered 411 cars and 453 motorcycles and had issued 1,327 licences. Driving licences were available on demand to anyone over seventeen, there being no test, but a licence could be forfeited for serious or repeated offences.

For speeding the fines were £10 for a first offence, £20 for the second and £50 subsequently. In 1909 the committee urged the police to take more action under the 1903 Act, although up to 30 September 1908 there had been 145 prosecutions in the county for 'driving to the danger of the public', 215 cases of exceeding the 20 m.p.h. speed limit and 244 other offences under the Act, with a 91 per cent conviction rate.[11]

By this date the maintenance of the 654 miles of main road in the administrative county was divided between fifteen 'claiming' municipal boroughs (97 miles) and fifty-two 'claiming' urban districts (211 miles), the remainder being vested in the county council but delegated or managed by contract. From 1 April 1911, however, the county council required that all the main roads not claimed by other councils should be maintained under the direct control of the county surveyor. The two non-claiming municipal boroughs were Lancaster and Widnes.

ROAD CONSTRUCTION TO 1914

Although the local authorities were generally hostile to steam haulage, they were quick to adopt the use of the steam roller for road building and mending. In 1876 Liverpool Corporation took delivery of the first production roller built by Aveling & Porter of Rochester, almost certainly the first local authority in the country to own such a machine. It weighed twenty-two tons and was cumbersome and ungainly but the borough surveyor reported that for £1 a day running costs he had much-improved roads – which were more easily cleaned – and a smaller bill for macadam.[12] By the 1880s the steam roller had been developed into the standard machine which was almost universally employed until well after the Second World War and by the 1890s most larger authorities possessed at least one.

In 1904 the former county surveyor of Shropshire spoke enthusiastically about the widespread use of steam rollers in compacting loose material on a macadam surface and providing a smooth road for motor cars, but warned of the problem of dust, caused by the sucking action of the wide pneumatic tyres of motor cars. This was very injurious to

Stone-knapping was a typical roadside scene throughout the nineteenth century and well into the twentieth. A roadman sat beside his length of the highway with a heap of rough stone, and laboriously broke it down to a size suitable for use in macadam *(Lancashire County Library: Colne Local Studies Collection).*

Stone-crushing was a more efficient, but more costly, alternative to knapping. Because the crushed stone had then to be taken to the road site the old method was still favoured by many highway authorities, particularly for small jobs. This animal-powered roller crusher, of the type more commonly used for ore in lead mines, was recovered from a small gritstone quarry adjacent to the old road from Bacup to Todmorden, and was re-sited and preserved in Bacup
(John Priestley).

the macadamed road crust, because it drew out the binding material which held the macadam in place and led to the disintegration of the crust itself.[13] It was this which was primarily responsible for the damage to the Preston and Blackpool road during Aviation Week 1909, while in 1910 it was said that there was a need to tar-spray the main roads radiating from Preston, because of damage caused by the steel-studded tyres of motor cars.

In 1905 the county surveyor prepared a report on the dust problem and in 1906 he authorised tests of various proprietary remedies. The length of Garstang Road, Preston, between Withy Trees and the Black Bull was chosen for one experiment because the road was fronted by houses and Fulwood U.D.C. was already watering the road twice a week. A 20 per cent solution of 'Duststop' was applied by water cart after loose dust had been removed. This only remained effective for about three weeks and its use showed little advantage over watering. Early experiments with tarmac also gave mixed results: one attempt to use iron slag from the Wigan Coal and Iron Co. proved a failure, probably because of poor mixing. However a quarter-mile length of heavily trafficked road at Turton was paved with granite aggregate laid by 'Tar Mac' of Wolverhampton (a predecessor of the famous civil engineering firm) and this was more successful. Experiments by Northern Quarries at Grange, using limestone aggregate tarmac as 'Quarrite', were also satisfactory.[14]

Other methods were also tried. Setts were, of course, very widespread in urban areas, especially where tramways had been laid. A modification used where there were local concentrations of heavy traffic was called

Road repairs at Cross Hillocks, on Chaddock Lane, Astley (now the A572) in about 1890. This road had formerly been a turnpike and was eventually a county main road. The repair work in progress involves sett paving: note the load of setts in the barrow, and (on the left) the heavy punner with which the setts were thumped into place (*Wigan Heritage Service Archives*).

'armouring' and consisted of spreading a layer of random granite cubes, not in courses as with 'setts' but racked[15] with chippings and fixed with boiling pitch. The vicinity of Star Paper Mills on Livesey Road, Blackburn and the heavily used road at Turton were chosen sites. The term 'armouring' was also applied to a scheme for spreading small rough granite cubes over existing macadam – no doubt the use of steam rollers produced a tolerable surface but its roughness compared with tarmac and its effect on tyres, can be imagined.

Tarmac had its problems. In 1909 it was reported that a £3,485 contract had been let to W. H. Stansbury & Co. to macadam the Clitheroe and Whalley main road, partly with tarred limestone and partly with tarred Pwllheli granite. The contract was to include maintenance for five years, but the Pwllheli granite (laid from Barrow printworks to Whalley station) was a complete failure and the company asked to be released from the contract. It then went into liquidation and the county council only recovered £300.[16]

The county surveyor eventually recommended the use of granite setts on concrete for all heavily trafficked roads. Although setts were largely used in towns there were examples in rural locations on steep

hills, where the uphill lane was sett-paved to give horses a better grip than tarmac or tar spray would have allowed. For the same reason Pwllheli granite was preferred to Penmaenmawr granite, which tended to polish. Half a million tons annually were imported through Liverpool and Preston docks. An example of half-width setts survived until after the Second World War on the uphill lane of Fishergate Hill, Preston, where it had assisted the horses leaving the railway goods depot at the bottom.

For less heavily-trafficked roads tar 'painting', as it was first called, was tried with varying success. Tar, heated in small boilers, was poured over the existing macadam and brushed on. This soon led to the more familiar 'tar spraying', for which larger tanks were used. Sometimes the old surface would be broken by 'scarifying' before spraying, the process then being called 'grouting'. Tar spraying then, as sometimes now, was not without problems. Characteristically, for example, the tar would 'fatten up' – go soft and sticky – in hot weather. The stickiness was a problem in the summer of 1909, when the county had to make a payment of 17s. 6d. to Jake Webster for damage done to his trousers by tar spraying while he was cycling past.

The tar from town gas was not at first considered suitable, as it

198

Road surfacing at Shear Brow, Blackburn, in the early 1920s. This useful secondary road from Sudell Cross to Four Lane Ends, Revidge, is being reconstructed, with a steam roller consolidating the macadam surface. Instead of the usual tar spray the surface seal is a cement grout, as implied by the concrete mixer and the prominently displayed bags of 'Ferrocrete'. All this suggests that the carefully-posed picture was being taken for publicity purposes *(Lancashire County Library: Blackburn Local Studies Collection).*

contained water-soluble compounds which were thought to cause pollution. This problem was highlighted when, in 1913, it was proposed to tarmac the main road from Chorley to Bolton through Adlington and Horwich. Chorley R.D.C. and the Bleachers' Association objected, claiming that pollution of adjacent reservoirs would make the water unsuitable for bleaching. The county council then proposed using setts fixed in concrete, but the Roads Board – which had approved a grant of £9,722 towards the tarmac surface – threatened to cancel this if setts were used. The county therefore had to borrow the whole sum which, including the extra cost of setts, amounted to £29,643.[17]

The county surveyor held that many rural main roads were insufficient to bear the weight of mechanical vehicles and recommended that the addition of three inches of tarmac was a desirable improvement. The traditional summer patching with chippings and small macadam was no longer efficient, as motor cars scattered the stones. It was therefore wasteful of material and effort and waterbound macadam was no longer an acceptable surface on main roads. However, tarmac required more expertise and a highly skilled labour force, which was not available because the district council staff were 'jacks of all trades', not specialists in highway work.

A further threat to the stability of the macadam roads was the 'motor waggon', or lorry. From 1905 these were restricted to twelve tons, the gross and unladen weight being painted on each vehicle and they could be compulsorily weighed within a quarter of a mile of a weighbridge. The county council erected a weighbridge at the rear of County Hall in March 1905 and in 1913 all police superintendents, inspectors and sergeants became authorised officers for the weighing of 'heavy motor cars', as they were officially termed. The speed limit of a motor waggon was 8 m.p.h., or 12 m.p.h. if on rubber tyres.

The rapid growth in their use was highlighted by the county surveyor as early as July 1903 after small censuses had been conducted. On the Blackburn-Darwen main road from 12 February to 11 June there were 798 single journeys, with an estimated weight of 20,000 tons *per annum*, while between Blackburn and Walton Cop in the week of 7–13 July there were seventy-nine single journeys by motor waggons with trailers and twenty-six without trailers, weighing 60,000 tons *per annum*. As all traffic in 1901 on this road was estimated at 63,000 tons, by 'the extraordinary method of conveying goods by motor wagons the total weight passing over the road nearly doubled'.[18] A further report in 1910 stated that the number of motor waggons registered in 1908 in England and Wales was 4,507, of which at least 500 were running regularly in Lancashire. In addition, Widnes Corporation had started a bus service and the Lancashire and Yorkshire Railway was running a bus from Chorley station to Whittle-le-Woods.

The Development and Road Improvement Fund Act of 1909 increased the licence duty on motor vehicles and taxed petrol, to produce an annual income of £1 million. The revenue could be used to fund new improvements, although not ordinary maintenance and repairs, but funds were withheld until needed for unemployment relief. Not until July 1914 did the Local Government Board, 'in the light of the economic situation', ask the county council for a list of schemes which would be easily implemented and employ the maximum amount of labour. Projects requiring land acquisition were not considered suitable but in fact the submitted list included several such schemes, including a new road (previously suggested by Burnley Corporation) through Towneley Holme to the Todmorden road and a new road from the Blackpool boundary to Poulton-le-Fylde. In October 1914 a further list was requested: it included the road from Skerton Bridge to Kirkby Lonsdale Road in Lancaster and various widenings and resurfacings. The annual estimate for main roads was now (March 1913) £282,274 and £10,756 for bridges.

Relaying the track of the Burnley Corporation tramways, at the junction of Church Street (A58) and Yorkshire Street (A671) in 1927. The photograph gives an excellent impression of the method of construction of the tramway – and also shows that at this date it was still possible to take complete possession of the main road junction in the centre of the town. Note how the setts within the tramway curtilage differ from those in the remainder of the road (*Lancashire County Library: Burnley Local Studies Collection*).

ROADS IN TOWNS

The use of setts for urban roads has already been mentioned: they rapidly became widespread not only because of local concentrations of heavy traffic but also because of the development of tramway networks. Horse-drawn omnibuses ran as early as 1824 on the Pendleton turnpike, through Salford to Manchester. They rapidly became very popular in larger towns and cities but the example of railways suggested that steel wheels on iron rails would enable a horse to pull a heavier vehicle with more passenger capacity. This meant that rails had to be fixed and maintained in the public highway in a way that did not interfere with ordinary traffic.

Experiments in Birkenhead in 1860 were not entirely satisfactory but in 1861 a novel three-rail track was laid from Pendleton to the Manchester boundary – Manchester Corporation having refused permission – whereby the horse-bus ran on flat outer rails but with a fifth wheel running along a centre guide-rail with double flanges. The fifth wheel could be raised to allow the vehicle to run along an ordinary road.[19] It worked with some success but by 1871 the grooved tramway rail had been invented. Laid flush with the road surface, it permitted the tram to run with normal flanged railway-type wheels: this type of rail is in use today wherever trams have survived, as in Blackpool, or on the Manchester Metrolink system.

The Tramways Act of 1870 permitted local authorities and private companies to construct and lease tramways. In the case of private

undertakings the leases usually ran for twenty-one years, after which the local authority had powers to take over. By the late 1870s most Lancashire towns of any size had horse tramways. Irrespective of who operated them, it was necessary to obtain the agreement of the local highway authority on such matters as route, the need for road widening and the method of track-laying and upkeep. With the development of steam haulage in the 1880s several systems were either converted or built anew – particularly in east Lancashire, where the steep hills made horse tramways a difficult proposition. These included Accrington (1886), Blackburn and Over Darwen (1881), Burnley and District (1881), Haslingden (1888), Rossendale Valley (1889) and the Manchester, Bury, Rochdale and Oldham Steam Tramway (1883) which had proposals for one hundred miles of route but, despite its grandiose title, only built thirty-three.[20]

These systems all had leases which expired in the early years of the new century. Blackpool had by then constructed the world's first proper electric tramway and in 1898 the inter-urban tramway to Fleetwood had opened. These pioneering schemes inspired others and as leases expired between 1908 and 1910 most municipalities exercised their right to acquire tram systems and convert to electric traction. Only a handful

THE TRAM TERMINUS, CHERRY TREE.

remained under private control and the only system not electrified was the short network centred on Morecambe, closed in 1920–26.

In the north-west of the county most systems were isolated from their neighbours but in south and east Lancashire the network was dense and interconnected – although with a different gauge for the east Lancashire towns. A continuous, if somewhat devious, route extended from Liverpool Pier Head to Summit, north-east of Rochdale. The size of undertakings varied considerably, from the three miles of Lancaster Corporation tramways (1903–30) to Manchester's 123 miles and Liverpool's ninety. At its peak the south Lancashire network involved no fewer than forty-seven local authorities and two companies.

A standard method of on-street tramway construction soon evolved. The rails were carried on a concrete foundation and were held to gauge by transverse tie-bars. The road surface was then brought up to rail level by setts. The Tramway Acts required the operator to maintain the surface of the public road not only between the rails and between double lines of track but also for eighteen inches on either side. Setts provided a convenient method for forming and maintaining these wayleaves and, where the road was still macadam, it soon became necessary to pave the full width kerb to kerb with setts. Setts also made maintenance somewhat easier, since it was possible to remove sections

The Blackburn Corporation tramway terminus at Preston Old Road, Cherry Tree, in about 1903. At this date the boundary of the borough was here; in the foreground the road is surfaced with waterbound macadam, but within the borough, and along the tram route, it is partly paved *(Lancashire County Library: Blackburn Local Studies Collection)*.

to gain access to the rails and then to replace the paving, without too much difficulty.[21]

Councils and tramway operators were often in dispute. The local authorities complained of the state of the tramway wayleave, while the operators retorted that the condition of the council-controlled sections of the road was so poor that ordinary traffic tended to follow the tramway, thus holding up the tramcars and increasing wear and tear – although one frequent cause of failure of the early tramway surfaces was the inferior quality of the concrete. Where the street had been paved with setts before tramways were built these were recoverable as the property of the highway authority – in 1903 Atherton U.D.C. reported that it had a good supply of secondhand setts consequent to the laying of tram tracks and requested an increase in the county grant to make use of them. The county then circulated the district councils requiring that, when new tramways were laid, the value of materials which it had paid for should be safeguarded.

Thus sett-paving spread until it was regarded as typical in all urban areas and on most inter-urban roads in the south of the county. No early twentieth-century picture of a Lancashire town was complete without tramlines and setts, both trams and paving being crucial elements in those powerful, haunting, evocative images. In many photographs taken before 1914 one of the most striking features, except in the biggest cities and the busy resorts, is the remarkable scarcity of any other traffic – and they surely cannot all have been taken early on a Sunday morning!

The urban areas had very serious problems of highway capacity, maintenance and administration by the late nineteenth century, resulting not only from the development of tramways but from the extremely rapid growth of towns in the previous half-century. The trend towards suburban living and the separation of dwelling and workplace became more pronounced and the need for ever-larger numbers of people to commute to work in the centre grew accordingly. This had an inevitable consequence both for public transport – which was one of the main factors in making it possible – and for highway capacity.

The gradual introduction and enforcement of bye-laws after the early 1870s and the consequent regulation and standardisation of building standards, produced the solid terraced housing which to many outsiders is so typical of the Lancashire industrial town. The somewhat monotonous grid-iron pattern of so many late Victorian and Edwardian housing areas was derived from the setting of minimum standards of density and layout under the urban bye-laws and from the attendant regulation of street widths and plans. Such housing and these characteristic street patterns, represented a very great improvement on what had gone before and they were found very widely – not just in the industrial centres but also in the 'working-class' ends of places such as Southport and Lytham.

As the great industrial cities spread outwards across the rural fringes during the 19th and early 20th centuries, thousands of miles of new streets were laid out. The process was usually undertaken without any coherent plan and the street patterns which emerged were often fragmented and un-coordinated. This 1895 map shows the growth of Openshaw, on the eastern edge of Manchester: new terraced streets are beginning to fill up the open land on either side of Ashton Old Road, a 1732 turnpike (running left–right on map) while the winding align-ment of Clayton Lane (running north–south) betrays its origins as a country road (OS 25″ 1st ed. CIV 12).

Usually – although every town had its local variations – the terraces faced onto a street, had small yards to the rear and were separated from the next row by a passageway, primarily for the removal of 'night soil' from the privies but also giving rear access to the property. This resulted in every pair of terraces sharing a front street and a rear passage. Cross streets were needed at intervals and, for large estate developments, new roads to give access from the existing built-up area – these often incorporated the alignments of older lanes. These developments added many miles of highway to the existing responsibilities of the towns, but they had to be constructed and surfaced to an acceptable standard – otherwise the local authority would refuse to adopt and the streets remained the responsibility of the landlord or frontage owner. The Public Health Act of 1875 and Private Street Works Act of 1892 gave highway authorities the permissive power to 'make up' and adopt unmade streets compulsorily, at the expense of the frontages, but rear passages were often left unsurfaced even when the front street was made up.

In Lancashire setts were widely used in these late Victorian housing areas: indeed, this, too, has become one of the enduring images of the industrial town. They are popularly though erroneously known – especially to outsiders – as 'cobbled streets'. True cobbles are rounded and less regular – they were often beach pebbles – and they were used for minor lanes and side streets. Examples of both types still survive, although in the 1950s and 1960s they were ripped out and resurfaced wholesale. Today streets paved with setts or cobbles are regarded by many people as attractive and they are enjoying a considerable revival, particularly in conservation and improvement areas, in pedestrianised town centres and in streets where traffic-calming measures are in use.

The more expensive housing tended to form ribbon development on the main roads, especially where these were served by trams – main road frontages were still considered the most superior and desirable sites as late as the 1930s. This housing often takes the form of semi-detached villas with front and back gardens. The Watling Street–Victoria Road development in Fulwood, served by Preston tramways, is a typical example. In some places, such as St Annes and Layton on the Fylde coast, there were very large areas of such housing, but all Lancashire towns can show examples.

New industries were also appearing in the late Victorian period, to add to the tradition of textiles, coalmining, heavy engineering, chemicals and metal-working which had been so significant in the development of the turnpike, canal and railway networks. For example, Preston became noted for the production of electrical equipment and tram cars. The continuing expansion of Liverpool docks was a major traffic generator, while in Stretford a country estate, Trafford Park, was transformed into a vast trading estate for new industry after the opening of the Ship Canal and Manchester Docks. Although the original aim was to use rail transport – the estate, like the Ship Canal, had its own locomotives and railway system – the road links became increasingly important during the 1920s and '30s. Symbolically, Henry Ford's first British factory opened here in 1910, producing the famous Model 'T' until the move to Dagenham in 1929.

The clearance of the densely-packed slums in the inner areas of bigger towns eventually allowed the highway authorities and planners to redesign road layouts but this was a rarity before the Second World War. One important exception was Rochdale, where in 1903 the corporation began the process of culverting a lengthy stretch of the River Roch and laying-out new roads. The section through the town centre from Yorkshire Street to the old Wellington Bridge was opened in 1904 and in 1910 it was extended to the west side of Newgate. The final section, from there to Weir Street, was not completed until 1926. Also in 1903, to facilitate the improvement of the tramway network, a new street and bridges were constructed between Bury Road and Spotland Road, called Mellor Street after Rochdale's first town clerk.

Blackpool Corporation made a concerted effort to extend and improve the promenade, especially after the town became a county borough in 1904. Queens Promenade was extended almost to Bispham, parallel with the Fleetwood tramway reservation, while the extension of the promenade southwards to Squires Gate was intended to meet Clifton Drive, which was constructed by St Annes and Lytham U.D.C.s during the late nineteenth century. These roads, too, were also tramway routes. Southport constructed the new promenade and underwent major expansion on a grid-iron of streets north, south and east of the older part of the town.

A major change in south Lancashire was the opening of the Widnes–Runcorn transporter bridge in 1905. The growing chemical industry of the area, partly prompted by the opening of the ship canal in 1894, required a better crossing of the Mersey than that offered by the old ferry. Although the London & North Western Railway had bridged the river at this point in 1868, the transporter was the first road bridge over the Mersey below Warrington. Vehicles were carried on a platform suspended from a high girder which trundled over the river and canal about 150 times each day. It was cumbersome but a major improvement upon the ferry and it survived until the present bridge was opened in 1961. It was a toll bridge, from 1912 vested jointly in the county councils of Lancashire and Cheshire.

SUMMARY, 1880–1914

At the outbreak of the First World War, therefore, many changes of fundamental importance were under way. Although the horse was still the prime mover of traffic, mechanical haulage by steam and subsequently by motor had already forced the abandonment of McAdam's surfacing for all except the minor rural or estate roads.

Town streets were almost universally paved with stone setts, while in the rural areas tarmac had covered much of the old 'macadam'. The following sections of this chapter outline the further changes and new construction consequent on the growth of motor traffic in the years between the wars.

THE WAR YEARS, 1914–1918

Despite the request from the Roads Board in July 1914 for 'quick start' schemes to deal with unemployment, few materialised. Some delays resulted from the need to acquire land, but much more important was the effect of the war. In May 1915 the government informed all highway authorities of restrictions on capital expenditure. All new works were to be abandoned, except where necessary for public health or war requirements, unless the work was approaching completion.

Labour shortages presented increasingly serious difficulties. In 1916 the director of the Roads Board appealed to highway authorities for labour to work on new roads to the Western Front: in Lancashire a conference of road authorities was held and as a result 517 men volunteered, including sixty-two from the direct works force of the county council. Three of the five county district surveyors had joined up with commissions and the county areas had to be rearranged so that coverage was provided by the two who remained.[22]

By then no important work was in progress – the final blow came in November 1917 with a directive from the Road Stone Control Committee of the Ministry of Munitions, severely restricting the supply of stone for highway repairs.[23] Quarry owners were to supply only 20 per cent of the contracted amount of roadstone to local authorities and then only for roads of national importance carrying substantial military traffic. During the first part of the war some routine work continued, funded mostly from revenue, but in 1917 the Main Road and Bridges Committee resolved to limit grants to district councils for secondary roads to half the average expenditure over the previous three years. This was mainly because of the wartime restrictions, although there was concern that the cost of grants was rising too quickly.

In Furness, where most main roads were still surfaced with water-bound macadam, severe difficulties were created by heavy wartime traffic. A motor bus service for civilian workers was introduced between Barrow and Ulverston by British Electric Traction Co. [B.E.T.]. The result was that expenditure on maintaining this section of road was £1,882 in 1914–5, compared with £365 in the previous year.[24] To cope with this exceptional problem, which was worsened by other types of increased traffic, the Local Government Board approved a loan of £10,000 to surface the road in tarmac. The county council then instituted proceedings against B.E.T. and after March 1917 claimed an estimated £4,983: the dispute was not resolved until 1924, when the county accepted £1,500 from the company.[25]

In Lancaster considerable damage was done to the Lancaster and Kirkby Lonsdale main road during the construction of a new munitions factory by Vickers in 1916. Here the Local Government Board agreed to a scheme for a section of new road from Skerton Bridge along Ladies Walk to the existing main road, with the widening of the latter as far as the borough boundary at the Aqueduct. The cost was £19,879, shared between the county council (42.5 per cent), Lancaster Corporation (26 per cent) and a Road Board grant (31.5 per cent).[26]

Among the few schemes exempted from the wartime ban on construction, perhaps the most important was the completion of the new bridge over the Ribble linking Preston and Penwortham. This was opened on 9 June 1915 and superseded the very fine bridge of the late 1750s. The old bridge was closed to vehicular traffic in December 1915 but it is still in use for pedestrians and cyclists. The new bridge, with great foresight, was built sufficiently wide to take two lanes of traffic in each direction – something which is invaluable today. A new lifting bridge over the Sankey Canal at Warrington was also completed in 1915.

A traffic survey conducted on the Manchester to Liverpool road in January 1916 recorded 282 single motor waggon journeys in six days, compared with just twenty-five in a comparable survey in 1912. Similar experiences were recorded from other parts of the county and in the long-term this had two effects. First, there was much damage to road surfaces so a backlog of repairs awaited the local authorities when the war ended. Second, the transfer of freight traffic from rail to road was greatly accelerated by the shift which took place during the war and by the increased use of motor lorries for military traffic.

NEW ROADS AND TRAMWAYS AFTER 1918

Between the wars Liverpool Corporation continued to expand its tramway system and designed a network of new suburban roads which incorporated tramway reservations. J. A. Brodie, city engineer from 1896 to 1926, held progressive views about urban transport and planning. In 1910 he formulated the 'linear park' concept, whereby new outer suburbs were to be built to house the displaced occupants of cleared inner-city slums. The new developments would be at lower densities and served by wide parkway-type roads. Crucially, however, he recognised that fast and cheap public transport was needed to

Urban expansion and the Liverpool tramways: J. A. Brodie, the City engineer, favoured the expansion of the tramway network on 'green track' routes to serve the new suburban estates on the perimeter. This 1917 view shows Broad Green Road (now the A5080), the first of the new tramway routes; the tracks are segregated in a central reservation with hedges on either side. The route, which extended to Bowring Park, was opened in 1914–15 *(Liverpool City Libraries)*.

compensate for the longer journeys to work and he therefore favoured dual-carriageways with rapid tramways on the central reservation. Liverpool was already committed to a 'wide roads' policy contained in its Corporation Act of 1902 and the 1908 Streets and Building Act, so the new policy accorded well with the old. Brodie's concept involved tramways which, unlike railways laid on ballast sleeper tracks, were bedded on clinkers which were then grassed over – this resulted in the characteristic Liverpool 'grass track' tramways.[27]

The main areas of Liverpool's housing expansion were towards Speke in the south and Norris Green to the east. The first 'grass track' was opened to Bowring Park in 1914. They were also laid along Menlove Avenue and on to Woolton (1924), Princess Road, Aigburth Road (1921), Muirhead Avenue Extension (1923), Mather Avenue (1924) and beyond. The ring road, Queens Drive, although a 'wide road' and one of Brodie's suggestions of 1910, never carried a tramway. After Brodie had retired the work continued, with new tramways in the Norris Green area. The extensions southwards included Edgelane Drive and Childwall Road. The final tramway extension was along the East Lancashire Road from Lowerhouse Lane to the city boundary, in an existing central reservation, in 1938–40. This served the Napier aero-engine works and in 1942–4 was temporarily extended to the Royal Ordnance factory at Kirkby. Despite all this pioneering work and progressive planning,

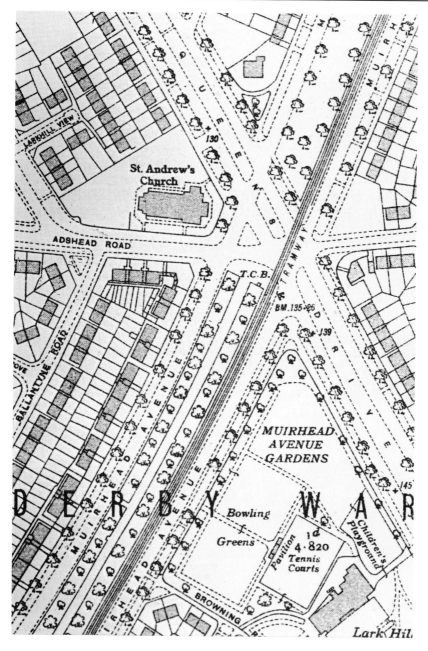

The progressive 'Brodie system' of dual-carriageways and tramways on central reservations was found in much of outer Liverpool until the precipitate abandonment of the network in the mid-1950s. This 1937 map extract shows the intersection of Muirhead Avenue with the ring road, Queens Drive - the latter never carried a tramway although sufficient space was left for one (OS 25″ CIV 8).

Liverpool very shortsightedly abandoned its tramway network with unseemly haste in the mid-1950s: the last tram ran in 1957.

Associated with the Liverpool network development was the need to reconstruct the inter-urban tramway from Liverpool to Prescot, originally built by a private company in 1902. In 1921 it was acquired by Liverpool Corporation but because the line was in a very poor state

Urban expansion and the Manchester tramways: Manchester Corporation also experimented with reserved track tramways, although not with the same enthusiasm as Liverpool. This view of Kingsway (A5070) taken shortly after its completion in 1930 shows scarcely any road traffic, but suburban housing development is already beginning to encroach upon the neighbouring fields *(Manchester Public Libraries, Local Studies Unit).*

the city council decided to rebuild it as a 'grass track'. The Prescot road – then the main route to Manchester – was very heavily-trafficked and road vehicles were damaging the tramway. The last mile inside the city was relocated to the central reservation and in the county area several diversions were made to take the tramway off the road and through green fields. The city council purchased the extra land and laid the new double tracks but the cost of the roadworks was borne by the county council with a 50 per cent grant from the Ministry of Transport. The conversion was completed in 1924, giving a through tram route of eight miles from Pier Head, the last four being on grass track. Although at the onset the road was largely in green fields, housing development rapidly spread around the route until there was continuous development from Liverpool to Prescot.

In Manchester the need for new housing areas was similarly acute and here, too, tramways on separate reservations played a part. Tramways radiated from the city along the existing main roads – the former turnpikes – and ribbon development in the late nineteenth century meant that many of these routes were becoming heavily congested. The only area near the city with plenty of vacant land lay between

Stockport Road (A6) and Chester Road (A56), served by the former
Wilmslow turnpike (B5093) and Barlow Moor Road from Chorlton
to Didsbury (A5154). To open up the new areas Palatine Road (B5167)
was built from Withington to Barlow Moor, with an on-street tramway,
but subsequently two completely new arterial roads were constructed:
Princess Road (A5103) in 1924 and Kingsway in 1926–7 (A5079). Both
roads were laid out on the 'Brodie' system, pioneered in Liverpool,
with dual carriageways and a rapid tramway in the central reservation.
Although other tram extensions were considered these two routes were
the only reservation tracks in Manchester: in the mid-1930s the city
council decided to abandon trams, although the Second World War
meant that the final closure was not until 1948.

However, the road development southwards from the city was
continued without tramways. Palatine Road and Princess Road were
carried across the Mersey using new bridges – the latter as Princess
Parkway – to serve Wythenshawe, the vast overspill town which
Manchester began building after its 1926 boundary extensions. The
two roads met at Northenden and then Parkway continued as far as
the Stockport–Altrincham road (A560). Since the 1960s the construction
of the M56 and M63 has changed much of this road system beyond
all recognition.

Just as in the early years of the century new tramways and their
maintenance were major concerns of the highway authorities, so the
abandonment of tramway networks began to cause difficulties after the
late 1920s. The Tramway Acts obliged the operator merely to reinstate
the road as it had been when the tracks were laid and, in the county
area, this was more often than not waterbound macadam. However,
by the 1920s the traffic growth and changes in road design meant that
such a surface was no longer acceptable – sett paving or tarmac were
required and agreement had to be reached with the tramway operator
to contribute the equivalent cost of waterbound while the county
funded the additional costs using Ministry of Transport grants.

One of the first instances was on the A57 from Prescot to Rainhill,
when the St Helens service was converted to trolley buses in 1926. In
1931 came the biggest single change, when the South Lancashire system
in Atherton, Leigh, Hindley and Ashton-in-Makerfield, together with
Wigan's service to Ashton, all switched to trolley buses. By the mid-
1930s the scale of tramway abandonment meant that the county had
to make an annual budget provision of £100,000 for road reinstatement.
In cases where the track and its surround was in good condition the
lines were left *in situ* and the whole road sheeted over with bitumen
macadam but in 1940, when the government was calling for the urgent
recovery of tram rail for its steel content, much of this had to be
re-excavated.

THE FIRST POSTWAR YEARS —

ROAD CLASSIFICATION

In February 1919 local authorities were informed by the Roads Board that the Treasury would be prepared to make generous grants for the restoration of roads which had fallen into disrepair during the war. The programme of work was to be equivalent to that for the year ending 31 May 1914 but the county surveyor warned that the increases in wages and material costs meant that the expense would at least double that of 1914. In its preparations for a major programme of work, the county council not only approved the purchase of a steam waggon but also acquired its first steam roller, bought second hand from Blackpool for £500 – repairs to make it usable cost another £150!

By 1913 tar was being used very extensively for surfacing, being delivered to various railway stations in 2,000-gallon tankers but the county council was extremely dissatisfied with the poor quality and slow delivery of the commercial tarmac supplies, particularly in the northern areas of Lancashire. It therefore decided to manufacture its own tarmac and in May 1914 a contract was agreed for the supply and erection of plant at Carnforth, to use slag from the local ironworks: the plant had an output of one hundred tons a day and much of the delivery was by rail.

In February 1923 the operation of the Carnforth plant was criticised by the district auditor, who urged closure because a loss of £7,528 had accumulated. The county surveyor disputed this figure, claiming that there were only two commercial firms which could tender for less and these had proved unable to supply the required quantities. From November 1924 winter manufacturing was abandoned, because it was proving uneconomic to dry the aggregate – necessary for adhesion of the tar – so in winter chippings were produced for the next summer's tar spraying. Finally, in July 1933, the county admitted defeat: the works were no longer able to compete with improved supplies by commercial firms at the low prices then prevailing and the plant was sold for £350.

The first postwar roadmending programme was budgeted as follows. It is interesting to note that, despite the great increase in traffic, granite setts and waterbound macadam were still being widely used: old methods died hard.[28]

	Main roads £	Secondary roads £
Tarmac	72,673	46,103
Granite setts	66,949	23,808
Tarspray	25,839	630
Drainage		953

Waterbound sheeting	18,456
Wood paving	6,000

Completion of Caton Road, Lancaster	3,000
Completion of the main road in Eccles	21,746
Widening at Lumb in Rawtenstall	5,800
Bridge works (various)	6,699
Granite sett paving in Colne	4,052
Tarmac in Mossley	1,436
Work in Worsley	1,049
Work in Barton-upon-Irwell	1,257

In 1919 the Ministry of Transport was established and one of its first tasks was to undertake a national scheme for the classification and numbering of roads. As a prelude to this, a nationwide traffic census was held, with 196 census points in Lancashire. In November 1921 the county council was notified of the mileage of classified roads.★ [29]

1921 status	To be Class I	To be Class II	Unclassified	Total
Main roads	593	46	17	656
Secondary roads	90	339	703	1,132
District roads	7	11	2,517	2,535
Total	690	396	3,237	4,323

★ In the table the mileages are rounded to the nearest whole number

These mileages were significantly less than the council had recommended, but even so the proportions in Class I (16 per cent of the total) and Class II (9 per cent) were slightly above the national average. Class I roads were to receive 50 per cent grants from central government and Class II roads 25 per cent grants (later increased to 60 per cent and 50 per cent respectively). In rural areas and urban districts with low rateable values, the ministry offered grants of 75 per cent to bring newly classified roads up to main road standards: for Lancashire the first lists included the routes from Skelwith Bridge to Broughton-in-Furness (A593), Lancaster to Pilling and Shard Bridge (A588), Penwortham to Leyland (B5254/A5083) and Chorley to Croston (A581). As the scheme settled down in the early 1920s several roads were upgraded to Class I status, including the A5084 from Greenodd to Torver, the A687 at Cantsfield, the road from Scarisbrick to Maghull (A5147) and the A5080 Liverpool to Warrington via Cronton road.

The old designations of 'main' and 'secondary' roads, inherited from the mid-nineteenth century, continued for a time because the grants from the county to the district were based on this classification but eventually the two systems were brought into line: by 1939 all non-classified roads had been 'dismained'. In March 1931 the title of the county Main Road and Bridges Committee was simplified to 'Highways and Bridges Committee'.

Consequent upon the classification of roads was the development of a national system of numbering. In March 1922 the ministry offered to assist local authorities in signing and numbering the new Class I or 'A' roads – the logic of main road numbering was to divide England and Wales into sectors bounded by the great highways radiating from London to Berwick (A1), Dover (A2), Portsmouth (A3), Bristol (A4), Holyhead (A5) and Carlisle (A6). All other roads were numbered according to the sector in which they fell, moving clockwise. Thus roads in Lancashire starting west of the A6 have numbers beginning with '5' and those east of the A6 begin with '6'. Where a route is continuous the numbering runs through – the A57, for example, runs from Liverpool to Lincoln, the A49 from Ross-on-Wye to Preston and the A34 from Winchester to Manchester. The Class II or 'B' roads follow a similar system, determined by the 'A' road numberings.

Further changes followed the adoption of the Trunk Road Act of 1936, whereby the Ministry of Transport became the highway authority for designated routes of national importance. The numberings were not altered on signposts, but maps often distinguish trunk roads by the '(T)' notation. After 1936 several Lancashire routes became trunk roads: the A6 from Salford to Preston and Kendal, the A59 from Liverpool to Preston and on to Skipton, the A56 in Stretford, the newly-opened A580 East Lancashire Road, the A49 from Warrington to Bamber Bridge and the A62 from Manchester to Leeds. Since the Second World War there have been further alterations. Trunk road status did not continue within county boroughs. For example, the A59 ceased to be a trunk road on the Preston boundary at Penwortham Bridge and then resumed that status at Brockholes. The trunk road mileage in Lancashire was 147 miles and since this was financed entirely by the government the ratepayers had some relief.

In the early years of classification further roads continued to be 'mained'. One notable example was the road from Preston to Lytham. The section over Freckleton Marsh was still a private toll road and the county responsibility only began at Freckleton village. Not until 1922 was agreement reached with the Clifton and de Hoghton estates for the abolition of tolls and the construction of a new road along the northern edge of the marsh, from Clifton Gate to the main road in Freckleton. The building of a completely new road was necessary because the toll road was by this time in a state of complete disrepair. The through route subsequently became the A584 but traces of the old road are still visible on the marsh to the south.

In February 1920 the lease on the Windermere ferry was advertised and under the Ferries (Acquisition by Local Authorities) Act of 1919 the county councils of Lancashire and Westmorland took over the service jointly from 1 March. In November the joint committee bought the steam ferry, other boats and equipment and two cottages valued at £3,606 12s – by 1922 the service was running at a loss and fares were increased.

Urban congestion in Market Street, Manchester (then the main A6) in about 1936: by the 1930s the growth in car usage had led to acute congestion in town and city centres. This view shows a mix of lorries, cars, taxis and trams, but it was the last – with their fixed tracks – which received most of the blame for the problem. Most towns therefore decided to abandon trams in favour of the more 'flexible' motor-bus: the idea of keeping out the other forms of traffic was as yet undreamt of. Manchester's last tram ran in 1949: just over forty years later, trams were again running on the streets of the city (Manchester Public Libraries, Local Studies Unit).

TRAFFIC, UNEMPLOYMENT, BYPASSES AND RING ROADS

By 1921, as a result of the traffic censuses undertaken before classification, the ministry and the local authorities had accumulated a considerable volume of data about road usage. This tended to confirm that there had been a very rapid increase in 'mechanically propelled road traffic' since 1913. Traditionally this has been attributed to the motor car, but the increase in the use of the motor lorry during the First World War had a very significant impact. At the end of the war the government disposed of a large number of military vehicles, many of which were bought – usually with subsidies and grants – by ex-servicemen who then started transport and haulage businesses. This greatly increased the volume of short and medium distance motor lorry haulage. The transfer of traffic from rail to road gathered pace, a trend encouraged by the very neglected state of the rail network after years of war and under-investment.

A week-long census at Barton Moss, on the Manchester to Warrington road (A57), in December 1919[30] had produced the following comparison with 1912 traffic levels:

	1912	1919
Motor cycles	108	130
Motor cars	128	366
Motor omnibuses	1	3
Motor vans (covered)	39	206
Motor lorries (rubber tyred)	94	2010
Trailers (rubber tyred)	1	336
Motor lorries (steel tyred)	32	11
Trailers (steel tyred)	18	4
Light tractors (steam)	4	3
Trailers	4	3
Traction Engines (steam)	2	1
Trailers	6	2
Total of mechanical vehicles and trailers	437	3075
Horse-drawn vehicles	1089	793

This indicates a seven-fold increase in the numbers of mechanically-propelled vehicles, including trailers and includes an increase of over

twenty times in motor lorries. Horse transport had only fallen by about a quarter, since there had been a general growth in traffic. The total tonnage had increased more than ten-fold.

The Ministry of Transport census in 1921[31] gave the following figures:

Road	Motor cycles	Private cars	Vans	Buses/ charas	Comm'l vehicles	Horse drawn
Blackpool–Preston	5612	8114	315	2381	933	545
Preston–Lancaster	4592	5944	701	1746	1104	267
Garstang–Blackpool	924	1590	70	724	101	367
Liverpool–Preston	337	654	115	8	756	700
Liverpool–Warrington	590	1243	450	162	3855	635

For some reason the roads from Preston to Blackpool and Lancaster were surveyed during Whit Week, which probably accounts for the large volume of charabanc traffic. The very heavy use of the Liverpool to Warrington road by motor lorries is particularly obvious and overall traffic in Lancashire was considered to be the heaviest of any county.

By this time the problem of large motor vehicles using unsuitable roads was becoming acute. From 1923, for example, Ulverston R.D.C. had to impose weight restrictions on many of its rural roads although as a concession to the tourist trade it allowed charabancs with up to fourteen seats. Damage by exceptional loads also continued. In August 1925 a

Manchester firm (probably Norman Box) hauled a 'stator' (part of a dynamo) weighing almost ninety-one tons on an eight-wheeled trailer along the Manchester–Warrington road. The setts, only laid in 1924, had to be relaid or replaced all the way from Eccles to Barton Moss Lane.[32]

The post-war economic recovery was soon followed by rising un-employment and falling wages. In Lancashire a roadman could earn 61s. a week in 1919, including bonuses of 38s. This fell rapidly to 56s. 4d. in August 1921, 44s. 10d. in August 1922 and 40s. 3d. in August 1923. In November 1921, in an attempt to reduce un-employment, the Ministry of Health offered grants of 32½ per cent for road schemes that could be started that winter but, as the county surveyor pointed out, Class I roads were already earning grants of 50 per cent if started with Ministry of Transport approval! One of the first unemployment relief schemes was for a new wide road between Lancaster and Morecambe, bypassing the old route through Torri-sholme. By mid-1922 several other schemes were well under way:[33]

Road	Cost in £	Labour Force
A570 St Helens–Clockface	48,046	155
A568 St Helens–Widnes	20,401	50
Eccleston–St Helens	51,262	50
A57 Liverpool–Manchester, at Knotty Ash	174,426	265
A586 Blackpool – Garstang, new road at Poulton	72,637	163
A59 Ormskirk bypass	69,042	80

Many lesser improvement schemes were added to the list and a pattern emerged of road improvement in the urban area of south Lancashire and the construction of new roads approaching the coastal resorts. Grants were made quite freely until the economic crisis in the late 1920s resulted in substantial reductions in expenditure. Fortunately this state of affairs was relatively shortlived and by May 1933 grants were once more available for new schemes.

It is more convenient to consider major projects geographically rather than chronologically. The A6 Manchester–Preston–Carnforth trunk road, part of the route from London to Carlisle, was of national significance and was an early candidate for improvement. At Blackrod a new 2-mile bypass was designed not only to avoid the village but also to ease the gradient on the steep Blackrod Brow. It should have started as an unemployment relief project in the winter of 1929–30, but was delayed first by the need for a compulsory purchase order and then by the 1932–3 moratorium on spending. Work finally began in May 1933.

Two bridges on the A6 were also tackled. The first was at Bloody Bridge, the skew bridge over the Leeds and Liverpool Canal at Dux-bury. In January 1894 this had been repaired by Leonard Fairclough, from nearby Adlington – one of the earliest contracts by what was later to be one of Britain's greatest road construction firms. It was rebuilt in steel in 1924–5. The second bridge was at Walton-le-Dale, over the Ribble. The turnpike bridge of 1779-81, although structurally sound, was only thirty feet wide: it was therefore widened to eighty feet, with dual carriageways, in 1938–9, although the associated road works were delayed by the Second World War.

North of Preston several stretches of road were widened and improved, but the largest project was the construction of the Garstang bypass. The 3½ mile single carriageway road was proposed in November 1924 as an unemployment relief scheme and, after several delays, was opened in October 1928. Designed to bypass the narrow High Street in Garstang, which was also the site of a street market, the new road began at the old turnpike gate south of Catterall and ended just north of the town. It was one of the earliest bypasses and its design had much in common with nineteenth-century turnpikes, being a mixture of new road and the improvement of existing lanes. The new section at the northern end included bridges over the Lancaster Canal and the Garstang and Knott End Railway. These had very steep approaches, while the improvement of the existing lane north from the junction with the Blackpool Road (A586) retained a winding alignment: both sections are substandard by the criteria of the 1990s. The short Bolton-le-Sands bypass was opened in 1928, but other proposed schemes were deferred until after the Second World War.

The A59 from Liverpool to Preston and Skipton, when disturnpiked and declared a main road, was merely a meandering lane. By the early 1920s it was becoming much busier and traffic congestion and dangerous alignments presented many problems. The largest intermediate town, Ormskirk, was a particular troublespot and in August 1922 a bypass was included in a list of unemployment work schemes. The route followed a tight arc west of the town centre and the road was completed late that year. Unfortunately there was no control over ribbon development and the road frontages were rapidly built up – this was almost a classic case of an extremely serious planning problem. The results can be seen today: speed restrictions, numerous residential accesses onto the main road and continued congestion.

Elsewhere on the A59 some attempts were made to prevent a repetition of that problem. At Maghull the diversion which became Northway was first planned in 1927, but was not started until 1933. In the interim the need to prevent residential access was realised and agreement was reached for developers to provide service roads on the Red Lion Bridge–Dunnings Bridge length. This length was originally built as single carriageway, but south of Ormskirk the two miles of new road known as Aughton Diversion (completed 1937) and Aughton Swan was constructed to a very different standard. The Aughton stretch was lavishly laid out, with dual carriageways, cycle tracks, footpaths and a wide central reservation. The second part was not started until May 1939, but because it was considered to be of national importance construction was continued even after the war began. These three projects in the Ormskirk area illustrate well how the conception of roads and their design altered rapidly during the inter-war years.

North of Ormskirk the main work was the upgrading of the section between Penwortham and the river Douglas. From Longton to Much Hoole there were short bypasses at Walmer Bridge and Much Hoole, with other lengths of widened road – most of these projects were completed in 1926. The Longton bypass featured in several programmes during the 1930s and in the early autumn of 1939 work was about to start, but the outbreak of the Second World War prevented any further work. Associated with it, but built in advance, were the dualling of the road through Howick and the widening of Liverpool Road in Penwortham itself. Part of the road west of the Douglas was also widened and a tiny bypass, only a quarter of a mile long, was constructed around Sollom village. East of Preston the A59 remained almost un-altered, apart from the diversion at Samlesbury airfield, started in July 1939 and, for obvious reasons, allowed to continue to completion after the outbreak of the war.

Little major work was done on the remaining trunk roads: the notorious A49 from Warrington to Preston, with its succession of congested built-up areas and its especially poor alignment, appeared particularly neglected. It was overshadowed by the proposals for motorways, which were emerging in the early 1930s and one of which, the north–south route which was the forerunner of the M6, paralleled it through the county.

In the early 1930s the county council reached agreement with the Leeds and Liverpool Canal Company for the replacement of Litherland swing bridge. The financial constraints of 1931–2 caused the postpone-ment of the scheme and the canal company, arguing that the council had broken the agreement, absolved itself of all responsibility for the old bridge. The county began construction of a lifting bridge in May 1933. In the meantime a scheme for a new road from Dunnings Bridge to Litherland had been prepared and agreement was reached with Lord Sefton who, as land owner, was prepared to make a contribution. This project, too, was delayed by lack of finance and it was not until November 1936 that work began. The dual carriageway road had 9-foot cycle tracks which could be widened to 16-foot service roads as development took place. It was classified as the A567 and provided greatly-improved access to the Bootle docks and the northern end of Liverpool docks.

THE MERSEY TUNNEL AND

THE EAST LANCASHIRE ROAD

Liverpool was the focus of road investment in the period between the wars. The Mersey road tunnel and the East Lancashire Road between Liverpool and Manchester were by far the largest transportation projects undertaken in north-west England since the construction of the Manchester Ship Canal. There had been a ferry from Liverpool to Birkenhead for many centuries. In 1822 steam vessels were introduced and in 1897 special 'luggage' or 'goods' boats for road vehicles began operating. The first tunnel under the river was for Mersey Railway, opened in 1886 with steam locomotives and converted to electricity in 1903. The growth in cross-river traffic reflected national trends: the total number of passengers per year on ferries and railways rose from 33 million in 1901 to 62 million in 1921, while goods vehicles transported by Birkenhead and Wallasey ferries increased from 380,000 to 640,000.

Woodside Goods Ferry: vehicles per year

1914	448,478	80% horse drawn
1919	284,768★	60% mechanical vehicles
1920	392,365	
1921	422,883	

★ motor vehicles could carry larger loads and so fewer journeys were necessary

The post-war increase in traffic meant that long queues built up at the landing stages. On Grand National Day 1932 the Woodside goods ferries carried:

	Number	*Percentage*
Horse	76	2.25
Steam	85	2.51
Commercial Motors	1,538	45.45
Motor Cars	1,532	45.27
Misc †	153	4.52
Total	3,384	100.00

† 'miscellaneous' included charabancs and motorcycles.

In 1921 a Merseyside Coordination Committee, representing the corporations of Liverpool, Birkenhead, Bootle and Wallasey, was established under the chairmanship of Sir Archibald Salvidge, leader of Liverpool City Council. In early considerations a bridge was ruled out, since navigation requirements meant that it would have required a headroom of 185 feet above high water, over a 2,200-foot span. The

THE MERSEY TUNNEL. — 12th Mar. 1931.
C.12. (Contract No 4) Shield under Dale St.

cost – £10½ million – and the length and gradient of the approaches made it additionally impractical. [34]

The first tunnel proposals were put forward in 1924, envisaging a double-deck scheme in which trams would run on the lower level. This was estimated to cost £6.4 million, the tramway element being some £1.75 million. The ministry offered a grant of £2,375,000 on condition that there were no tolls, a restriction which was unacceptable to Liverpool Corporation. Wallasey and Birkenhead, meanwhile, were unhappy with the prospect of through trams affecting the ferry revenues and Wallasey had already considered abandoning its tramway.[35]

In November 1924 the chancellor of the exchequer, Winston Churchill, offered a fixed grant of £2½ million and agreed to the imposition of tolls for twenty years. The scheme – minus the trams – was approved by parliament in August 1925 and work on the access shafts began at once. Because of increasing costs three further Acts were required and the toll period was extended to twenty-five years. The tunnel was opened with due ceremony by King George V on 19 July 1934. It

Construction of the first Mersey road tunnel in progress, 12 March 1931; the view is taken beneath Dale Street, when a 200-ton shield was being used. The cast-iron lining follows the shield and supports the rams propelling the shield forwards. Only the upper half of the tunnel is being excavated at this stage; the spoil is removed using skips on a narrow-gauge railway *(Stewart Bale Photographic Archive)*.

The formal opening ceremony of the Liverpool-Birkenhead tunnel was performed on 18 July 1934 by King George V and Queen Mary. The tunnel was named 'Queensway', and when the second tunnel was opened in the 1970s it was called 'Kingsway', even though there was then no king! Note the first pay-booths, to the left of the monumental column *(Stewart Bale Photographic Archive).*

was a remarkable feat of engineering and it immediately transformed the traffic patterns of Merseyside. There were disadvantages, though and these have increased over the years. Perhaps the most serious, in retrospect, is that because the tunnel entrances and exits are right in the heart of Liverpool, traffic is inevitably drawn into the city centre.

Mersey Tunnel Statistics[36]

Length:	Kingsway, Liverpool to Kings Square, Birkenhead, 2.13 miles long (2.87 miles including the branches to Princess Dock, Liverpool and Wallasey Docks)
Road width:	36 feet in main tunnel, 19 feet in branches
Lowest point:	170 feet below high water mark
Min. rock cover:	3ft. 6ins.
Material excavated:	1,200,000 tons using 560,000lbs of explosives
Tunnel lining:	cast iron segments 82,000; concrete 270,000 tons

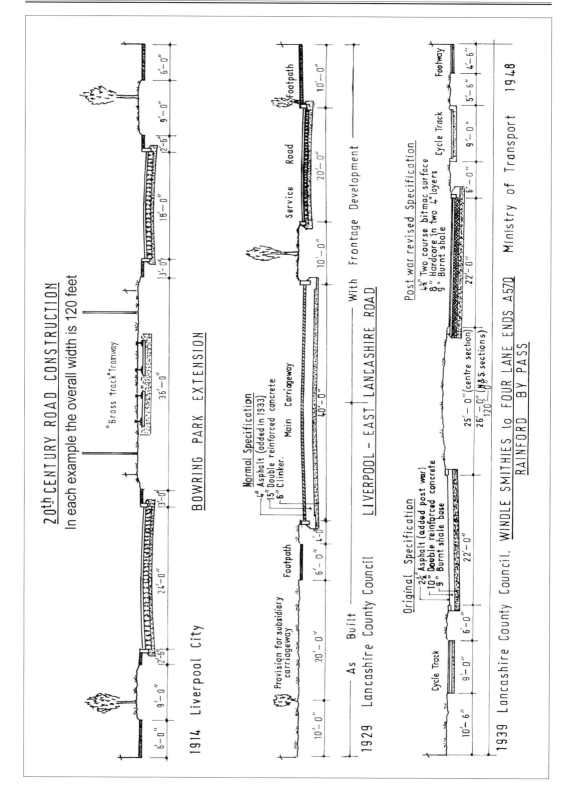

20ᵗʰ CENTURY ROAD CONSTRUCTION

In each example the overall width is 120 feet

1914 Liverpool City   BOWRING PARK EXTENSION

1929 Lancashire County Council   LIVERPOOL - EAST LANCASHIRE ROAD

1939 Lancashire County Council. WINDLE SMITHIES to FOUR LANE ENDS A570   Ministry of Transport 1948
RAINFORD BY PASS

Traffic forecasts proved to be seriously under-estimated. It was expected that two million vehicles would use the tunnel in its first full year, but this figure was reached in nine months and the second year saw 3,164,627 vehicles including 186,361 motorcycles and 237,751 pedal cycles.

The East Lancashire Road also had a long gestation period. Notwithstanding the construction of the Manchester Ship Canal and the existence of two barge canals and three competing railway routes from Liverpool to Manchester, manufacturers in the Manchester area were perpetually dissatisfied with the transport services available. The only main road between the cities ran through Eccles, Warrington and Prescot (A57) and in the early 1920s, except for the laying of sett paving, it was much as it had been left by turnpike trusts. Discussion on improvements started as early as 1912 but the war intervened and it was not until 1923 that a meeting of representatives of the ministry, the county council and the corporations of Liverpool, Manchester, Salford, Bootle, St Helens and Warrington, began serious planning.

The radical decision was made that improvement of any existing road would not be an adequate solution and instead a completely new inter-urban trunk route was required. This, with some of the radial arterial roads in the London area, was to be the first British example of this type of scheme, the ancestor of the motorway. The Ministry of Transport offered a grant of 50 per cent for the £3 million cost of a 27-mile single-carriageway road and suggested that other local authorities in the area should contribute. In 1925 the plan was slightly revised but the estimate was left unaltered and the ministry now offered a 75 per cent grant. There was some further delay but by November 1926 the ministry authorised an immediate start, to assist with unemployment relief. Most of the work was to be carried out by Lancashire County Council, but Liverpool would build its own length and the first twelve miles from the city were built by the unemployed from the Liverpool, Bootle and St Helens labour exchange areas.[37]

A design office was set up at Newton-le-Willows in 1927 and powers for bridging various railways were included in a Railways (Road Transport) Act 1928. At a formal ceremony on 29 April 1929 Sir John Aspell, the chairman of the county Highways and Bridges Committee, 'cut the first sod'. Progress was good: by November 1930, 809 men were employed on the Lancashire county length, with 220 hired two-ton lorries for earthmoving. If allowance is made for off-site work by suppliers it is likely that more than 3,000 men were involved. Most of the road was constructed of concrete and it was opened in sections as it was completed: a final tarmac surfacing was deferred because of the 1931-2 financial restrictions. By February 1932 it was

Twentieth-century road construction methods in Lancashire.

open to traffic from Liverpool to Windle, from Lowton to *The Greyhound* and from Astley to Walkden Road and in July 1933 the remainder was finished. The road was formally opened by King George V on 19 July 1934.

Although it was almost entirely new construction, the design of the road was far from ideal. In particular, it had twenty-four at-grade junctions with other roads and, because of the speed of traffic on the new road, these quickly became accident black spots. Some attempt had been made to avoid this problem, by incorporating 'circuses' in the design – setting-back the boundary at junctions in a circle, designed to give improved visibility – but rather belatedly the Ministry of Transport and the county surveyor recommended the building of roundabouts at nine of the most important junctions, the first being that with the A49 at Haydock in July 1933. At that date, too, the ministry at last approved the expenditure on a final surfacing with asphalt.

Only 2¼ of the twenty-eight miles were on the alignment of earlier roads. The East Lancashire Road was therefore not only by far the longest single piece of new road construction in the county since the Roman period, but its use of new alignments over a very long distance meant that it was completely different in conception from any of the

The construction of the Liverpool-East Lancashire Road, the largest road-building project in Lancashire since the Roman period, began in 1929. Much of the road comprised a 15″ reinforced concrete slab. In this view, taken in July 1932 at the Windle cutting, the slab is being laid in sections. Narrow- and standard-gauge railways are still being used for the handling of spoil and materials, as in the building of the Manchester Ship Canal forty years earlier *(LCC publicity booklet, 1934).*

The East Lancashire Road, photographed in April 1934 from the bridge spanning the Windle cutting near St Helens (as in previous view). There is a single 40-foot wide carriageway. The cutting required the excavation of 295,000 cubic yards of material *(LCC publicity booklet, 1934).*

turnpikes. It was built to a standard width of 120-feet with a single carriageway, although from the start it was envisaged that additional capacity would eventually be provided and so space was left for this. One proposal was that two additional 20-foot carriageways should be built for 'slow moving traffic' and although after the war a straightforward dual carriageway arrangement was adopted the older suggestion survived in the form of service roads – most notably in the stretch between Irlams o'th' Height and Wardleys, through Swinton.

Lay-bys were provided at intervals – a progressive feature – and these were equipped with water points for steam waggons, which might in contrast seem an anachronism, but these vehicles were still being constructed as late as 1937 and could be seen running on this road into the 1950s. Earthworks excavated totalled approximately 1.5 million cubic yards, the largest cutting being at Windle and 135 houses were demolished – sixty-nine were built to provide alternative accommodation. The normal construction of the road was of 15-inch thick double reinforced concrete, on six inches of consolidated clinker containing some 250,000 cubic yards of concrete. Two miles were on embankments, where settlement was anticipated and consisted of two-inch layers of hand pitching surface with four inches of tarmac. The main contract in Lancashire was let to Sir Lindsey Parkinson & Co. of Blackpool for £2,147,179 5s., while the surfacing was done by four specialist firms.

The length of road in Liverpool was constructed to the 'Brodie' standard, with dual carriageways and a grass central reservation which

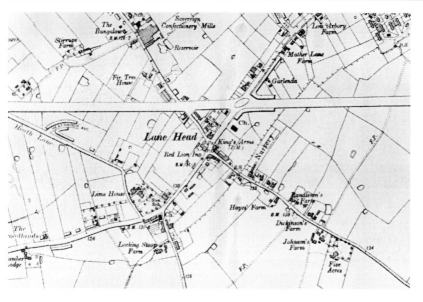

The East Lancashire Road sliced across the flat lowlands between Liverpool and Manchester with scant regard for the existing landscape or for the older road pattern – although not a motorway it shared many of the same qualities. It is shown here at Lane Head, Lowton, with its straightness and width in dramatic contrast to the previous highway network of the area. Note the early roundabout at the junction with Newton Road *(OS 6" 102SW, 1938)*.

eventually carried trams from Walton Hall Avenue. The final estimates of the cost of the road were that Lancashire County Council spent £2,538,842 2s. 7d. and Liverpool City Council £182,957 4s. 2d., a total of £2,721,799 6s. 9d., which compares with the initial estimate of £3 million – how rare it is that a project of this size and importance should be so significantly under-budget!

RING ROADS

Most of the large towns of Lancashire were the focus of a network of important traffic routes and particularly of former turnpike roads. As the built-up areas grew and as road traffic increased the traffic problems of these towns became correspondingly more acute. Conflict between local traffic and through traffic movements was a major concern by the 1920s and congestion in the town centres, where the multiplicity of local and through routes met, was especially severe. The cost of widening or realigning old roads in densely built up urban areas was usually regarded as prohibitive so in the inter-war period the ring road became a favourite device, intended to take through and long distance traffic around the outskirts of a town rather than through the centre.

However, in many places where such routes were built, the areas alongside were soon developed for housing and light industry – in large measure attracted by the excellent road access – and so the aim of reducing congestion was in considerable measure negated. Most inter-war ring roads are now well within the built-up area. In Preston,

Rossendale Road, Burnley, under construction in August 1925. This road (the A646) formed part of the project for a Burnley outer ring road, and it involved both new construction and the widening and improvement of stretches of existing road. One reason for the project was the relief of unemployment, so gangs of labourers were used instead of a steamroller for compacting and levelling the stone layer (*Lancashire County Library: Burnley Local Studies Collection*).

although the north-south traffic on the A6 passed very close to the town centre, most congestion was thought to be the result of traffic from east Lancashire to Blackpool. A new three-mile east-west ring road was therefore laid out in 1935–6 from New Hall Lane to Four Lane Ends and on towards Blackpool. Within a couple of years housing estates were growing up along much of the route and at holiday times it became extremely congested.

Blackburn built a ring road around the north and east of the town, just inside the borough boundary. The road was virtually a new route, except for a short length east of the notoriously difficult junction with the A666 at Brownhills, where part of Bank Hey Lane was incorporated and reconstructed: the overall length was just over four miles. On this road, too, housing development began, but in most instances it was very wisely kept back from the main carriageway by the use of service roads – the contrast between the Preston ring road, with its numerous junctions and the comparatively uninterrupted sweep of the Blackburn ring road, is very obvious. The Preston ring road was not designed for future upgrading and no spare land was left – it thus remains largely single-carriageway, in contrast to the Blackburn ring road.

The Bolton ring road, built in stages during the 1920s and 1930s,

was intended to take heavy industrial traffic travelling between east Lancashire, Yorkshire and Liverpool, although its very indirect route meant that it did not entirely fulfil its potential. The seven-mile road was partly new construction, but it also incorporated several stretches of existing lane, which is the main reason for its winding alignment. Even before the First World War Burnley Corporation had been pressing the county council to build a new road from Parliament Street to Todmorden Road but, although included tentatively in the 'quick start' list of 1914, this never materialised. During the 1920s an eastern bypass linking the Todmorden road with the Nelson road was built, to be followed by a western route from Padiham Road (A671) to Rose Grove and thence to the A56 at Summit. Some of this was new construction: an extension beyond the borough boundary to the Todmorden road was proposed by Burnley in 1924 but not completed until the mid-1930s.

Rochdale built a four-mile ring road, using some new construction – characteristically named Kingsway and Queensway, which were very popular titles for new roads between the wars – and some upgrading of existing routes. Although Bury Corporation had plans for new roads little was done there before the Second World War apart from the

Laying the road foundations on the new Rossendale Road at Burnley, 12 September 1928, with the Boggart Bridge chimney in the background. The methods being employed differ little in essentials from those used by Telford well over a century before. Note the use of skips running on very light temporary tramways (*Lancashire County Library: Burnley Local Studies Collection*).

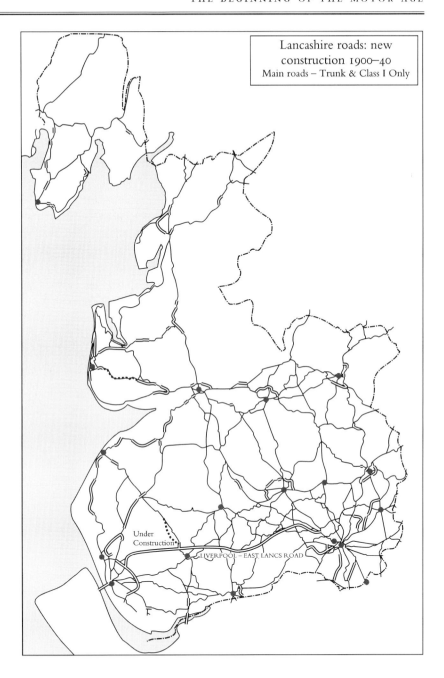

Lancashire roads: new
construction 1900–40
Main roads – Trunk & Class I Only

Under
Construction

LIVERPOOL – EAST LANCS ROAD

The construction of
new roads in Lanca-
shire, 1900–1940

building of a link from Manchester Road (A56), over a new Irwell
bridge, to Springs Road, Radcliffe (A668). This was a joint scheme
between the borough and the county council, which had different ideas
of what was desirable for a new road. Bury wanted a 70-foot overall
width and sett paving, while Lancashire pressed for a 60-foot tarmac
road. The government refused a grant until the differences were resolved

and eventually Lancashire conceded – for an unemployment relief project setts were preferable, as they were labour-intensive. The new road bypassed a winding section of the existing route but it was never classified and did not become part of a more comprehensive scheme.

Oldham did not try to build a ring road but instead constructed a north-south relief road, the new 4½-mile long Broadway from the A627 Rochdale Road via Chadderton to the A62 Manchester Road in Failsworth, completed in 1929. At one stage Stockport Corporation proposed that the road should be extended to form an eastern bypass for Manchester, but this far-sighted suggestion was not pursued.

The traffic problems of Warrington in the early 1920s were particularly severe because there was only one bridge across the Mersey. Although the bridge itself was rebuilt in 1915 it remained badly congested, while in the very centre of the town there was conflict between traffic passing north to south on the A49 and east to west on the A57, which until the opening of the East Lancashire Road was the main route from Manchester to Liverpool. Within the borough boundary a partial ring road was built: from the A49 at Longford north of the town it used older roads as far as the A57 Manchester Road. A new road, Kingsway North, was then constructed to link with a new bridge over the Mersey and on, via Kingsway South, to the A50 Knutsford Road just short of the Manchester Ship Canal. However, no new crossing of the canal was provided and the swing bridge continued as a major bottle neck. The route was quickly surrounded by housing estates and this, together with the substandard alignment and incomplete route, meant that it was much less useful than its planners had intended.

THE COASTAL RESORTS

The schemes described above were intended mainly for commercial traffic and to relieve town centre congestion. In the west of the county, however, traffic problems developed rapidly during the 1920s because of the increased use of private cars, buses and charabancs for leisure trips. The roads to the west coast had never been turnpiked and as a result, even where adopted as main roads, were in no condition to meet traffic demands. The improvement of access to the three main Lancashire resorts – Morecambe, Blackpool and Southport – was therefore a county council priority from the 1920s until work stopped in 1939.

The new road from Lancaster to Morecambe (A589), an early unemployment relief scheme, is noted above. In 1929 plans were drawn up for another new route, from the northern end of Morecambe Promenade to the A6 at Bolton-le-Sands. This, too, was built as an

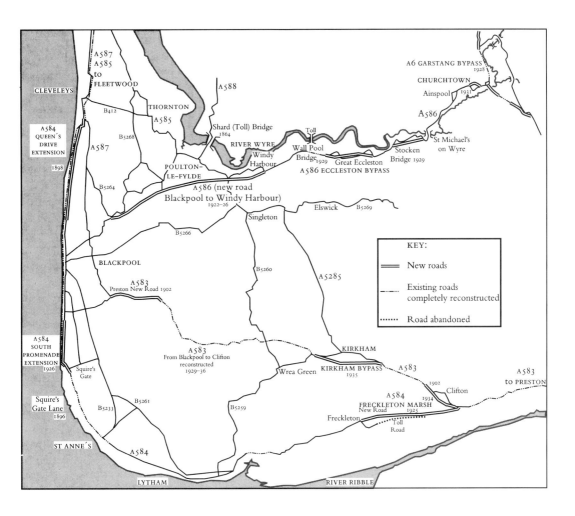

Improving the roads
to the Fylde coast,
1890–1940

unemployment project, with 75 per cent of the cost being met by a government grant under the Unemployment (Relief Works) Act of 1920. Morecambe & Heysham Council carried out the scheme, which was conditional on the employment of 'distressed labourers' from elsewhere in the county.

Blackpool, as the greatest of the coastal resorts, had the most serious traffic problems. Improvements to the Garstang road, giving access from the north, were being planned well before the First World War and a new road to Poulton-le-Fylde was included in the 1914 list of possible unemployment schemes. The road was eventually started in 1922 and was extended to Singleton, Larbreck and Windy Harbour in 1926 to form a bypass for Poulton. Great Eccleston and Churchtown village were bypassed in 1937–8 and other improvements were made during the 1930s. The Blackpool–Garstang road was upgraded in sections, with

233

separate stretches of road being dealt with as and when the opportunity arose.

This was in very marked contrast to the work being undertaken, at the same time, on the Preston to Blackpool road. This, much the busiest route to Blackpool, was particularly narrow and winding, with extreme congestion in the villages and towns through which it passed – notably Kirkham. In February 1924 a conference between Blackpool Corporation and the county resulted in agreement on upgrading, but although various widenings and diversions were put in hand at Plumpton, Newton and Ashton the grant support was not agreed with the government until 1928. At this point it was decided that a comprehensive three-year programme to reconstruct the whole road was necessary. This was a project second only to the East Lancashire Road in scale and involved bypasses of Clifton and Kirkham with major widening and realignment throughout the remainder of the route.

Widening work began in February 1929 and the Kirkham bypass was started, after financial restraints had delayed the project, in 1933. Grants of up to 75 per cent were paid, although the road was not classified as a trunk route until 1946. The 11½ miles of 40-foot carriageway was completed in 1936: because the county had planned for an overall width of 60-feet no cycle tracks or dual carriageway were provided – the absence of the latter has since been a major cause of concern on safety grounds, since this road is now, to use the American terminology, an 'undivided highway', with four fast lanes of traffic and no central reservation. The winding alignment and, in particular, the very large number of junctions throughout the route from Preston to Blackpool mean that this road now falls well short of modern design standards. The huge growth in traffic on this route is indicated by the table below:

Traffic tonnage
(3 day average counts)

Year	1911	1913	1922	1925	1928	1935
Tons	799	1,368	7,212	15,039	19,914	32,281

Southport, too, was approached by narrow winding roads passing through congested towns and villages. Conscious of the need to improve access, Southport Corporation was particularly active in pressing for new roads during the early 1920s but on its own initiative could build only within the borough boundary. It constructed Preston New Road, the fine wide approach to the town from the east, which bypassed Churchtown and pointed out towards county territory, but in August 1924 the county council declared that it did not consider a new arterial road from the Preston direction to be justified by the traffic figures.

Later, in the early 1930s, this view was reversed and work began on a series of new roads and diversions between Tarleton and Crossens, bypassing Mere Brow. The later sections were built to full late–1930s standards of road design, with dual carriageways, cycle tracks and footways, whereas the earlier sections were less advanced – the contrast between the three-lane road westwards from the Tarleton crossroads and the generously-proportioned stretches nearer to Southport is still very apparent. Work was in an advanced state when the building restrictions of November 1939 were imposed so completion was permitted, but the final stretch, from Banks to the Southport boundary, was deferred until the early 1960s.

Southport Corporation also built Waterloo Road and Lulworth Road, linking Lord Street with the old Liverpool Road in Ainsdale. Beyond the borough boundary, however, the road to Liverpool degenerated into a country lane, which was extremely indirect and had many right-angled bends. Notwithstanding this, it was not until February 1937 that the county council began work on a new 4½-mile road bypassing Formby. This was designed to the latest standards – 120-feet wide, with concrete dual carriageways, cycle tracks and footpaths. It opened in October 1938 and was said to be the longest continuous dual carriageway in the county.

The road from Southport to Ormskirk and Rainford was also in need of upgrading. It was very attractive to weekend and holiday traffic, not only from St Helens and the south but also (after 1934) from the Manchester area via the East Lancashire Road. Southport Corporation, as part of its vigorous road-building policy, constructed Scarisbrick New Road within the borough, but the county council was content to make small-scale piecemeal improvements to the road thence to Ormskirk. This policy perpetuated the very substandard alignment of this road – the unbypassed villages of Pinfold and Scarisbrick suffer the consequences today. South of Ormskirk the road was widened in 1938 from Scarth Hill to Bickerstaffe and Rainford U.D.C. asked that a bypass of that village should be constructed as a matter of urgency. As there were other problems on the road, particularly a bad bend at the 'Bottle and Glass Brow' south of Rainford, the county prepared a scheme for a completely new road from Bickerstaffe to the East Lancashire Road at Windle. Work began in February 1939, concentrating on the Rainford bypass section.

Although good progress was made the work was not sufficiently advanced to be exempted from the wartime building restrictions and in spring 1941 it was suspended. The War Department requisitioned the completed section in 1943 for the storage and repair of military vehicles including tanks, while the Ministry of Supply took land on the southern section for a cotton store. The road was derequisitioned in 1946 and the government paid over £50,000 to compensate for damage caused by tanks and other wartime use. After the war several houses near Windle which were on the line of the new road were required for emergency housing and the design was altered to allow them to remain, rather oddly, on a widened central reservation.

In April 1946 the whole A570 route became a trunk road and the county council urged the Ministry of Transport to complete the road in order – a familiar plea – to relieve unemployment in the Liverpool area. A fresh problem then arose: the shortage of cement threatened to delay the project. James Drake, the county surveyor, persuaded the ministry to modify the original design, which had involved ten-inch thick reinforced concrete, and substitute two four-inch layers of broken stone with bituminous topping, all on a nine-inch base of burnt colliery shale. This was a revival of the macadam method of construction used on the turnpike roads a century and a half before! The road was formally opened on 13 December 1950.

ACCIDENTS AND SAFETY

As road traffic grew in volume and speeds increased, the number of accidents rose sharply. In the first years of the century accidents were still sufficiently rare to merit special mention in council minutes, but by the 1920s they had become very frequent and statistics were produced to illustrate the seriousness of the problem. In the year 1936–7, for example, the county council recorded a total of 6,253 incidents within its police area (the administrative county together with the borough of Bury). There were 282 deaths including fifty-eight pedal cyclists and 133 pedestrians. The 5,980 non-fatal injuries included 2,397 involving pedal cyclists and 1,969 to pedestrians. This was, however, lower than in the worst years, 1933–5: the fall, which continued thereafter, was probably attributable to improved road safety education, safer new roads and the beginning of comprehensive traffic regulation.[38]

The Road Traffic Act 1934 introduced the mandatory speed limit of 30 m.p.h. on roads in built-up areas, which were defined as areas where the street lighting was not more than 200 yards apart. The system was flexible, as it still is – a highway authority could by direction de-restrict sections of such roads or, alternatively, deem other roads to be built up. The Act took effect on 18 March 1935 and was applied forthwith to all illuminated roads in the county administrative area. Another step towards improved safety was the painting of white lines. In November 1925 the Ministry of Transport approved these for use on dangerous bends and the highway authorities in Lancashire began the protracted process of introducing this now universal feature. Automatic traffic control signals – better known as traffic lights – were also introduced in the late 1920s. The first submission by the county council for a 60 per cent government grant was in response to a request from

Stretford U.D.C. for a set of lights at the junction of Chester Road (A56), Edge Lane and King Street.

RIBBON DEVELOPMENT AND BUILDING LINES

The problem of residential and other development along the frontages of existing and new roads has already been mentioned. Ribbon development drastically reduced the effectiveness of new roads, by recreating the problems of congestion, numerous access points and lack of space for improvements which the roads had been designed to avoid. The Ormskirk bypass, built through open country in the 1920s, was well within the built-up area ten years later and much of its value was lost. The 1925 Public Health Act empowered local authorities to define 'building lines', in an attempt to ensure that future development did not creep too close to the road edge and hence increase the cost of, or preclude, future widening. The Road Improvement Act of the same year allowed them to designate 'improvement lines' on main roads which might require major work in the future – in other words, to reserve land and protect it from development. The list of the first roads in Lancashire so defined reflects the priorities in the highway programme. It includes the roads from Preston to Blackpool, Liverpool and Southport and from Southport to Liverpool and Ormskirk.

Eventually over two hundred miles of road were protected under these Acts, but since detailed plans had to be prepared to justify designation the workload on the surveyors' department was considerable – even though many of the projects were not implemented for many years. The effects of these restrictions and of reserving land for future projects were often apparent in housing developments of the 1930s, where garden fences were set back and an area of 'no man's land' existed up to the carriageway edge. The A57 at Bruche, east of Warrington, was a classic and very long-lived, example.

In 1934 Lancashire County Council complained to the government about the effects of ribbon development. Planning powers to control this undesirable phenomenon were limited, although some refusals were upheld at inquiries. Eventually, pressure from highway and planning authorities and amenity bodies resulted in the passing of the 1935 Restriction of Ribbon Development Act, which stated that no new access could be made onto any road classified before 17 May 1935, nor any building erected within 220 feet of the middle of the road, without the consent of the highway authority. The restrictions also applied to any road which might be built in the future. The county Highways and Bridges Committee wisely considered the Planning Sub-Committee to be best suited to deal with the expected applications:

by March 1936 405 applications had been received and by February 1937 the number exceeded 1,700.[39]

The 1935 Act was of tremendous importance for highway design and town planning and had a dramatic impact upon the problem. The differences between the road schemes built in the years after 1935, which generally function effectively as uninterrupted through routes and those – such as the ring roads in Bolton and Burnley or the Ormskirk bypass – where adjacent development was uncontrolled, are very obvious today. Indirectly, too, the Act helped in the protection and preservation of the rural landscape, for no longer was there a serious danger of rural roads being lined with development only one house deep.

The rural roads themselves were subject to improvement, however. After 1926 the Ministry of Transport was prepared to make grants of 20 per cent for strengthening and widening of the more important unclassified roads, to meet the needs of the mechanically-propelled traffic now using them. In some cases these were former 'secondary roads' which were still receiving 25 per cent grants from the county council. The urban spread in south-east Lancashire has now obliterated much of the network of lanes, but in the north and west of the county the results of the improvements of the 1920s and 1930s can still be recognised. For example, in the Fylde and Lonsdale, where hedgerows have not been completely eradicated, the hedge on one side of a lane may be irregular, with abrupt changes of direction and contain mature trees and a variety of shrub species. The opposite hedge may have a smooth alignment, following the road edge, be devoid of truly mature trees and contain only one or two species of shrub. This is the consequence of early road-widening, whereby one side of the original road was realigned but the other remained untouched.

THE EARLY YEARS OF THE MOTOR CAR:

A RETROSPECT

This chapter has been primarily concerned with the impact of mechanical transport on former turnpike roads, which had been designed only for horse-drawn traffic. Initially there were problems because of the great increase in vehicle weight and especially from the use of traction engines. As well as producing conflicts between the owners and the local authorities, this traffic made it necessary to lay stronger and more durable road surfaces, with particular emphasis upon sett paving on the busier roads and in towns. This trend was accelerated by the introduction of trams, which encouraged urban sprawl and ribbon development. In Liverpool pioneering attempts were made to design new roads incorporating tramway reservations.

238

The increasing speed of traffic and especially that of the light motor car with its rubber tyres, damaged waterbound macadam surfaces. The resultant dust problem encouraged the introduction of tar spraying and by the 1930s tarmac surfaces were becoming general. Motor lorries were very numerous after the First World War and at first appeared to take highway authorities by surprise, but the high levels of unemployment in the early 1920s and the financial support offered by central government led to the construction of improved or completely new roads for industrial and leisure traffic, culminating in the East Lancashire Road, the rebuilding of the main road to Blackpool and the construction of the Mersey Tunnel. In Lancashire the local authorities showed great initiative in planning and designing such schemes, although most of the ring roads which they built fall well short of modern specifications.

Then, as now, progress in public works was uneven. The early 1930s were a time of severe recession and tight financial restrictions, which delayed many schemes so that they were still in progress or being planned when war broke out. Some were then stopped, only to be resumed at the end of the 1940s, while others were never started. By that time the highway authorities in Lancashire were thinking not in terms of small-scale improvement but of radical change – the planning of motorways was in progress.

The postwar development of motorways, in which Lancashire was the pioneer, has perhaps tended to overshadow the engineering achievements of the inter-war years. The evolution, in little more than twenty years, from rough setts and waterbound macadam to asphalted main roads and tarmac even on rural roads was as great a change as that implemented by the turnpike trusts. Many of the new roads, ring roads and coastal routes built between the wars are in use today almost unaltered, coping with changes in vehicles and traffic density which were inconceivable in the 1930s, just as the road traffic of the 1930s was unimaginable only fifty years earlier. By 1939 there was hardly any horse dung on the streets and that was a dramatic change!

7

The Motorway Era

INTRODUCTION

S INCE the end of the Second World War the roads of Lancashire
have seen changes incomparably greater in scale and impact than
any which have gone before – beside these developments even the
Roman roads and the turnpikes seem modest. As elsewhere in the
country, this change and the huge growth in private and commercial
traffic which is inextricably linked with it, have been the subject of
much debate. The implications for the role of public and private
transport, for environmental evaluation and protection and for land use
planning, may well be seen as an equally important and crucial phase
in the evolution of transport networks.

Lancashire's place in the history of British roads during the late
twentieth century is assured, irrespective of the long-term judgments
about what happened over that period. Britain's first motorway was
built in Lancashire, as part of the country's first detailed road building
strategy and many techniques of design and construction which orig-
inated there were soon to become commonplace. Although not as
complete as some had hoped, the motorway network which developed
in the county by the mid-1970s was more comprehensive than that in
any other part of Britain.

One man dominates the story between the late 1940s and the early
1970s. In 1945 James Drake was appointed county surveyor and bridgemaster of Lancashire, a post he was to hold for twenty-seven years. Born
in Accrington, a graduate of Manchester University, he had held a number
of appointments with local authorities in the north west and, as a dedicated
Lancastrian, began the task of providing an adequate highway network
to meet the needs of his native county, following the years of neglect
during the war. At that time the emphasis was on planning for the future
and in 1947 the county council accepted his suggestion that a road plan
should be prepared, which could be incorporated in the forthcoming
county development plan. The road plan would cover the existing
highway network within the area of the administrative county and would
include recommendations for improvement, the estimated cost of the
proposals and a programme of works to be undertaken.

Within the geographical county there were at that time eighteen county boroughs, such as Barrow-in-Furness, Manchester and Preston, whose councils were highway authorities in their own right. The plan could not, therefore, be fully comprehensive, but needed to take into account traffic movement in and out of those areas. At the outset certain basic principles were established. It was considered that for the road system to be described as 'adequate' it must allow its users to move economically, at a generally acceptable speed and under conditions of maximum safety. It was recognised that, in a period of financial restraint which was likely to continue for some time, there would be no point in adopting an idealistic approach, with every possible road scheme included.

The principal types of traffic movement were carefully analysed – that passing through the county on long distance journeys, cross-border movements to and from points within the county and traffic movement within Lancashire. The results showed that the existing road network was, despite the improvements of the 1930s, quite unable to cope effectively with all these movements. It was also clear that the situation would deteriorate further as the volume of traffic increased. Considerable lengths of main road were continuously lined with property, in a form of ribbon development, with unrestricted access causing frequent stoppages and low speeds. There were a number of notorious bottlenecks, particularly where main traffic routes converged, and congestion was endemic, especially at peak times.

Many roads were too narrow even for pre-war traffic volumes. In the built-up areas widening was considered to be impossible because of the high cost of acquiring property. Elsewhere, the policy of providing dual carriageways had already been established and in 1938 it was decided that 434 miles of single carriageway should be upgraded to that standard. By the start of the war, however, there were only nineteen miles of dual carriageway road within the county. Features such as poor sight lines, sharp bends with little or no super-elevation and narrow bridges, were major causes of accidents. Inadequate or non-existent footways, indiscriminate parking on the carriageways of main traffic routes and the absence of lay-bys for public service vehicles, all created potential hazards. The frequency of night-time accidents pointed to the need for improved street lighting. It was clear that the situation would deteriorate further as the volume of traffic increased.

In developing the plan several assumptions had to be made. Firstly, it was considered that, apart from the addition of a limited number of national routes, the country would not be able to afford to spend significantly more on roads than in the immediate pre-war period. In that context, the expenditure on the roads of Lancashire should be an

equitable proportion of the national roads budget. Secondly, the improvements and new construction would be completed in thirty years.
Thirdly, the volume of traffic throughout the country would reach a
peak in twenty years' time and would then be approximately double
that of 1938.

The minor roads in the county were in reasonable condition and,
as the cost of these roads was largely borne by the local authorities
concerned, it was considered that the future level of expenditure should
be based on that incurred in 1938–9. The trunk, class I and class II
roads were, however, a different matter. They had to bear the brunt
of heavy through traffic and it was felt that their importance warranted
the adoption of a fairer system of funding than hitherto. Lancashire,
with its heavy industries and popular holiday resorts, had to cater for
a weight of traffic quite out of proportion to the mileage of its main
road system. It was therefore contended that resources should be
allocated according to population as well as road mileage.

In deciding on the design standards to be applied in implementing
the road plan it was recognised that, if these were to be too generous,
the costs would rise sharply but the additional benefits would not be
commensurately increased. It was felt that, as the urgency of the traffic
problems was so great, it was preferable to achieve an adequate standard
on as much as possible of the system, rather than to concentrate on
obtaining a much higher standard on only a limited mileage of road.

At that time, basic standards for rural roads and some pre-war census
data were all the guidance which was available. In later years, when
highway engineers were subjected to the issuing of an abundance of
government circulars and guidance notes, it was difficult to appreciate
that, in the mid-1940s, there was very little information on, for example,
the capacities of urban roads and the design requirements for achieving
a higher standard of safety. Terms such as 'traffic engineering' and
'transportation planning' were not yet part of the language – at least
on this side of the Atlantic.

The intention was that the road plan should not only contain
proposals for an improved road network, but also that it should be a
practical working document. A great deal of traffic data was therefore
collected, from which projections of future traffic flows and urban road
capacities were made. This enabled the future network to be defined
on a basis of three categories of traffic routes.

The first category comprised twelve express routes with dual carriageways, totalling 217 miles in length. Ninety-four miles would be
to motorway standard and all these routes were chosen to attract the
highest possible volumes of traffic. They included the north–south
motorway and the Liverpool–Manchester–Yorkshire route, both of
which had been included in a ten-year construction programme of

THE MOTORWAY ERA

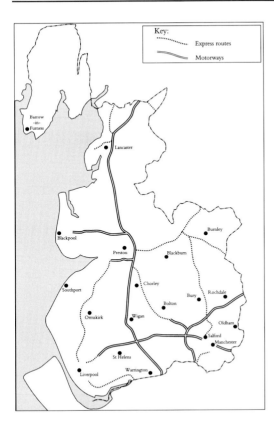

The 1949 *Road Plan for Lancashire*: proposed motorways and express routes.

national routes announced by the Minister of Transport in 1946. Among other roads in this category were the western sector of the Manchester Outer Ring Road and the routes between Liverpool, Preston and Yorkshire, Manchester and Preston and Manchester, Bury, Accrington and Whalley.

The function of the 409 miles of road in the second category was to connect the large towns to the express routes, or to give fast inter-urban links. Approximately half the length was to be dual carriageway, with the proposed links from the north–south motorway to Blackpool and Morecambe constructed as motorways.

The routes required for through movements of lesser importance formed the third category. They were to connect smaller towns to the major road network or to larger towns and it was decided that this need could be satisfied largely by the existing classified roads, with only limited new construction. Only eighteen of the 282 miles in this category were to have dual carriageways.

Of the 908 miles of road in the three categories, one-third would be new. The existing network comprised 1189 miles of trunk, class I and class II roads, only half of which were to be included in the revised system, with the remainder declining in importance and becoming local in character.

In order that the new and improved roads should be as safe as possible, a major pioneering research programme was undertaken. By analysing the accidents which had occurred at numerous junctions, a new understanding was obtained of how different layouts, traffic controls and other features affected the number and types of accident. As a result, firm guidance was given regarding the design requirements for improvements to existing junctions and the layout of new ones. The research also showed how accidents were related to the main features of a road, such as the visibility at bends and junctions, speed limits, street lighting, pedestrian crossings and the provision of cycle tracks. Using this information, it was possible to forecast the accident savings which could be achieved for each scheme within the proposed network, as an element in establishing its economic justification.

By applying the standards of layout and design which had been thus determined, the cost of the proposals was assessed. With the exclusion of the cost of the north–south motorway and the Liverpool–Manchester–Yorkshire route, which it was considered should be met by the government, the estimated expenditure on the roads within the three categories amounted to £146.9 million. With the addition of a sum of £12 million for the improvement of the other 2748 miles of road within the county, the total estimate for the work required was £158.9 million. No attempt was made to assess the priority of the various schemes but it was recognised that, in due course, some form of cost/benefit analysis would have to be applied.

Although the plan concentrated on the need for new and improved roads as a means of reducing congestion and the number of accidents, it also recommended policies for road maintenance and for dealing with the many and varied problems associated with the 2060 existing highway bridges. By making additional provision for the implementation of these policies, the total estimated cost of the proposals in the plan amounted to £170.9 million. On the assumption that the existing system of grants from the Ministry of Transport would continue throughout the thirty-year period of the plan, it was calculated that the net annual expenditure to be borne by the county council would be £1.74 million.

In 1949 the *Road Plan for Lancashire* was approved by the county council and the various proposals were included in the county *Development Plan*. This enabled future land use to be controlled, firstly by establishing improvement lines for those existing roads which required widening and realignment and secondly by protecting 'corridors of interest' for the proposed new roads. In due course the *Development Plan* was accepted by the government and therefore, in effect, the road plan of 1949 received the general approval of the Ministry of Transport. However, because of the large financial commitment involved the ministry, not unexpectedly, did not endorse it in its entirety.

The road plan was, however, of the greatest importance because not only did it form the basis of highway strategies in Lancashire for more than thirty years, but also many of the procedures which were developed in its preparation were subsequently adopted nationally. In particular, it contained what was probably the most comprehensive and well-researched practical advice available at that time on the principles of safe highway design. In recognition of this new expertise a traffic engineering section was established within the county council, probably the first of its kind in Britain. The pursuit of safety on the county's roads was unrelenting and in the mid-1960s a computer system was set up to record and analyse accidents on all main roads, in order that early remedial action could be taken at 'blackspots'.

ADMINISTRATION AND FINANCE

The system of highway administration and finance was outlined in the previous chapter. The Trunk Roads Act of 1936 had transferred to the minister the responsibility for the major national routes and in 1946 a further Act extended the mileage of such roads in Lancashire to a total of 266 miles. With a few exceptions, none of the roads within the county boroughs was given trunk road status. This had the unfortunate effect of creating a situation whereby the standard and condition of a 'through' route could change dramatically at a county borough boundary. Also in 1946, the number of classes of road was increased by the introduction of a class III category, which qualified for a 50 per cent grant and the rate of grant for class I and class II roads was raised from 60 per cent and 50 per cent to 75 per cent and 60 per cent respectively.

As the highway authority for trunk roads the minister became entirely responsible for the cost of any work carried out on such routes. The maintenance and operational aspects, such as winter gritting and snow clearing, were undertaken by certain of the local highway authorities acting as the agents of the minister. Their costs were fully reimbursable and they received a fee for administration. Similar arrangements applied to improvements and new construction, subject to the local authority having the necessary staff resources and with a different scale of fees to cover the design costs. Within Lancashire the county council acted as the minister's agents for the major part of the trunk road network, the remainder being the subject of direct agency agreements with nineteen of the non-county borough and urban district councils.

Outside the county boroughs, the county council was the statutory highway authority for all of the 2052 miles of classified roads. Those non-county borough and urban district councils with a population of over 20,000 were, however, entitled to 'claim' the right to maintain these roads within their areas and certain of the other councils were given similar delegated authority by the county council. A total of ninety-six councils acted in this capacity in respect of 1058 miles of road.

With the exception of the unclassified roads, which were entirely financed from local revenue, the adequacy of the road network was to a large extent dependent upon the allocation of resources by central government, as a consequence of the funding arrangements. The local authorities could simply have adopted a low profile and left the initiative with the ministry, not only in respect of trunk road schemes but also as far as the improvement of the classified road network was concerned. Instead, however, they chose to adopt a positive approach, often by joint action and with local knowledge of the need and justification for

new and improved roads within the county and lost no opportunity
of submitting proposals to the ministry. Therefore it became the policy
of the county council to prepare selected schemes well in advance, so
that they could proceed quickly in the event of funds becoming
available.

The management of the various programmes was controlled by the
engineers within the Ministry of Transport at both national and regional
level. A good working relationship developed with the staff of the
various local authorities, on the basis that as professional engineers they
had a common interest in dealing with the serious traffic problems
which beset the county. They did, however, have different views on
traffic forecasts, which influenced the standards to be adopted in design
and construction. The local authority engineers tended to look a long
way ahead and to demand higher standards, whereas the ministry's
objective was to contain the cost of individual schemes, in order to
be able to undertake a greater number with the available funds.
Unfortunately, the insistence on applying this policy led, in some cases,
to problems which became apparent within only a few years of completion and these are referred to later.

There is no doubt that the concerted efforts of all the authorities in
Lancashire were, during the following three decades, instrumental in
developing a highway network which was the envy of the rest of the
country. One of the factors in this success was the formation of the
Road Construction Units (RCUs). Before 1967 the design and supervision of almost all the major trunk road schemes in Lancashire was
undertaken by the county council under the agency arrangements.
However, the ministry was responsible for all the statutory procedures
and for obtaining the necessary land. In the 1960s, as the programme
of trunk road construction expanded, it became apparent that to cope
with the increased workload a new organisation was needed. The
RCUs were based on a working partnership between the ministry and
the participating county councils in each of the six regions in England.
The first, that for the north west, was established in Preston in April
1967, with James Drake as its director, on secondment from the county
council, for an initial period of eighteen months.

The headquarters of the unit consisted of a small number of specialist
civil servants and county council staff and was primarily concerned
with the statutory procedures, financial control and the overall supervision and management of the programme. The design of the projects
and the day-to-day supervision of construction contracts were the
responsibility either of sub-units formed of experienced members of
staff from the participating counties together with a few seconded
ministry engineers, or of firms of consulting engineers. In the north west
the participating counties were Lancashire and Cheshire and in each

case the county surveyor acted as the chief engineer of the sub-unit. Whereas the earlier trunk road and motorway projects, such as the whole of the M6 through Lancashire, were undertaken by the county council as the minister's agent, later schemes became the responsibility of the RCU.

THE MOTORWAYS

The purpose of a motorway is to enable traffic to travel safely at relatively high speeds and therefore, in contrast to other types of road, various restrictions in its use must be applied. Pedestrians, pedal cycles, animals and certain classes of slow-moving motor vehicle, such as agricultural tractors and mopeds, are excluded and the public utilities may not lay mains and services. Access must be strictly controlled, with vehicles entering and leaving the motorway only at properly designed interchanges.

National plan for motorways put forward by the County Surveyors' Society in 1938.

Although Britain had lagged behind other countries in the construction of motorways, there were many who had advocated the principle of this type of road since the beginning of the century. Even the then prime minister, Arthur Balfour, had expressed the view that there was a case for highways constructed for rapid motor traffic and confined to that use.

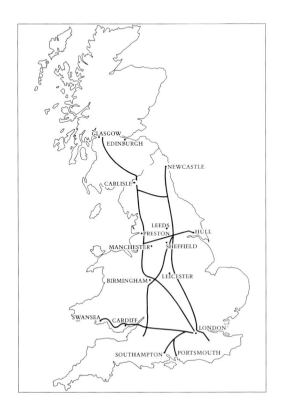

Nevertheless, it was not until the mid-1930s that serious proposals for a national system of motorways were published. The Institution of Highway Engineers (later to be renamed the Institution of Highways and Transportation) and the County Surveyors' Society both suggested motorway networks which included a north–south route through Lancashire. At the same time the county council, concerned at the increasing volume of traffic passing through the major urban areas of Warrington, Wigan, Preston and Lancaster, was giving detailed consideration to such a scheme. In 1937, therefore, it submitted to the Ministry of Transport a proposal for the construction of a motorway, sixty-two miles long, bypassing those towns.

The construction of the German *Autobahnen* was then in full swing and, although ostensibly intended to assist industry and alleviate the high rate of unemployment, their strategic military role was undoubtedly a crucial factor. This programme generated considerable interest in Britain and James Drake, who was then borough surveyor of Blackpool, joined a group known as the German Roads Delegation on a tour of inspection. It fired his enthusiasm, to the extent that in 1939 he recommended to his council, albeit unsuccessfully, that a proposed ring road of Blackpool should be constructed as a motorway. The Minister of Transport, Leslie Burgin, also visited Germany and must have been equally impressed, as he personally recommended that approval should be given to the scheme put forward by Lancashire County Council. Although the war precluded any positive action, the case for motorways had been established.

THE NORTH—SOUTH MOTORWAY (M6)

In 1946 the Minister of Transport published a map of his future road programme, which envisaged the construction of 800 miles of motorway within a ten-year period, including the north–south route through Lancashire. James Drake obtained the approval of the county council to proceed with preparation and preliminary design work for the new route, which was subsequently to be numbered M6. It was found that its basic alignment, as envisaged by the county council in 1937, was

The Ministry of Transport road programme announced in 1946.

still appropriate and only comparatively minor adjustments had to be made. It was recognised that in view of the economic situation at that time, the construction of a short section of the route which could be shown to be capable of producing an immediate benefit would have a far better chance of proceeding quickly than one of greater magnitude. Priority was therefore given to the 8¼ mile Preston bypass section, which would give relief to the conurbation by removing north–south through traffic from the A6.

In 1949 the Special Roads Act was passed, giving highway authorities powers to build roads with restricted access and laying down the formal statutory procedures, covering such matters as establishing the alignment, enabling alterations to be made to side roads and private means of access to land and property and compulsorily acquiring the land needed for construction. The process involved

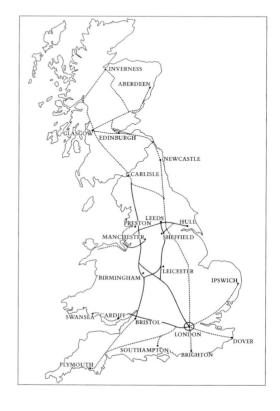

advertising the proposals and, in the event of any valid objections being unresolved, the minister was obliged to hold a public inquiry. The year 1953 was an important milestone, in that not only did the minister take the first step in the statutory procedures, but he also announced that construction of the Preston bypass was to be included in his expanded road programme, to commence in the 1956–57 financial year.

The county council, of course, gave its full support to the scheme and resolved to carry out the widest possible public consultation on the proposals. James Drake suggested that, rather than relying solely on drawings to illustrate the proposals, a large model should be constructed and, in order that the design programme should not be delayed, members of his staff, keen to see the project proceeding, agreed to build the model in their own time. At subsequent public meetings it was of major value in explaining the scheme. The route followed a line very close to the eastern edge of the built-up areas of Fulwood, Preston, Walton-le-Dale and Bamber Bridge, with only one farmhouse and three other dwellings directly affected. For many years a corridor to allow for the future construction of the motorway had been protected against development and in several instances housing estates had been built immediately adjoining its western boundary.

Following the advertising of the proposals, only a few formal objections were received and these were resolved by agreement. The minister was therefore able to confirm the various statutory orders without a public inquiry. This was quite remarkable, in the light of the vociferous opposition to similar proposals which was generated elsewhere in the country as motorway schemes became the subject of formalised and lengthy public inquiries, often disrupted by objectors not directly affected by the proposals. Part of the explanation lies in the fact that there was close personal involvement of members of the county council and of the county surveyor in the consultation process. As a result, those affected had full confidence that their interests would be properly considered, both in the detailed design of the works and during construction. Furthermore, the alignment of the new road had been defined and anticipated for over twenty years and therefore was no surprise.

It could be argued that, as there had been no previous experience of motorway construction in Britain, the public could not appreciate the full impact of the construction and use of a road of this magnitude. In consequence, those likely to be affected when other sections of the motorway came to be considered might have been inclined to raise strong objections. In the event, however, by adopting a similar approach, all the statutory procedures for the whole of the sixty-two miles of the M6 through the county were completed without difficulty. Only one public inquiry was held and at that the sole objector failed to appear at the hearing!

When the Preston by-pass opened in 1958 it had dual two-lane carriageways. This view, where the motorway cuts through the northern escarpment of the Ribble Valley, shows the wide central reservation which allowed for a third lane to be added in each direction. Concrete marginal strips mark the edge of the carriageways and the hard shoulder is unpaved *(Lancashire County Council Surveyors' Department).*

Based on experience of motorway construction and operation in Italy, Germany and the United States, various design principles had been established for use in Britain. Motorways would always have dual carriageways, each with either two or three traffic lanes depending on the estimated future traffic flow, separated by a central reservation. There would be no speed limit. Acceleration and deceleration lanes would be provided at interchanges, to enable traffic to enter and leave the motorway in safety. The alignment would have large radius curves and the carriageways would have easy gradients. There would be no raised kerbs and hard shoulders would be provided on the nearside of each carriageway for use in emergencies. Contrary to the recommendation of James Drake, the ministry decided that a 'positive' drainage system, using conventional gullies, would not be provided. Instead, surface water run-off would be collected in stone-filled trenches, known as 'french' drains, located either in the central reservation or behind the hard shoulders.

Earth-moving equipment excavating the 60-foot deep cutting through the northern escarpment of the Ribble Valley during the construction of the Preston bypass *(Lancashire County Council Surveyors' Department).*

At its southern end the bypass was to connect with the A6 at a roundabout close to its junction with the A49, enabling north–south traffic to and from both Manchester and Warrington to avoid the Preston area and designed to accommodate the future southward extension of the M6. At the other end it was also to connect with the A6, at a roundabout on the northern edge of Fulwood a mile west of the general alignment of the north–south route.

The major obstacles along the route were the valleys of the Darwen and the Ribble. Crossing these required major bridges and embankments and deep cuttings through the valley edges, to keep within the limiting gradient of 1 in 25 – the standard adopted for motorways in Britain. Through the northern escarpment of the Ribble valley a cutting sixty feet deep was required and it was anticipated that the excavated material would be used to form an adjoining embankment of equivalent height. At Samlesbury, where the A59 trunk road runs adjacent to the river, a 'partial-cloverleaf' interchange was to be provided.

The county surveyor, on the basis of his own traffic predictions, considered that the carriageways should be constructed with three lanes each, but for financial reasons the ministry insisted on two-lane carriageways only. It agreed, however, that the bypass should be designed with a wide central reservation to allow for the addition of a third traffic lane to each carriageway a later date. Such an operation could be carried out with minimum disruption and without the need for any structural alterations to bridges. James Drake was soon vindicated – traffic increased so quickly that the third lanes were constructed only eight years later!

There was no experience in the use of hard shoulders on British roads and a considerable reduction in cost was achieved because a hard

shoulder was not provided at overbridges and underbridges, where the risk of a vehicle breaking down and blocking a traffic lane was considered to be minimal. The form of construction was to be merely that of a hardened grass verge, but subsequently this was found to be quite inadequate for supporting a heavy vehicle, particularly if a jack had to be used for changing a wheel.

Lancashire had two main sources of material for road construction. In the south there were massive deposits of burnt red shale, which had been accumulated during many years of coal mining, while in the Clitheroe and Carnforth areas existing quarries produced high quality limestone aggregates, properly screened and graded to meet any specification. The form of carriageway construction was to be such that the fullest possible use was made of mechanical plant and the county council had therefore carried out several pilot projects in which a pre-mixed waterbound limestone macadam, to be known as 'wet-mix', was developed as a material for the base. As noted in the previous chapter, it was common practice in new road construction, particularly

The bridge carrying the M6 Preston by-pass across the River Ribble and the A59 at Samlesbury, photographed shortly after its opening in 1958. This was the first motorway bridge to be constructed in Britain (*Winter & Kidson, Preston*).

where major earthworks were involved, to defer the laying of the final surface until the carriageways had been subjected to traffic use. Initially, therefore, only a temporary surface was laid, so that any early deformation could be remedied before completion, thereby ensuring a high standard of running surface over an extended period.

In designing the Preston bypass it was decided that the carriageway construction should consist of a sub-base of burnt red shale, varying in thickness from twelve to thirty-six inches depending on ground conditions, followed by a nine-inch layer of 'wet-mix' and a surface consisting of a 2½-inch thick tarmacadam base course and a ¾-inch temporary wearing course. The final hot-rolled asphalt surfacing would be laid at a later date.

Twenty-two bridges were required, the choice of type and the materials of construction being determined by the engineering problems at each site and the need for their appearance to be in harmony with the surroundings. At Samlesbury, the three-span bridge over the Ribble and the A59 was designed as a steel box girder structure, a comparatively new form of construction. The interior surfaces of these boxes were to be painted and, in view of the fact that these surfaces were not exposed to the elements, consideration was given to methods by which the frequency of maintenance painting might be reduced. It was found that if the access manhole covers were properly sealed, the humidity of the interior of the boxes could be controlled by placing silica gel inside, thereby giving the paint treatment a much extended life. This became standard practice in future steel box girder structures. The other major bridge, carrying the bypass across the valley of the River Darwen, was of a more conventional design using multi-span welded steel plate girders.

The construction of the bypass began in June 1956, under the supervision of James Drake. Whereas separate contracts were awarded for the construction of the two major bridges, Tarmac Ltd. was appointed the main contractor for all the other works, with Leonard Fairclough Ltd. of Adlington, an old-established Lancashire firm, as the sub-contractor for the remaining twenty bridges. The contractors planned their operations for completion within the two year period allowed, on the assumption that the weather would be reasonable. Unfortunately, however, the work was severely disrupted by rain which continued almost without a break. It was known at the outset that the sub-soils were generally very poor, with a predominance of sandy clay. In one area this was known locally by the vivid term 'cow-belly' – an apt description! The exceptionally bad weather, which resulted in the contractors being granted a five-month extension of the time for completion, prevented the heavy earth-moving plant from operating satisfactorily and caused the loss of considerable quantities of excavated material. In normal circumstances this would have been suitable for embankment construction, but it had to be tipped off-site and replaced by imported fill.

Later road schemes generated a great deal of debate about the environment. On that first motorway extensive landscaping was carried out, not only within the boundaries of the road but also on adjoining land, acquired after negotiation with the owners, and in the areas where unsuitable excavated material had been tipped. This was followed by an extensive tree planting scheme and the provision of hedges along the motorway boundaries and in the central reservation. In order to reduce monotony for drivers, which had been reported as prevalent on motorways in other countries, the painting of bridge steelwork in different colours became the standard practice in Lancashire.

The ministry had decided that lighting was only needed at the Samlesbury interchange. However, towards the end of construction, when most of the lighting columns in the interchange had been erected, the minister visited the site. On viewing the interchange from the south escarpment of the Ribble valley he expressed concern at the effect on the surroundings of such a large number of columns in such a small area and immediately ordered their removal. Several years later, when it became apparent that lighting motorways could substantially reduce night-time accidents, the policy was changed and lighting was installed on some of the busier sections of motorway, including the Preston bypass. Safety considerations were, eventually, to outweigh environmental objections.

On 5 December 1958 the Preston bypass, Britain's first motorway, was opened to traffic. In view of the national importance of the event the ceremony was performed by the prime minister, Harold Macmillan and a granite plinth marking the occasion was erected at the Samlesbury interchange.

In January 1959, however, a small amount of frost damage affecting the carriageways occurred as a result of an exceptionally rapid thaw, when the temperature rose from 8°F to 43°F within a period of thirty-six hours. Since there was no speed limit on the motorway it was decided that, for safety reasons, it should be temporarily closed to enable remedial action to be taken. This situation had arisen primarily because of the exceptionally wet weather, which meant that there was still a high water table in the formation below the carriageways. As the hard shoulders were not paved and, therefore, were permeable, surface water run-off was able to drain directly into the formation, thereby exacerbating the problem. Furthermore, the burnt red shale used in the sub-base had not been screened or graded and, where it contained an excess of fine material, capillary action took place, drawing ground water to the surface. In the circumstances, the thin temporary surface of the carriageways proved to be inadequate to resist the effect of the freeze/thaw cycle when subjected to heavy traffic.

Apart from local repairs to the carriageway, immediate steps were taken to improve the drainage system as part of the remedial works and the final four-inch thick surface of hot-rolled asphalt was laid within twelve months, much earlier than originally intended. In 1963 the hard shoulders were reconstructed and paved, their distinctive red surface giving a contrasting colour as an aid to drivers. In the next few years further improvements were made. The hedge in the central reservation, which had been planted to prevent dazzle from the head-lights of oncoming vehicles and as part of the landscaping, had suffered from the salting of the road in winter and was removed. In its place a safety barrier was erected to prevent out-of-control vehicles crossing from the opposing carriageway and the edge-marking of the carriage-ways was improved by laying plastic white lines to give a better definition than the original concrete marginal strip.

The appearance of this first section of motorway therefore changed considerably as it was improved to a standard comparable with later designs, but the lack of continuity in the hard shoulders remained as a deficiency which could not easily be remedied. It was never envisaged that they would be used for purposes other than emergency parking. However, on later sections of motorway with continuous hard shoulders it was found that, when a breakdown or accident occurred and traffic was brought to a halt, the hard shoulders could be used by emergency vehicles trying to reach the scene. Of equal, or even greater, importance, they could be used as additional traffic lanes when it was necessary to close the normal running lanes for maintenance purposes. Without this facility, the situation on the Preston bypass was a continuing source of difficulty for the maintenance engineers and the emergency services.

Many of the bridges had been subjected to test loading before the bypass was opened and much valuable information was obtained on their performance. However, following several failures during the construction of box girder bridges in Britain and abroad during the late 1960s, national concern was expressed at the adequacy of this type of design. Temporary lane closures were therefore applied to all such bridges, including that at Samlesbury, until an independent check had been carried out. It was found, however, that Samlesbury Bridge was one of the few which did not require any strengthening.

The temporary closure of the bypass in January 1959 led to much criticism, which failed to recognise that, under a financial regime which emphasised maximum economy in design and construction of a type of road new to Britain, it was probably inevitable that problems would arise, from which lessons could be learned. The designs of further sections of motorway then being prepared were revised to include

The bridge carrying the Lancaster bypass of the M6 over the River Lune, at Halton east of Lancaster. This impressive structure is unfortunately not seen by the motorway user *(Castle Cement, Clitheroe).*

stronger carriageways with materials of a higher specification and to allow for the laying of the permanent surface in the initial construction. 'Positive' drainage was to be provided and the construction of the hard shoulders improved. This, of course, meant that the cost per mile for comparable motorways was substantially increased and was well in excess of that for the Preston bypass, even after its remedial works and subsequent reconstruction were included. Despite its problems, the construction of the bypass undoubtedly gave good value for money.

The construction of the Lancaster bypass section of the M6, the county council's second priority, had followed a year after the work on the Preston section had started and in many respects it was similar. It would bypass Lancaster on the eastern side, with connections to the A6 at each end and would have dual two-lane carriageways with a wide central reservation for later widening. However, because of the close proximity of the Carnforth quarries, the sub-base was to be in limestone. In 1955 the minister announced that he had included it in the construction programme and work started in July 1957.

The bypass was 11½ miles long and it was not intended to provide an intermediate interchange. However, this would have made access for emergency vehicles very difficult. The only road of any importance crossed by the bypass was the A683, leading from Lancaster north-eastwards along the Lune valley and, as the nearest emergency services were based in the city, it was decided that a connection should be provided for their use only. The design standards of this junction would therefore be lower than those of a normal interchange, with the carriageways on the slip roads separated only by double white lines. Subsequently, however, representations were made for the junction to be opened for general use and this was eventually agreed. The result is a unique example of a sub-standard interchange on a British motorway.

The major obstacle along the line of the bypass was the River Lune. The design chosen for the 400-foot long bridge at Halton incorporated a reinforced concrete fixed arch with a clear span of 230 feet and a rise of forty-four feet. Because of their width, bridges carrying motorways are normally designed in two halves with a narrow gap in between. In constructing an arch, massive temporary support is necessary. The contractor therefore built a temporary timber gantry across the river to carry the scaffold and shuttering for the first half. This was later lowered slightly, winched sideways as a complete unit on to a second gantry, raised to its correct level and used to form the second arch. The bridge is a very impressive structure, in an attractive setting, of which the users of the motorway are unfortunately not aware.

Work was well advanced when the problems of the Preston bypass became apparent, but immediate steps were taken to improve the design. The Lancaster bypass was opened to traffic in April 1960 and within the next few years the hard shoulders were paved and the third lanes were added.

In June 1958, while the Preston and Lancaster bypasses were under construction, the route of the twenty-seven miles of motorway between Thelwall and Preston was confirmed. Two major bridges were required

Thelwall Viaduct, carrying the M6 over the Mersey and the Manchester Ship Canal, was built between 1959 and 1963. At that time it was the longest motorway bridge in Britain *(Lancashire County Council Surveyors' Department)*.

– the thirty-six span Thelwall Bridge (commonly known as the Thelwall Viaduct), over the Manchester Ship Canal and the River Mersey and the six-span Gathurst viaduct across the Douglas valley west of Wigan. Because of their size and complexity an early start on their construction was vital and work began in September 1959. This was one of the earliest examples of the system of 'advance works' in motorway construction, a practice which became generally accepted as a means of dealing with particularly difficult obstacles.

Thelwall Viaduct is 4,414 feet long and rises to a height of ninety-three feet above the ship canal. It was of sufficient width to accommodate dual three-lane carriageways and a central reservation but, in order to reduce the cost of the structure, hard shoulders were not provided. This proved to be the cause of accidents when vehicular breakdowns blocked the running lanes and is a source of serious traffic problems when lanes are closed during maintenance operations.

Ground conditions were particularly difficult, with soft alluvial deposits over the whole of the site. The land between the canal and the river had been used for the disposal of canal dredgings and was overlaid by a layer of silt some forty-five feet deep. In consequence, the reinforced concrete piers, which varied in height from thirty to eighty feet, had to be carried on piles up to 130 feet in length, to provide a satisfactory foundation. The superstructure consists of steel plate girders supporting a reinforced concrete slab deck. The erection of the girders in the 336-foot main span across the canal had to be undertaken without affecting shipping, which included ocean-going vessels of up to 12,000 tons and the contractors completed this difficult operation by cantilevering the girders from each side of the crossing. When opened to traffic in July 1963 this was the longest motorway bridge in Britain.

The main works, which included a further seventy-nine bridges of various designs, began in February 1961. The contractor was a consortium of two north-west firms, Sir Alfred MacAlpine & Son Ltd. of Cheshire and Leonard Fairclough Ltd. Although other national firms of contractors were involved in the programme of construction within the county, this consortium, with its local background and experience, was to be successful in winning many of the later motorway contracts.

Early site investigations had identified a wide variety of soil conditions, with clays of varying plasticity, soft and hard grey shales, dry and very wet sands, peat, sandstone and even coal, all of which required different forms of treatment. For nineteen miles the motorway passed through mining areas and in several places the seams were exposed during construction. Some 13,000 tons of good quality coal were excavated and handed over to the National Coal Board, which had rights of ownership. Unrecorded shallow mine-workings were also found and, depending on their depth, were either back-filled or

Broughton interchange on the M6 north of Preston provided a connection to the A6 in Fulwood. It was designed to accommodate the future M55 serving the Fylde Coast towns and was the first three-level interchange in Britain when it opened to traffic in January 1965 *(Lancashire County Council Surveyors' Department)*.

protected by reinforced concrete slabs, as were many old mine shafts, some up to 900 feet deep. Future subsidence was expected over a length of almost ten miles and the carriageways, drainage systems and eight bridges were designed to cater for up to thirteen feet of settlement.

In contrast to the Preston and Lancaster bypasses, a stronger form of carriageway construction was adopted with, in general, a base of 6½-inches of cement-bound granular material overlaid with 3½-inches of dense bitumen-bound macadam. However, in the areas likely to be affected by subsidence, the bitumen-bound material was used for the full depth, to give greater flexibility. The Thelwall to Preston section of the M6 was opened to traffic in July 1963 and included, at Charnock Richard, Lancashire's first motorway service area.

Work on the 13½ miles of motorway linking the Preston and Lancaster bypasses began in September 1962. With no intermediate interchanges, it was to be the longest stretch between junctions on a British motorway at that time. The route closely followed the West Coast main line railway and, south of Garstang and within a corridor less than half a mile wide, there are now these two modern transportation facilities, as well as the old A6 and the Lancaster Canal. The southern interchange, at Broughton, had to cater for the future M55 serving the Fylde Coast. A conventional two-level layout with a roundabout would not have allowed continuous flow between the two motorways and so a three-level interchange was designed. It was the first of its kind in Britain and included the impressive eleven-span Fylde Junction Higher Bridge, 1300 feet in length.

Snowhill Lane bridge at Scorton on the Preston–Lancaster section of the M6. The stylish and innovative design of bridges such as this, which received a Civic Trust Award, was a feature of the county's motorways *(Lancashire County Council Surveyors' Department)*.

Tenders had been invited for different types of carriageway construction and the lowest, which was accepted, provided for twelve miles of the length to have dual three-lane concrete carriageways. The 10½-inches thick reinforced slab was to have a lower layer of concrete 7½-inches thick, using limestone aggregate and a top layer with granite aggregate to give a high skid resistance. The contractor adopted various methods unique to Britain by employing items of specially imported equipment to form a 'concreting train'. In order that it should operate as efficiently as possible, it was essential that it should be able to move forward at a steady rate. The earthworks, drainage, carriageway base and the majority of the forty-four bridges had therefore to be completed by the spring of 1964, to enable the concreting to be carried out during the summer. The concreting train could lay, in a single operation, the full thirty-six feet width of the slab for one of the carriageways. The maximum length laid in a twelve-hour working day was 2520 feet, a European record at that time.

The 'concreting train' used in the construction of the carriageways on the Preston–Lancaster section of the M6 (Lancashire County Council Surveyors' Department).

In January 1965 this section of motorway, including the service area at Forton, was opened to traffic. Apart from a short length north of Carnforth, the M6 in Lancashire was then complete. The sixty-two miles of motorway had twelve interchanges, 174 bridges and twelve miles of link and slip road, while thirty-two miles of other road had been diverted or realigned. In terms of Lancashire's modern history, geography, economy and landscape the building of this motorway and its long-term effects, are of the most fundamental importance.

THE STRETFORD–ECCLES BYPASS

Although the completion of the M6 was a priority, the county council had given early attention to the needs of the other parts of Lancashire where there were serious traffic problems. The 1949 road plan had identified the western sector of the proposed Manchester Outer Ring Road as one of the express routes to be constructed as a motorway, to bypass Stretford and Eccles and to serve the large Trafford Park industrial area. It would also relieve the Barton swing-bridge which carried the busy A575 across the Manchester Ship Canal and where serious traffic delays occurred when the bridge was closed to allow shipping movements. Therefore the main feature was to be a high-level bridge carrying the motorway over the canal.

As the A575 was a class 1 road the bypass was eligible for a 75 per cent government grant and in 1953 it was included in the programme of grant-aided schemes. In the same year a nearby steelworks was having difficulty in finding a disposal site for its slag and the county council therefore made arrangements for this to be tipped and compacted on

Barton swing bridge, which carried the A575 over the Manchester Ship Canal, became a major bottleneck because of the growth in the volume of road traffic. One purpose of the new Barton high level bridge was to provide an uninterrupted canal crossing in this area *(Salford Local History Library)*.

the site of the south approach embankment of the proposed bridge. A public inquiry into the road proposals had been held, but the work was actually carried out in advance of the minister's decision. In that a favourable decision might not have been forthcoming, the county council undoubtedly took a risk in proceeding with this work at such an early stage. It would, however, have been economic to re-excavate the embankment and move the material to another site, instead of paying the cost of importing fresh material from other sources and the not unreasonable county view was that the minister was certain to give his assent. By using some 400,000 tons of 'free' material nearly £100,000 was eventually saved. This embankment, which was completed at insignificant cost, was the first physical step in the construction of a motorway anywhere in Britain.

With four intermediate interchanges, giving an average spacing of only 1¼ miles, this was probably the first urban motorway in the country. Standards for such roads had not yet been determined but, as some sections of the route passed through residential areas, the need to reduce land acquisition to a minimum was recognised in the designs which were adopted. The county council's traffic forecasts indicated that dual three-lane carriageways were needed, but the ministry would only countenance the issue of grant for a dual two-lane scheme. The county council therefore had no alternative but to proceed accordingly.

The construction of the bypass, which included a total of twenty-two bridges, started in April 1957 when work began on the first of several contracts. Although shorter than Thelwall Viaduct the Barton Bridge,

The Barton high level bridge, carrying the new Stretford–Eccles bypass over the Manchester Ship Canal. *(Lancashire County Council Surveyors' Department).*

2425 feet long and with eighteen spans, was similar in many respects. However, a different method, using bailey bridge equipment, was adopted for the erection of the girders in the span crossing the canal.

Mining subsidence of up to twelve feet was expected at the northern end of the bypass and provision was therefore made for the decks of the bridges carrying the motorway over the Bridgewater Canal to be jacked-up to maintain the required headroom. At the public inquiry objections had been made to the northern terminal roundabout at Worsley, because of the perceived detrimental effect on the surroundings. On completion of the work, however, the county council received a Civic Trust award for the design and landscape treatment. When the bypass, at that time numbered M62, was opened in October 1960 it represented another 'first' for Lancashire – the first 'county motorway' in Britain (that is, the county council was the highway authority, not the Ministry of Transport).

THE MANCHESTER–PRESTON MOTORWAY (M61)

The 1949 road plan had proposed an express route between Manchester and Preston, to be achieved by improving sections of the A6 and constructing several town and village bypasses. However, by the early 1960s it became evident that there was a strong case for building a new motorway, linking the proposed M62 at Worsley with the M6 near Preston. Advance works began in February 1967 and included the

Worsley Braided Inter-
change, *circa* 1970.
The interchange,
which was the largest
in Britain, connects
the M62 (foreground
and top right) with
the M61 (top left).
The A580 and
A666(M) also connect
but are not visible in
this view *(Lancashire
County Council and
others,* Motorways
across the Pennines,
1971, p.16).

construction of major culverts, the diversion of the aqueduct carrying
the main water supply from Rivington Lakes to Liverpool, the building
of a major bridge at the junction with the M6 and the removal of
350,000 cubic yards of peat from mosslands. Work on the construction
of the twelve miles of dual three-lane motorway from the Horwich
interchange to the M6, bypassing Adlington and Chorley, began in

January 1968. This first section of the M61, with a service area at Anderton, was opened in November 1969.

The outstanding feature of the 6½-mile section of the motorway south from Horwich was the construction of the Worsley Braided Interchange, connecting the M61 with the M62, A580 (East Lancashire Road) and the A666(M) Kearsley spur. At that time the largest free-flow interchange in Britain, with fifteen separate routes, it covered an area of about two square miles and was designed to carry approximately 160,000 vehicles per day by 1979.

The siting of the interchange on Kearsley Moss was largely determined by the fact that, due to the considerable depth of peat, the area had never been developed in the past so very little property was affected. However, the ground conditions presented many difficult engineering problems in design and construction. Different horizontal profiles were examined along the various routes in order to obtain the cheapest solution. An early design for one section would have required a bridge over a mineral railway, the excavation of twenty feet of peat and its replacement with suitable filling material. Subsequently, it was found that the underside of the peat could be drained by an outfall about half a mile in length and the motorway profile was redesigned to pass under the railway, reducing the amount of imported filling by three million cubic yards and saving over £2 million. In total, some 1¼ million cubic yards of peat were excavated and deposited in tipping areas alongside. A very large and unsightly chemical waste tip, which had been one of the main sources of pollution in local watercourses for over fifty years, was removed and the material, sealed with clay, was used in a motorway embankment.

The opening of this section in December 1970 marked the completion of the M61.

THE LANCASHIRE–YORKSHIRE MOTORWAY (M62)

During the 1930s the need for a fast road route across the Pennines had been the subject of much discussion between the highway authorities in Lancashire and Yorkshire. It was eventually agreed that it would be an extension of the East Lancashire Road, but little positive action was taken before the war except for the reservation of land for the future construction of an all-purpose road then known as the Yorkshire Branch Road. Although the route was included in the 1949 *Road Plan for Lancashire*, it was not until 1961 that the Ministry of Transport invited the county councils of Lancashire and the West Riding to survey and recommend a route for the new motorway.

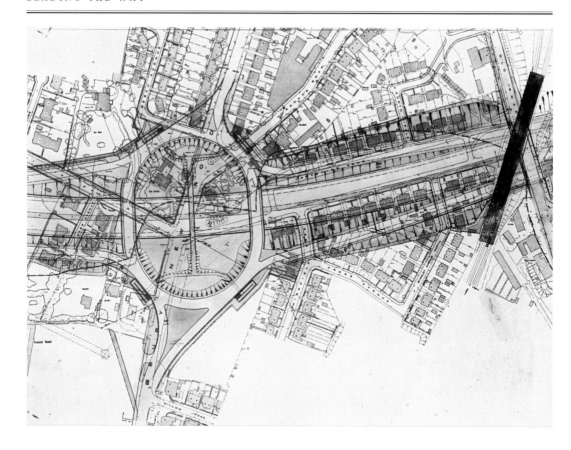

Reconnaissance on foot was followed by an aerial survey of the whole area and extensive traffic surveys were carried out on both sides of the Pennines. Since it would probably be the highest motorway route in Britain, meteorological data were also examined to identify the alignment which would be least affected by fog, snow and high winds.

The section within Lancashire, which was to be an extension of the existing Stretford–Eccles bypass (M62), presented the design engineers with two principal and contrasting problems. Firstly, there was the task of finding a route through urban areas in the west and north of the Manchester conurbation with its residential property and old industrial workings, and a network of roads, railways, canals and rivers to be crossed. The second problem was the long and steep climb up to the county boundary, where the obstacles were not existing roads but rather the lack of them.

A study of existing records showed that the geology of the route was divided into two sections. The lowland section from Eccles to Milnrow lies on the fringe of the Lancashire plain. Almost the whole of this area is covered by a blanket of glacial deposits and several peat

The plan for the M62 interchange at the A56 Bury New Road, with Besses o'th' Barn railway bridge crossing Bury Old Road at the right hand side. The proposal shows the land requirement for the construction of the three-lane motorway compared with the narrow strip of land reserved in the 1930s for the all-purpose Yorkshire Branch Road (*Lancashire County Council Surveyors' Department*).

266

mosses. West of the River Irwell, coal measures had been extensively worked and further subsidence seemed unlikely, but to the east of the river the coalfield was still being exploited. Significant subsidence could therefore be expected, both during construction of the motorway and after it was opened to traffic. In the foothills east of Milnrow there were mudstones, shales, coal seams and sandstone which was fissured, weathered and steeply bedded. Millstone grit formed the Pennine massif and, except for rocky outcrops, the whole of the moorland was covered by a layer of peat up to six feet thick.

Traffic forecasts indicated that dual three-lane carriageways would be necessary. The widths of the strips of land which had been reserved in urban areas such as Prestwich since the 1930s were therefore quite inadequate and unfortunately more than one hundred houses had to be demolished and the residents rehoused.

Work on the first of several advance contracts began in March 1966. The aim was to build bridges at key locations in order to provide access for construction traffic along the line of the motorway and thereby avoid existing roads. High in the Pennines, at an altitude of over 1200 feet, major rock excavation was required and a route had

The spectacular Rake-wood Viaduct, carrying the M62 over the Longden End Valley east of Rochdale. This view emphasises the rugged terrain on this section of the motorway (*LRO MBV 23*).

to be opened up to allow the haulage of the material westwards, for use in embankments. One of the early contracts, therefore, was for the construction of the spectacular six-span 840-feet long Rakewood viaduct, crossing the Longden End Brook 140 feet above the valley floor. The very exposed site was subject to severe weather conditions.

In May 1968 work began on a series of main contracts for the nineteen mile section of motorway from Eccles to the county boundary. It was a massive operation, requiring the movement along the line of the motorway of almost 16½ million cubic yards of material, including ten million cubic yards of rock. Near the summit the rock strata dipped steeply into the north face of the cuttings which in places were 120 feet deep. This resulted in sizeable landslips, which necessitated the removal of additional material and the provision of terracing to stabilise the slope. At these locations a wide concrete-lined ditch was provided behind the hard shoulder of the motorway, to serve not only as a drainage channel but also as a 'rock catcher' to prevent any loose rock from rolling onto the road.

The summit cutting of the M62 at Windy Hill is over 100 feet deep, and represented a huge engineering task. Of all Lancashire's motorways the M62 was by far the most challenging *(Lancashire County Council Surveyors' Department)*.

Apart from the many crossings of existing roads and private accesses, and junctions with a number of major roads, interchanges to connect with three other motorways had to be constructed – at Worsley, linking with the M61, at Simister with the Middleton Link (M66) and at Thornham with the A627(M) Rochdale–Oldham motorway. Other important structures included the Irwell Valley Bridge and the three-level Besses o'th' Barn railway bridge, carrying the Manchester–Bury railway over the A56 and the motorway, both of which had to be designed to allow for severe mining subsidence.

The motorway was opened in stages and at a later date a service area was provided at Birch, near Middleton. Concurrently, further sections of the motorway were completed within the West Riding of Yorkshire and the historic significance of linking the two counties by this engineering feat of our age was recognised in October 1971, when the twenty-seven miles between Eccles and Outlane near Huddersfield was formally inaugurated by Her Majesty the Queen.

THE SOUTH LANCASHIRE MOTORWAY (M62)
AND ASSOCIATED PROJECTS

During the 1950s the East Lancashire Road (A580) became severely congested, especially at its many junctions and with only a single carriageway it had a notoriously bad accident record. As noted in the previous chapter, it had always been the intention to widen the road at some future date and sufficient land had been acquired for that purpose. It was therefore comparatively easy to upgrade the existing road by providing dual carriageways and improving some of the junctions. In the early 1960s the entire length of the road was improved in this way.

The Ministry of Transport felt that this improvement to the A580 would be adequate for Liverpool–Manchester traffic in the foreseeable future. However, the county council, supported by the other local authorities in the area, took the view that a South Lancashire motorway was necessary. This proposal was eventually accepted by the ministry. Within Liverpool it was intended that it should start at the proposed Inner Ring Motorway, but there were serious objections because of the scale of the property demolition likely to be required and the loss of amenity. Following several public inquiries it was decided that the western terminal of the motorway should instead be at Queens Drive. At the eastern end it was to connect with the existing M62 by means of a large interchange to be built at Eccles.

For some time the county council and Eccles Borough Council had been concerned at the deteriorating traffic conditions on the A57 within the borough. It was proposed that it should be bypassed by a 'county' motorway, the M602, extending eastwards from the Eccles interchange through to the Salford city boundary. In order to minimise disturbance, part of the new road was to run immediately alongside the Liverpool-Manchester railway and through several derelict areas, but nevertheless many property owners and residents were affected by the scheme. Shortly after the announcement of the route, early in 1962, the county council agreed to buy any properties offered to it, thus enabling the owners to obtain alternative accommodation when suitable premises came on the market. Many properties were purchased in advance under this arrangement, which was then most unusual but is now standard practice.

Through the built-up area the bypass was to be mainly in a deep cutting, which had the advantage of making the road less intrusive, reducing the level of traffic noise affecting nearby property and simplifying the design of the overbridges. In order to reduce the extent of the land and property required and to provide support for the adjoining

269

The Eccles bypass
(M602) built between
1969 and 1971. This
shows the complexity
of constructing a
motorway through an
urban area, with Mon-
ton in the foreground
and the Liverpool-
Manchester railway
line and Eccles town
centre at top right
(LRO MBV 23).

land, long retaining walls of up to thirty feet high were constructed. However, 353 houses had to be demolished, of which 293 had been built before 1914. Two churches, forty-seven shops, two public houses and a small number of other premises were similarly affected.

The construction of the interchange and of the bypass began in December 1969. The urban situation presented many problems not normally associated with rural motorways. There were thirteen side road diversions and many public utilities were affected – for example, the replacement of a length of the Eccles main sewer required the driving of a thousand feet of 54-inch diameter tunnel up to forty feet deep, much of it through the underlying sandstone. The 1¾ mile long three-lane motorway was opened to traffic in November 1971. Apart from removing heavy traffic from the A57, there were other benefits to the area resulting from the building of new houses and churches, as a replacement for those which had to be demolished.

The construction of the 13½ miles of the M62 between Tarbock and Risley began in September 1971. At Tarbock there was to be an interchange with the M57 Liverpool Outer Ring Road, then under construction and at Croft, north of Warrington, a major interchange connecting with the M6. Two intermediate interchanges were to be provided, at Rainhill Stoops and at Winwick, to connect with the A57 and the A49 respectively.

For over a mile the motorway was to be built on the disused main runway of Burtonwood Airfield but, because of mining subsidence, it was necessary to raise the level by up to ten feet and break the continuity of the runway pavement. It was somewhat ironic that use was being made of this facility, as one of the first major road schemes carried out by the county council after the war (and paid for by the Air Ministry) was to enable the original runway to be extended at the time of the Berlin Airlift in 1949. Burtonwood Road, which was to be severed by the runway extension, had provided a convenient through route between St Helens and Warrington. The most suitable alternative was to improve approximately 2½ miles of existing road and build half a mile of new road, including bridges over the West Coast main line railway and the St Helens Canal. These were the first prestressed concrete bridges to be constructed in Lancashire.

Ground conditions were bad along much of the route of the motorway and at Winwick an embankment nearly half a mile long and up to thirty feet high was built in advance to ensure that settlement would be completed before the carriageway was constructed on the top. The scheme required the building of thirty-seven bridges, including the five-span Winwick Quay Viaduct over the West Coast main line railway.

At Croft the interchange with the M6 provided not only for the heavy flow of through traffic on the two motorways but also for a major flow from the Liverpool direction turning south to the M6 and vice versa. It was therefore decided that easy curves with a design speed of 70 m.p.h. should be provided for these movements, while the other slip roads were designed for a speed of 40 m.p.h. Nevertheless a very large area of land was required, but by providing access to parts of the interchange some agricultural use was still possible. Elsewhere, unsuitable excavated material was tipped and landscaped.

The section of motorway between Tarbock and the M6 was opened to traffic in November 1973, with a service area at Burtonwood.

Between the M6 and Eccles the route presented engineering challenges which, although not new, had never been experienced on such a scale. It crossed the notorious Chat Moss and other peat mosses, over which Stephenson had built the Liverpool and Manchester Railway in the late 1820s. For that project rafts of branches and brushwood were laid and then covered by layers of sand and gravel as a base for the railway track. As settlement of the peat took place the sleepers carrying the track were raised, by packing with ballast, to maintain an acceptable profile. Similar amounts of settlement on the carriageways of a motorway are unacceptable, as the deterioration and continual adjustment of the running surface would be potentially hazardous, as well as very expensive.

It was technically feasible to build an embankment which would compress the underlying peat and drive out the water, but since this required large amounts of imported material the cost would have been prohibitive. The peat was up to twenty feet deep so the possibility of cutting through it and constructing the carriageways on the stable underlying clay and sands was investigated. The critical factor was whether a drainage system could be provided for use during construction and for the discharge of surface water on completion. It was found that this could be achieved by laying a three-quarter mile length of 84-inch diameter pipe from Barton Moss to outfall in the Manchester Ship Canal and this was carried out as advance works during 1970.

Work on the main contract began in April 1972. Nearly two million cubic yards of peat were excavated and, to support the plant carrying out the operation, massive steel and wooden rafts were used. The excavated peat was tipped on adjoining land which was later returned to agriculture. Stone buttresses had to be constructed to stabilise the remaining peat on the sides of the cuttings.

When opened to traffic in August 1974 this ten-mile section of dual three-lane carriageway provided Merseyside with first-class motorway links to Greater Manchester, West Yorkshire and beyond. A year earlier, work had begun on the remaining three miles of the motorway between Tarbock and Queens Drive, where provision was made in the design of the junction for a further extension into the city. It is, however, extremely unlikely that this will ever be built. The opening of this section, in November 1976, therefore in effect completed the M62 in Lancashire.

OTHER MOTORWAYS OF THE 1960S AND 1970S

It had long been recognised that there was a need to link Rochdale and Oldham by means of a new high-standard route and it was eventually agreed that this should form part of the motorway network. The designs for the M62 therefore included overbridges and slip roads at Thornham to accommodate a future interchange. The A627(M) was to be 3½ miles long and from its terminal roundabouts new lengths of all-purpose road were to be built to serve the town centres and other parts of the two boroughs. From an intermediate interchange at Slattocks a link road would provide a motorway connection to Middleton.

Although Rochdale and Oldham county borough councils were highway authorities in their own right they agreed to Lancashire County Council acting as their agents for the project. The section of new motorway south of the M62 was accepted as a potential trunk road, attracting a 100 per cent grant, while the remainder of the scheme was eligible for a 75 per cent principal road grant. Construction began in March 1970 and, because of the urban character of much of the area, 102 properties had to be demolished.

This was an unusually difficult project. For a comparatively short length of new road the earthworks were very substantial, involving 2½ million cubic yards of excavation in sands, silts, gravels and clays, all with a high water table. In the sixty-foot deep cutting immediately north of the M62, water was found only six feet from the surface, which at that point was 600 feet above sea level and near the summit of a hill. At the Slattocks interchange artesian pressure caused water to burst through into excavations being carried out in the overlying clay. A permanent 'safety valve', consisting of eleven well-heads, was therefore installed. Three of the well-heads within the roundabout of the interchange were then incorporated in a landscaped lagoon, which also collects water from other sources – a unique feature in a motorway interchange. The A627(M) was opened in January 1972, three months ahead of schedule.

The *Road Plan for Lancashire* of 1949 proposed a Liverpool Outer Ring Road, extending from Sefton Town in the north to Gateacre in the south and comprising sections of new road and the improvement of existing roads. In the following decade, however, major industrial and housing development took place on the fringes of the Merseyside conurbation and it became apparent that this scheme would be inadequate. The Merseyside Conurbation Traffic Survey of 1962 emphasised the urgent need for greatly improved road facilities and the county surveyor then proposed a completely new road built to motorway standards with grade-separated interchanges. It would serve the rapidly developing areas of Kirkby, Croxteth and Gateacre and would link with the proposed Liverpool–Preston and South Lancashire motorways.

The local authorities accepted it as a priority scheme and in the mid-1960s preparation and design work began. The proposed route ran from the A565 Liverpool–Southport road at Thornton for fourteen miles, to connect with the A562 Speke–Widnes Link Road near Ditton.

Despite passing through densely populated areas it necessitated the demolition of only five dwellings. To a large extent this was due to the existence of the Green Belt, which the planning authorities considered was not incompatible with the motorway.

Following a start on advance bridgeworks to carry railway lines over the motorway, work began on the 3½ mile section between the A59 and A580 in April 1970. Some 70 per cent of the motorway was carried on embankments, most of the filling material being unburnt colliery waste from old pit heaps in the St Helens area. Thus a useful contribution was made to the removal of dereliction in the county. The completion of this section, two years later, was of particular benefit to industrial traffic passing between the new Seaforth Docks and the A580, as a through route to connect with the M6.

Work had already begun on contracts for the six-mile section between the A580 and the interchange with the South Lancashire motorway at Tarbock and for a link road to serve Huyton. In November 1973 the length from the A57 at Prescot was opened at the same time as the M62 between Tarbock and the M6. With the completion of the section between the A580 and the A57, in April 1974, a continuous 9½ mile section of the Liverpool Outer ring Road, between the A59 and the M62, was open to traffic.

THE FURTHER DEVELOPMENT
OF THE COUNTY ROAD NETWORK

The building of the motorways was, of course, only part of the road development programme within Lancashire. There were many plans for the improvement of existing roads and for the provision of new all-purpose roads in areas where the network was inadequate. For example, the transporter bridge between Widnes and Runcorn, opened in 1905 and crossing both the Mersey and the Manchester Ship Canal was quite unable to cope with the volume of road traffic wishing to use it. In 1947 the Lancashire and Cheshire County Councils sought parliamentary powers for the construction of a jointly-funded high-level fixed bridge, which was to link with a proposed new road serving the Speke area.

It was to have either three or five spans, but the Manchester Ship Canal Company objected to the scheme, claiming that one of the piers would have an adverse effect on the waterway. A single span suspension bridge was proposed as an alternative, but aerodynamic tests on a model of the bridge showed that the close proximity of the existing railway bridge would produce severe oscillation during high winds. A suspension bridge was therefore unacceptable – a further factor in its rejection

The Runcorn–
Widnes bridge was
built in 1956-61 to
replace the old trans-
porter bridge. The
bridge is now listed as
a building of architect-
ural and historical
interest. This view is
looking south, with
the Victorian railway
viaduct to the right
(*Runcorn–Widnes
Bridge Joint Committee*,
Runcorn–Widnes
Bridge: Official Open-
ing [*1961*]).

was the publicity given to the dramatic failure of the Tacoma Narrows
suspension bridge in America a few years before.

A steel arch bridge capable of carrying a three-lane carriageway was
then proposed and fresh parliamentary powers were obtained in 1954-5.
It was to be similar to the Tyne and Sydney Harbour bridges, having
a central arch 1082 feet long with a rise of 252 feet from its bearing
level to the top chord and side spans of 250 feet. The deck was to be
carried by steel wire rope hangers suspended from the arch ribs. With
approach viaducts on both sides of the river and associated roadworks
the total length of the scheme was some three miles. Work started in
May 1956 and when the bridge was opened by Princess Alexandra in
July 1961 it had the longest span in England and the longest arch span
in Europe.

In the early 1960s the government persuaded the Ford Motor
Company to establish a manufacturing plant on a 'green field' site at
Halewood. It was agreed that a single-carriageway road serving the site
would be constructed within nine months and upgraded to a dual
carriageway within eighteen months. It would connect with the A562
to the east and with Speke Boulevard to the west and was to be the
first stage in the construction of the Speke–Widnes link, which would
be a high standard all-purpose road. The major part of the scheme was
within the area of the administrative county and, because of the need
to proceed quickly and the short time available to prepare contract
documents, it was decided that the road should be built by county
council direct labour. Later, it was agreed that there should be a flyover

link into the factory, with a bridge constructed under contract. The project was completed on time, in November 1962.

Subsequently, approval was given to the extension of the road through to Widnes and the principle of undertaking the roadworks by direct labour and constructing bridges under contract was continued. The decision to adopt this policy was largely determined by the need for large quantities of filling material in the construction of embankments and the possibility of using chemical waste from large heaps lying on or adjacent to the eastern end of the route. This material, known locally as 'galligoo', was a by-product of the soda ash industry and had been deposited between the 1850s and the First World War. Although it had a very high moisture content and was extremely difficult to handle and compact, there were major economic and environmental advantages to be gained from its use. However, there were problems in defining the precise specifications for competitive tender documents. Direct management by the county council's engineers allowed a flexible approach to be adopted.

Apart from the 'galligoo', other industrial waste was used in the construction, including burnt red colliery shale, pulverised fuel ash from power stations and excavation material dumped in a local quarry during the construction of the Manchester Ship Canal in the early 1890s. New roads are often condemned for their adverse affect upon the environment, but this scheme is a good example of the considerable benefits to be gained by the use of potentially dangerous and unsightly waste in road construction – a policy adopted throughout Lancashire wherever possible.

The three miles of new road were opened in February 1966 and included six bridges of which the largest, crossing the electrified Crewe–Liverpool railway, was the first in the country to be built over a railway with 25kv overhead lines.

By the late 1950s the growth of traffic had created severe congestion in Liverpool and Birkenhead, particularly around the approaches to the 1934 Mersey Tunnel, the capacity of which was quite inadequate. Early in 1959 the local authorities agreed to investigate the provision of a new bridge or tunnel and, following a traffic survey and a study of the engineering aspects, six tunnel and two bridge schemes were put forward. The favoured option was a six-lane bridge, but there were serious objections to this, mainly because the clearances for shipping would necessitate high-level approaches, with consequential adverse environmental effects.

The *Highway Plan* which resulted from the Merseyside Conurbation Traffic Survey in 1962 recommended a tunnel as the best solution to the problem. It would be less environmentally intrusive and give greater flexibility by allowing a two-lane bore to be provided as a first stage at a lower initial capital cost. The new tunnel, to be called Kingsway, was one mile downstream from the existing crossing. It would form part of a road system connecting the projected Liverpool Inner Motorway with the proposed M53 along the Wirral and was designed to keep traffic away from the congested city centres. In Liverpool the route occupied the site of an abandoned canal and an old goods station and on the Wirral side it followed part of the disused Seacombe Railway. The profile of the tunnel provided for a maximum gradient of 1 in 25 and a rock cover twenty feet thick below the river channel. Through the rock, the tunnel was to be lined with precast reinforced concrete segments designed for erection by a tunnelling machine and covered by welded steel plate. Elsewhere, as the tunnel rose out of the rock into boulder clay, a cast-iron segmental lining was to be used.

Parliamentary powers were obtained in 1964 and work on a pilot tunnel began early in 1966, with the aim of exploring the ground, establishing facilities for drainage and ventilation and carrying out grouting trials on any rock fissures which might be encountered. The size of the bore of the main tunnel was governed by the requirement that it should provide two 12-feet wide traffic lanes and a headroom of 16 feet 6 inches. An internal diameter of 31 feet 7 inches, at that time near the limit of tunnelling machine experience, was therefore necessary. Construction began in March 1967 and the 'mole' employed on the task completed the bore in twenty-seven months. The 7300 foot tunnel, together with its approach roads, was opened to traffic in June 1971, having cost almost £32 million.

Meanwhile, the overall transportation needs of the Merseyside conurbation had received further consideration. The population was expected to increase, over twenty-five years, from 1.4 million to between 1.6 million and 2 million and some 200,000 people would move out to the new towns of Skelmersdale and Runcorn. It was recognised that changes of this magnitude would inevitably lead to major growth in road freight and private car usage, over and above national trends. It was therefore decided that a major investigation of all the relevant issues should be undertaken. Three years later, in 1969, the report of the Merseyside Area Land and Transportation Study (MALTS) urged, among other recommendations, the immediate duplication of Kingsway, the Wallasey tunnel then under construction. This was accepted and, using the same 'mole', the main bore was begun in November 1970. With the benefit of earlier experience a considerably improved tunnelling rate was achieved and the second tunnel was completed within fourteen months and opened to traffic in February 1974.

In other parts of Lancashire several local bypasses were built. The A59 trunk road through Longton, four miles west of Preston, was narrow and tortuous. Proposals for a dual carriageway bypass were

The Backbarrow by-pass, west of Newby Bridge, was one of the first post-war schemes carried out on the A590 to improve the trunk road serving the Furness area. The bridge was constructed of concrete but to enhance its appearance and enable it to blend into its attractive surroundings it was faced with local stone *(Lancashire County Council Surveyors' Department).*

drawn up before the war and most of the land required for the scheme was purchased, but progress was halted in 1939. It was not until July 1956 that the work began on the construction of Lancashire's first post-war village bypass. Design standards had changed during the intervening period and the provision of cycle tracks was dropped, but the widths of carriageways and the central reservation were increased.

The only bridge was that carrying the bypass over the Preston–Southport railway and, as the area is flat, the only significant earthworks were those for the approach embankments. This was one of the factors in the decision to construct the carriageways in reinforced concrete. The 2½-mile bypass was opened to traffic at the end of 1957, but only a few years later the railway line was closed. The increase in the volume and speed of traffic during the next decade meant that a serious accident blackspot developed at the junction with Chapel Lane. However, the redundant bridge was brought back into use in 1973, when a short length of the lane was diverted through it and the gap in the central reservation was closed to prevent accidents.

Some bypasses were built to solve a local traffic problem while others involved the general upgrading of longer sections of road to produce an improved through route. For example, the A671/A56 route between Padiham, Burnley, Nelson and Colne passes through built-up areas and is mostly subject to a 30 m.p.h. speed limit, while in several places it serves as a main shopping street. The B6247 and B6249, through the villages of Higham, Fence and Wheatley Lane on the northern side of the Calder valley, were increasingly being used as an alternative. The county council therefore undertook the comprehensive improvement of this route, starting with a one-mile north-western bypass of Padiham. The carriageway was constructed in concrete during 1963 and was used as a trial for many of the techniques later employed in the laying of the concrete carriageways on the Preston to Lancaster section of the M6. It was followed by a series of other schemes to give a much improved single carriageway road over four miles in length bypassing the villages.

A bypass for Wheelton, on the busy A674 Blackburn–Chorley road, had been needed for many years, but did not have a high priority. However, because of the collapse of a major retaining wall on the approach to the village in 1966, the road had to be closed. A bypass was constructed as a matter of urgency and was opened in the summer of 1967. In north Lancashire a relief road was built at Ulverston to take through traffic on the A590 out of the centre of the old market town and on the same road a bypass was constructed at Backbarrow. In the early 1970s a short bypass was built around Hawkshead, where the network of narrow lanes, thronged in the season with tourists, was suffering severe environmental damage because of through traffic.

Among the new roads constructed in the late 1960s and early 1970s were some of regional significance which had been included in the second category of routes in the 1949 road plan – for example, the Farnworth–Kearsley bypass. The A666 carried very heavy traffic flows between Blackburn, Darwen, Bolton and Manchester, passing through the centres of Farnworth and Kearsley. The need for a bypass was self-evident, but there was some reluctance on the part of the local authorities to accept that the proposed route, to the east of both towns, would provide the best solution. In due course, however, the scheme was accepted and, as it would ultimately provide the residents of Bolton with a direct link to the motorway network, the borough council agreed to meet one-third of the cost.

The route lay on the west side of the Croal valley, which was dissected by a series of ravines, some very narrow and filled with a mixture of waste materials. Before construction began a large number of old terraced houses, whose occupants had been rehoused, had to be demolished. Specialist contractors were engaged to remove human remains from a graveyard which was affected. The bridgeworks were extensive and included subways and major retaining walls. The road was opened to traffic at the end of 1968 and it was subsequently connected to the Worsley Braided Interchange by the A666(M) Kearsley Spur.

With the Calder valley as an important textile manufacturing area and Manchester as the commercial centre for the industry the need for improved road communications from the north-east Lancashire towns southwards through Rossendale had long been part of the road strategy. The main route was the A56 trunk road from Manchester to Burnley, passing through Bury, Edenfield and Rawtenstall. The A680, which served Haslingden and Accrington, joined this road at Edenfield, where there were traffic flows of 17,000 vehicles per day. The 1949 road plan proposed the general improvement of the route, with an eastern bypass of Bury connecting with the Lancashire–Yorkshire motorway and separate bypasses of Edenfield and the level crossing at Rawtenstall, a notorious bottleneck. The construction of an eastern bypass of Bury depended on the programming of the M62 so it was decided to concentrate on the Edenfield bypass. This was initially planned to run east of the village but detailed investigations revealed that a better route could be found to the west and that it could be extended to bypass the level crossing with a link to Haslingden.

In the summer of 1967 work began on the four-mile bypass, the first scheme to be supervised by the newly-formed North Western Road Construction Unit. The route follows the Irwell valley, the sides of which are covered with thick deposits of glacial silts and clays. Following an extensive site investigation during the design stage, a number of special measures were included to cater for the unstable conditions. For example, lightweight pulverised fuel ash was specified for several of the embankments to reduce the ground loading and deep toe trenches filled with granular material were incorporated to give stability. Despite these precautions there was serious ground movement during construction, a problem exacerbated by exceptionally wet weather.

As a high-standard all-purpose dual carriageway road with limited access it involved the construction of five major bridges, including a crossing of the river Irwell. At the northern terminal, Queens Square in the centre of Rawtenstall, a roundabout was built, of sufficient size to accommodate a future bus station, with subways to provide pedestrian access. The road was completed in the summer of 1969, but it was several years before a start was made on the nine-mile Bury easterly bypass, the M66, which extended the route southwards to connect with the M62.

In the Ribble valley the village of Whalley, with its ancient abbey, and the historic market town of Clitheroe had suffered for many years from the effects of traffic on the A59. Severe congestion often occurred in the centre of Whalley, where the A59 was joined by the A680, the main route from the towns of the Calder valley and south Lancashire, and long traffic queues frequently formed on the narrow approaches to the junction. A further problem was the very steep gradient encountered by southbound vehicles leaving the village. In Clitheroe the A59 was the main shopping street and the poor alignment and narrow carriageway, particularly in the vicinity of the castle, meant that conditions were becoming intolerable as traffic increased.

Before the war it was envisaged that separate bypasses would be provided and various routes had been investigated but little progress was made until the early 1960s, when a scheme for a combined 8¼ mile bypass was proposed. Only a single carriageway could be justified initially, but the road was designed so that it could be upgraded by the provision of a second carriageway at a later date. It was expected that this high-standard bypass would be more attractive to long-distance traffic thereby giving some relief to the towns along the Calder valley.

Construction began in February 1969. The works included a bridge across the river Calder, another to carry the Blackburn–Hellifield railway line over the road and a deep rock cutting near Chatburn spanned by a dramatic high-level bridge. The extra land required for the second carriageway was laid out as a wide grass verge, but within a few years, it became apparent that there was a need for a motorway along the Calder valley. This was later to be constructed as the M65.

The road was opened to traffic in January 1971, but although it gave considerable relief to Whalley the problem of traffic on the A680 remained. However, in May of that year work on the one-mile eastern bypass began. When opened to traffic a year later this not only removed further traffic from the village but also bypassed the notorious Whalley Brow. Clitheroe, too, gained a second bypass. At Pimlico, north of the town, a link road connecting with the main bypass was constructed to divert heavy quarry and cement works traffic away from the built-up area, with consequent environmental benefits. It was partly paid for by the quarry owners in recognition of the financial savings which they would make.

URBAN ROADS

The problems created by the concentration of traffic in urban areas had been recognised in Lancashire for many years. As the number of vehicles using the roads increased in the postwar period, road safety, congestion and the environmental damage caused by traffic became issues of serious concern. It was accepted that there was a relationship between land use and the demand for transport of all modes, but there were many factors militating against dealing with the problem as quickly as the public demanded. Many of the town plans being prepared at that time were unrealistic and the Buchanan Report, *Traffic in Towns*, published in 1963, led to a reappraisal in many instances.

The approach adopted in the 1949 road plan had been aimed at removing as much through traffic as possible from the urban areas, by constructing a network of new roads specifically intended for use by through traffic, together with local bypasses of towns and villages. Within the financial limits imposed by the government considerable progress was made in this respect, as noted elsewhere. Meanwhile action was taken to deal with urban problems by the introduction of traffic management measures such as one-way systems and the installation of traffic signals, while pedestrian safety was improved by the provision of 'pelican' crossings. However, road widening and new construction were limited because of the property demolition involved.

In Manchester the *City Plan* of 1945 suggested a range of major projects for new roads, but it was not until the late 1950s that the political and economic climate was favourable. In November 1958 officers of Lancashire and Cheshire County Councils, the county borough councils in the region and the Ministry of Transport met to consider the future traffic needs of the conurbation. All the other local authorities became involved and following a major traffic survey carried out during the summer of 1960 the SELNEC (South East Lancashire and North East Cheshire) Highway Plan was published.

Mancunian Way provided a southern bypass of Manchester's city centre and was the first urban motorway in the country *(Winter & Kidson, Preston)*.

It envisaged a large motorway and dual carriageway network of radial and other routes. Many of the main roads leading from central Manchester and Salford were to be widened and upgraded, the comprehensive redevelopment of the adjacent housing areas being fundamental to this policy. One of the major schemes, which was crucial to the proposals, was Mancunian Way, envisaged as a southern bypass of Manchester city centre. It was intended that eventually it would link with the proposed Eccles bypass and with the radial routes to Sheffield, Stockport and Ashton-under-Lyne. The road would act as a distributor for several heavily trafficked radial roads and link the railway marshalling yards at its eastern end and Salford docks in the west. Because of the number of junctions which would have been required if the road was constructed at ground level it was decided that it should be elevated for most of its length and designed as a motorway. Parliamentary powers for its construction by the city council were obtained in 1960. The road was carried on a thirty-two span concrete viaduct nearly three quarters of a mile long and, when opened to traffic in March 1967, the 1½ mile length between London Road (A6) and Chester Road (A56), and numbered A57(M), was the first true urban motorway in the county.

In Bolton part of an outer ring road had been built in the 1920s and 1930s, but it had provided only limited benefit to the town centre. After the war an inner ring road was proposed, but this was superseded by a scheme for an 'urban motorway box'. North-south traffic using the A666 was to be diverted on to the eastern side of the 'box', to be known as the 'eastern limb' of the inner relief road. This two-mile section of motorway-standard road linked into the Farnworth–Kearsley bypass to give a direct connection to the motorway system. At the northern end the terminal roundabout was close to the town centre, with car parks providing over 1000 spaces.

The route lay in the valley of the River Croal, which had acquired the worst characteristics of a derelict area in declining industrial surroundings. In part it followed the line of the Manchester, Bolton and Bury Canal, filled in twenty years earlier. The large quantity of excavated material which was unsuitable for re-use was tipped and landscaped in adjoining areas, giving the road the appearance of an urban parkway. Long sections of retaining wall up to thirty feet high were built, together with five bridges. Although it had many of the characteristics of a motorway, it was opened in December 1971 as a high standard all-purpose road.

In many other towns, during the 1960s and 1970s, relief roads were associated with the development of shopping centres and car parks. The concept of pedestrianisation was beginning to gain favour, although the major schemes to remove traffic from central areas did not appear until later. Circumstances differed. For example, in Preston the limited number of bridges over the Ribble necessitated the use of the main shopping streets, Fishergate and Church Street, by through traffic on the A59. This was the cause of severe traffic congestion in the town and, although a relief road had been planned since before the war, it was not until the late 1960s that a start was made on the construction of a length of dual carriageway on the northern side of the central area. Associated with the scheme were multi-storey car parks, one of which was built above what was said to be the largest bus station in Europe. A substantial part of Ringway, with its vehicular and pedestrian underpasses and a large footbridge, was opened to traffic in December 1971.

At Blackburn, in contrast, the roadworks in the centre were initially limited in scale, although sufficient to allow pedestrianisation of the main shopping street as part of a central area redevelopment. In Lancaster heavy congestion affecting Skerton Bridge, carrying the A6 across the River Lune, severely affected the movement of traffic through the town. In 1971–2 the disused Greyhound Bridge, which formerly carried the Green Ayre to Morecambe railway line, was converted to a road bridge to form part of a gyratory system with the Skerton Bridge, thereby giving considerable relief to the city centre.

Many comparable schemes were undertaken in towns throughout the county, with the aim of making their centres more pleasant places in which to live, work, shop and enjoy leisure facilities. Although initially there was resistance to pedestrianisation, mainly from tradespeople, the principle came to be accepted and, as town centre relief roads were built, more schemes came into operation.

THE ACHIEVEMENT, 1945–1974

When James Drake retired in 1972 the road network in Lancashire had been transformed by his own efforts and by the immense contribution of his dedicated staff and the engineers of the other local authorities. He was widely known as 'Mr Motorway' and his achievement was recognised nationally when he was knighted shortly afterwards. His pioneering advocacy of motorways, as expressed in the 1949 road plan, had laid the foundation of a fine regional highway system which was also a key element in the national network. Much remained to be done and many schemes which had featured in the 1949 plan or were introduced in the later revisions were still in the pipeline – particularly the proposals for new routes crossing the county in an east–west direction.

In mid-Lancashire there was a long-standing proposal for a motorway from north Liverpool to Bolton. A start had been made with the construction of a 3½-mile long bypass of Upholland, to serve Skelmersdale new town. With its connection to the M6 east of Wigan it was to be upgraded to motorway standard and extended, as the M58, through to the A59 and the Liverpool Outer Ring Road at Aintree. At Westhoughton, near Bolton, an underbridge had been included in the construction of the M61 to accommodate a future junction.

At Broughton, north of Preston, the three-level interchange had already been built to handle the large volumes of traffic expected from the proposed M55. This motorway would serve a resident population of 275,000 and bring great relief to Preston – which had a serious accident problem – and would represent a major improvement in access to Blackpool and the other Fylde Coast towns where the leisure industry was of such vital importance.

For many years road access to Furness had been the subject of much criticism, because of the state of the narrow and tortuous A590 trunk road. As this was the only route from the east serving the heavy

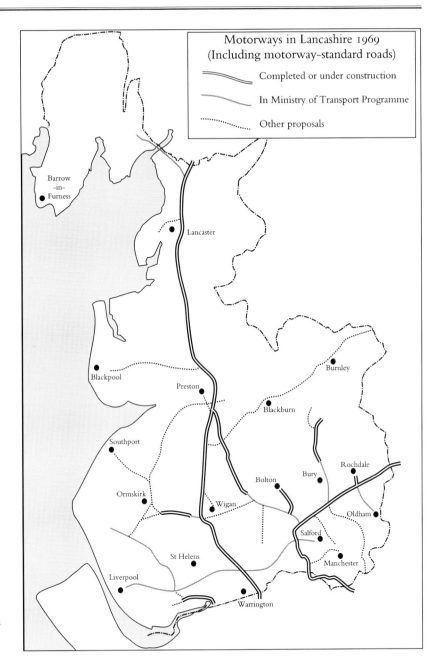

Motorways in Lancashire 1969
(Including motorway-standard roads)

⌇⌇⌇ Completed or under construction

⌇⌇⌇ In Ministry of Transport Programme

⌇⌇⌇ Other proposals

Barrow
-in-
Furness

Lancaster

Blackpool

Preston

Burnley

Blackburn

Southport

Rochdale

Bolton

Bury

Ormskirk

Wigan

Oldham

Salford

St Helens

Manchester

Liverpool

Warrington

Motorways (built and proposed) in Lanca-shire, 1969.

engineering industries of Barrow, it was claimed that the road deterred potential employers who were contemplating a move to the area. The county council had continually pressed the Ministry of Transport to improve the route and strongly supported the proposal for a crossing of the River Kent at Arnside, in Westmorland, which would greatly shorten the journey between the two parts of Lancashire. After a public inquiry in 1970 the minister rejected the proposal and decided that the A590 should be upgraded in a piecemeal fashion throughout its length.

In the early 1970s there were a number of changes which were to have a profound effect upon the future development of the road network in Lancashire. Several government departments were brought together to form the new Department of the Environment, with the improved coordination of land-use and transportation policies as a principal objective. Environmental issues were becoming of increasing importance and were a source of major objections at public inquiries into road proposals which were, as a result, not only delayed considerably in the decision-making process but were, in some instances, removed from the programme. These aspects were recognised in policy statements issued by the department and in the passing of the Land Compensation Act 1973, which allowed highway authorities to purchase extra land for landscaping and planting, to provide noise barriers and to insulate residential property in order to reduce the impact of new and improved roads.

The oil crises of the mid-1970s caused other problems. The rate of traffic growth decreased as a result of the substantial increase in the price of fuel and, as an economy measure, the government imposed cuts in the roads programme and a maximum speed limit of 50 m.p.h. which lasted for six months.

However, the most significant event during this period was the reorganisation of local government in 1974. The boundaries of the administrative county of Lancashire were substantially amended by the establishment of the metropolitan counties of Greater Manchester and Merseyside, the inclusion of part of the former West Riding within Lancashire, the creation of Cumbria which absorbed Furness and the inclusion of the Warrington area within the new Cheshire. The county boroughs ceased to exist and the new Lancashire County Council became the local highway authority for the whole of the county, with the majority of the fourteen new district councils acting as agents for certain highway functions. At the same time, the system of specific grants for highway schemes was replaced by a Transport Supplementary Grant, to cover not only the construction and improvement of roads but also support for public transport.

The development of Central Lancashire New Town in the Preston/ Leyland/Chorley area created a need for better communications with the north-east Lancashire towns, to enable them to participate in the social and economic benefits which would be generated. This led to pressure for the construction of a new high-standard road, subsequently to be known as the Calder Valley motorway (M65) from the M6/M61, south of Preston, through to Colne. Many would say that this should be the last motorway to be built in the county, but others consider that there will always be a need for the construction of roads of this type – for example, the completion of the motorway 'box' around Preston, which was first proposed in 1969.

It has been argued that the building of a motorway does not give the economic support which has been claimed. However, in Lancashire some of the most buoyant commercial and industrial areas are situated close to the nodal points on the motorway and trunk road network – the expanded town of Warrington and the industrial and business estates at Walton Summit and Haydock, for example. Elsewhere, at places such as Skelmersdale and Kirkby, it is accepted that the existence of excellent road communications has not prevented severe economic problems, which indicates that the relationship between roads and economic success is complex and heavily dependent on local circumstances. On the other hand, it has been amply demonstrated that well-designed new roads, such as motorways, are the best and safest means of providing for the movement of through traffic and give valuable environmental benefits to the areas relieved of that burden.

Epilogue and retrospect

ALTHOUGH the main body of this book ends with the reorganisation of local government and other changes in 1974, time has not stood still and much has of course happened in the ensuing years. This short Epilogue, which does not attempt to be comprehensive in its coverage, looks at some of the issues which have arisen in relation to road-building since that date and reviews some of the many developments in the geographical county of Lancashire during that time. As the previous chapter made clear, the twenty years from 1955 were a time of exceptional and vigorous activity in the building and improving of Lancashire's roads – perhaps, in retrospect, they will be seen as a 'golden age' of road-building. Many of the key elements in the 1949 road plan, some of them inherited from more tentative pre-war proposals, came to fruition, while ambitious programmes for future works were prepared by the county council and the other highway authorities in the region. In local and regional planning the late 1950s and the 1960s were likewise a time of great optimism and confidence. An inherited legacy of profound problems such as sub-standard housing was tackled with energy and enthusiasm. Over a quarter of a century later much of what was done in the two decades from 1955 may strike us as misdirected, and there was a strong reaction against the planning policies of this period, but there can be no denying the magnificent scale of the visions of the post-war years.

By the late 1970s new thinking in planning policies was evident as professionals and 'ordinary' people alike rejected the sometimes brutal and banal 1960s' architecture and the destructiveness resulting from wholesale redevelopment of urban areas. During this period the environment became, as it has remained, a subject of major political and popular interest and concern.[1] Road-building policies and programmes were increasingly affected by these changes in attitude – by new thinking on planning issues and by the growth of environmental lobbying. Here, too, optimism and confidence in the future were modified by experience and by changing perceptions of problems and solutions at national and local level. For example, a characteristic idealism was shown in the planning of Skelmersdale new town (designated in 1966) with its advanced and high-standard road network which was 'designed for a high level of car ownership' and, commendably, 'as an integrated communications system adequate for all future foreseeable needs'.[2] But the initial optimism of the plans for the town was tempered in practice as Skelmersdale experienced severe social and economic problems – the level of car ownership in fact remains one of the lowest in the country. Plans for later new towns – Warrington and Central Lancashire – were more pragmatic and their authors noted the changed circumstances within which the plans would be implemented: 'it is becoming increasingly apparent that the only realistic way of providing the whole community, including areas of existing development, with accessibility to reasonably priced transport is by adopting policies that in many situations restrict the use of private cars and which have a much more positive approach to the promotion of public transport . . . an effective policy must successfully embrace a wide range of elements, including the railways, public road transport, car parking, traffic management and facilities for cyclists and pedestrians'.[3]

In the conurbations some of the more ambitious plans of the 1960s did not come to fruition. In Manchester, for example, an important element in the comprehensive redevelopment of much of the inner city – a belt two miles wide around the central business district – was to be the building of new and improved radial and tangential routes. It was proposed that the roads to, *inter alia*, Stockport, Ashton-under-Lyne, Rochdale, Oldham and Denton should be upgraded to six-lane highways, with grade-separated junctions. The densely-packed terraced housing along these routes was to be cleared and replaced by new high-density modern estates, separated from the roads by landscaping. Traffic and housing policies were closely linked in the minds of the city planners. In its 1970 proposals for the comprehensive redevelopment of Newton Heath the corporation noted that 'in addition to improving housing conditions the opportunity will be taken to provide other facilities and improvements [including] the re-organisation of traffic . . . New primary roads will keep through traffic away from Newton Heath; Oldham Road is to be improved to motorway standard to link with the Failsworth By-pass while the new Intermediate Ring Road will follow the line of Hulme Hall Lane . . . There could be a third principal traffic route, D.23, sometime after 1987, which would be an additional ring road for the eastern part of the city'.[4] Within the redeveloped housing areas the road pattern was to be totally reorganised. However, most of the major new roads included in the city plan were never built. Between 1968 and 1973, for example, most of the properties along a three-mile stretch of Ashton Old Road (A635) were demolished and a broad swathe of land was reserved for the motorway-standard road to Ashton. A quarter of a century later the road has not materialised and the plans have been drastically scaled-down.

Similarly, in the early 1960s Liverpool City Council proposed an inner motorway which would 'provide direct and easy movement between all the radial routes, the tunnel entrances and a series of major car parks' and – under the original plan – would involve complex multi-level junctions and elevated stretches of road. By the late 1960s the problems of 'large areas [which were] beginning to look semi-dere-lict because of advance acquisitions' and of the escalating capital cost of the project meant that it was scaled down. The elevated sections were deferred indefinitely and eventually the eastern section of the motorway scheme itself, from Islington to Parliament Street, suffered the same fate. The likelihood of these revisions became apparent at an early date: by 1973 the city planning officer noted that changing public attitudes to roads in any case meant that these works might not have been required.[5]

So in the mid-1970s progress in road-building began to falter and many plans for urban roads were modified or dropped. However, projects such as town centre relief roads, associated with new car parks, bus stations, landscaping and – crucially – with the introduction of pedestrianisation schemes in shopping areas and environmentally-sen-sitive streets, continued to multiply. Today many towns in Lancashire have a central area relief road, and others are still being proposed. In Manchester and Salford the SELNEC plans of the early 1960s were replaced by a more modest but no less essential scheme, gradually implemented from 1985, for a five-mile inner ring road, passing as far as possible through derelict land and declining industrial areas in order to minimise costs and disruption to the community, and incorporating the existing A57(M) Mancunian Way. 'The Ring', as it was termed, was intended not only to revitalise the fringes of the two city centres (by, for example, giving excellent road access to new redevelopment projects) but also to allow the major upgrading of the city centre environment by facilitating extensive pedestrianisation and further de-velopment of the new Metrolink network, the conurbation's pioneering reintroduction of on-street tramways.

By the 1980s there was less undisguised concrete and a greater use of brick and more 'user-friendly' materials for the structures and land-scaping associated with new urban roads. The widespread 1960s policy of routeing pedestrians through subways or over footbridges was in-creasingly abandoned in favour of surface crossings. Landscaping was generally on a more intimate scale and, as with architecture in general, the design of the associated car parks, shopping centres and other facilities reflected the more aesthetically-sympathetic styles which had succeeded the harshness of the 1960s. Nevertheless, despite these major changes (and as with other road schemes) town centre proposals now caused controversy. For example, in Lancaster plans for an inner relief road, a key element in a policy aimed at reviving the fading fortunes of the central area, met with very strong opposition in 1988–9, because of the environmental damage which it was claimed would result in the areas just outside the core.

Outside the town centres other forms of road began to appear. The development of major housing areas, especially around the new and expanded towns, produced the 'distributor road', a term coined in the early 1960s when the principles of traffic management and the defining of road hierarchies were becoming increasingly sophisticated. These characteristically follow long curving courses around the outer edges of towns, linking with residential and industrial areas – they are not primarily intended as bypasses but rather are aimed at 'distributing' intra-urban traffic so that it does not have to pass through the centre or older residential areas. Their junctions with local roads very often take the form of roundabouts, like strings of beads on a necklace, which help to reduce overall speeds and make local access much more efficient. The A574, sweeping from Sankey to Winwick around the north-west side of Warrington, has eight roundabouts in 2½ miles. Built in the late 1980s, it serves large housing and industrial areas and new superstores with a regional catchment, and in consequence is a victim of its own success – it already suffers from acute congestion even at off-peak times.

In the more rural parts of Lancashire, where the planning and environmental aspects of road-building were as yet less contentious, roadbuilding continued apace in the late 1970s. The basic motorway network was completed by 1975, with the north–south M6 and the east–west M62 forming its main elements, each being a vital section of the fast-evolving national motorway system. The M61 and, to a lesser extent, the M58, connecting Manchester and Liverpool with the M6 for traffic to and from the north, were other crucial components of the system as they had been of plans since the 1930s. The M55 and Yeadon Way, its extension along the former Kirkham-Blackpool Central railway route, carried holiday, residential and commercial traffic to Blackpool and the Fylde. The M63 over Barton Bridge was part of the projected Manchester outer ring road, carrying heavy industrial and through traffic and (with the M56) providing a very important road link to Manchester airport. Other elements in the long-term planning were beginning to emerge. Lancashire County Council feared that the imminent development of the new town around Preston, Leyland and Chorley would present a threat to the economic security of east Lancashire. This was a major factor in its vigorous promotion of the M65 Calder Valley route, opened in stages between Blackburn and Colne from 1980 onwards. The county council hoped that this road

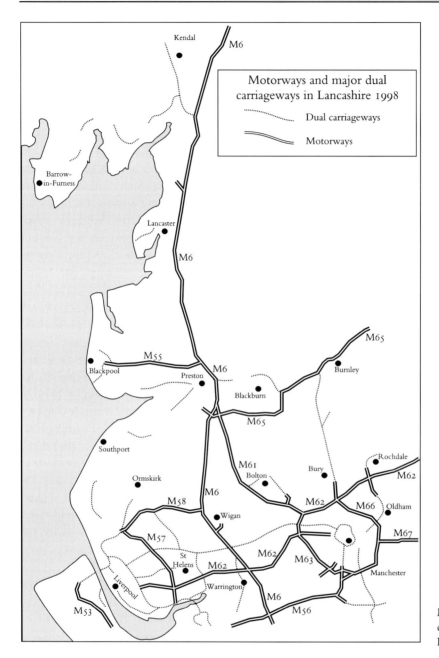

Motorways and major dual carriageways in Lancashire 1998

Dual carriageways

Motorways

Motorways and major
dual carriageways in
Lancashire, 1998

would be a means of protecting their vulnerable economies: 'the increased accessibility the completion of the new road would bring to the North East Lancashire cotton towns would, it is considered, dramatically increase their economic potential'.[6]

The completion of the outer ring roads of Liverpool (M57) and Manchester (M66) remained firm proposals. However, a combination of increasing controversy about the environmental consequences of road-building, together with ever-slower planning processes and ever-present financial constraints, resulted in the frequent deferral and delaying of these schemes. Not until the early 1990s were the remaining stages of the M57, M65 and M66 brought closer to fruition, and all three were dogged by argument and considerable opposition. The Liverpool outer ring road has been extended southwards from Tarbock, as an all-purpose dual-carriageway, to join the A562 at Ditton, but its possible northern extension to connect with the A565 Southport road at Ince remains uncertain because of the damaging impact which it might have upon woodland – for this reason the preferred scheme for a six-lane road was rejected by the Secretary of State for the Environment, who overruled the recommendation of the inquiry inspector.

The M66, which may be one of the last major motorways to be built in England, will thread a difficult path through the eastern side of the Greater Manchester conurbation, weaving its way between Middleton, Oldham, Ashton and Manchester. It involves sizeable engineering works (including the draining of part of the Audenshaw Reservoirs), and has angered conservationists because it will cut through the Medlock valley at Daisy Nook, a popular beauty spot, and will cross Ashton Moss, the last area of open land between Ashton and Manchester. The plans for the final stages of the M65, from Lostock Hall through Brindle and Lower Darwen to Whitebirk near Blackburn, were from 1993 to 1995 a *cause célèbre* of the anti-motorway lobby, with opposition centred on the sections crossing the northern end of Cuerden Valley Park near Bamber Bridge and through the steep-sided wooded valley at Stanworth near Blackburn.

On the existing motorways the huge and sustained growth of traffic levels meant that by the mid-1980s the infrastructure of the 1950s and 1960s began to reach design capacities. The consequence has been a succession of expensive widening schemes, all of them exceptionally complex and intricate to plan because of the need to fit the works in and around heavily-trafficked roads which remain in more or less constant use. The first major scheme of this type was the widening of Barton Bridge and the associated stretches of the M63, carried out between 1988 and 1991. Work on widening Britain's first motorway, the Preston bypass, to four lanes each way began in 1992. The project has included a complete remodelling of the interchange at Samlesbury, the provision for the first time of continuous hard shoulders, the modification of the interchanges at Walton Summit and Broughton, and (from 1996) the building of a new partial interchange to serve the Fulwood and Red Scar areas.

The M62 around the north of Manchester is among the busiest motorways in Britain, carrying a particularly heavy freight traffic, and

in a very delicate and difficult task the section from Worsley to the
A56 at Prestwich has been widened to eight lanes almost entirely within
the boundaries of the original motorway – a remarkable and ingenious
achievement, designed to avoid the need to take extra land in a densely
built-up district. The most ambitious of all the widening schemes has
been the building of a second Thelwall viaduct, just upstream from
the first bridge, so that the M6 can be widened from Lymm to Croft
and its junctions drastically remodelled. This huge undertaking was
made necessary by the endemic congestion on the bridge, across which
is channelled not only the extremely heavy traffic on the M6 itself,
but also the large volumes passing to and from the M62, M56, A57
and A50. The three mile section across the Mersey valley is one of
the nodal points in the national motorway network, and 'very heavy
congestion on the Thelwall viaduct, with long delays in both directions'
had become a familiar refrain of radio traffic reports by the 1980s.

The remainder of the inter-urban road network also experienced
continuing development in the 1980s and early 1990s, although here,
too, many longstanding projects have remained unbuilt or have been
deferred indefinitely. In the 1980s the Edenfield bypass was extended
around Haslingden and then dramatically across the moors and hillsides
to the M65 at Huncoat, the new road being dubbed 'the highway in
the sky'. This represented the completion of a scheme, first mooted
in the 1949 plan, to provide a high-quality route from north-east
Lancashire to the Manchester area. At that time it was intended to
connect the two key areas of the textile industry – when it was finished,
forty years later, it was expected to be a valuable commuter route and
to provide a further boost for the ailing economy of the Calder Valley
towns.

In south Lancashire similar considerations of providing a stimulus to
local industrial and commercial development were one of the factors
in the building of new roads in St Helens and Leigh. In the early 1990s
a new dual carriageway route was developed from the Widnes-Runcorn
bridge northwards to St Helens, bypassing Widnes and Sutton and
connecting with the M62. At Leigh a single-carriageway bypass followed the line of the old Bolton and Leigh railway, joining the East
Lancashire Road (A580) at the southern end and intended ultimately
to connect with the M61 in the north, avoiding Atherton. These routes
also made possible the opening up and partial reclamation of derelict
land as well as providing local bypasses. At Irlam, in the Mersey valley,
the A57 bypass built in 1990–2 was part of a project to reclaim and
improve land which was formerly the site of the steelworks, closed
some years earlier.

Smaller scale bypasses for individual communities have also remained
part of the road programmes throughout the county. In the south

Fylde, west of Preston, for example, Freckleton was bypassed in 1992 by a new dual carriageway, one stage in a possible long-term strategy for a road to skirt Warton, Lytham and St Annes and extend through to Blackpool. In the same area a new link from the earlier Yeadon Way extension of the M55 through Marton to Squires Gate provides much improved access to Blackpool's South Shore and helps to take the very heavy holiday traffic away from residential areas. In Furness parts of the main road to Barrow, the A590, have been improved by the construction of bypasses at Dalton and Greenodd and the town centre relief road at Ulverston, while the industrial and residential areas of north Barrow are now served by a much-upgraded northern access route to the town centre.

Other plans, often those 'in the pipeline' for many years, remain unfulfilled and may now never be implemented. For example, earlier proposals suggested that the southern section of the A59 should be bypassed by a new motorway linking Liverpool with the M6 just south of Preston. Later plans, one as recent as 1991, envisaged major upgrading with new dual-carriageway bypasses for Ormskirk, Burscough, Rufford and Tarleton, and the improvement of the remainder. In 1993, however, the government announced that the Burscough-Rufford bypass would be dropped from the list of future schemes and the Bank Hall diversion at Tarleton was subsequently dropped as well. Not only is the road not to be upgraded, but much of the existing route south of Tarleton has now been modified by the reduction to two lanes of the older three-lane sections and by the imposition of speed limits. In contrast, the building of a northern bypass for Ormskirk on the A570 St Helens-Southport road remains a 'firm' project to be implemented at an unspecified future date. The long-planned link from Wigan to Bolton has still not materialised, although it may yet be built as a series of local bypasses, and the eastern bypass of the Fylde Coast towns – intended, among other purposes, to cater for freight traffic using Fleetwood docks – has also been abandoned for the foreseeable future. Perhaps most dramatically, in 1991 the government announced its intention to build the Preston southern and western bypass, a fully-fledged six-lane motorway linking the M6/M61/M65 interchanges near Bamber Bridge with the M55 near Kirkham. Two years later, after it had encountered vociferous opposition from residents of South Ribble – though it had the wholehearted support of Lancashire County Council – the scheme was dropped from the roads programme.

Most new road proposals now meet with hostility from at least some sections of the community. Even if the principle of a project commands reasonably wide acceptance the details – and in particular the various possible alignments – are likely to produce vocal, highly organised and often very effective opposition. Many authorities, especially urban ones,

now place much greater emphasis upon the provision of public transport, including the rather remote possibility of substantial investment
in new infrastructure, and this is likely to become a major theme in
the next decade as the whole question of traffic restraint and the role
of the private car is questioned. Balanced transport policies, first mooted
in the late 1960s, are now becoming increasingly general.

However, underlying much of the retrenchment in road-building
which has been seen in the mid-1990s are not environmental but
financial constraints. The cost of building new roads today is so great,
because of the need for higher standards in both design and construction,
that their deferral or abandonment can represent a major saving on
future expenditure for national and local government. The 1980s and
1990s have thus seen the publication of a sequence of future road
programmes which have soon been followed by cancellations or post-
ponement of projects on cost grounds. In 1995, for example, the roads
programme nationally was substantially reduced with this in mind
although arguably environmental pressure also played a major part in
the decision.

The great man of Lancashire road-building was James Drake, a
leading figure of twentieth-century civil engineering. He was well
aware of the problems as well as the visionary nature of his work: 'the
building of a motorway is sculpture on an exciting and grand scale,
carving, moulding, forging and adapting materials provided by nature
– earth, rock and minerals – into a finished product, which must be
functional and pleasing to the eye, as well as economical and durable.
But in trying to accomplish this, one must be humanitarian and
remember that all this affects people. The civil engineer on motorway
projects, as on other public works, is the servant of the people, using
his specialist knowledge on their behalf for the good of the whole
community and, at the same time, mindful of their views and the rights
of the minority who are affected'.[7]

Those words (written in the late 1960s) were prescient, for the
attitudes of the community have been increasingly important in planning and building roads. What lies ahead is therefore uncertain. Financial
exigencies have combined with environmental concern and debate over
planning issues to produce a climate which is entirely different from
that of thirty years ago. Despite the fundamental dichotomy which
exists between, on the one hand, the wish or need to restrain the use
of the car and, on the other, the powerful arguments in favour of
car-ownership, a debate about the very principle of road-building is
now in progress. It has its roots in the growing reaction against roads
and cars detectable from the mid-1970s and may well foreshadow a
new stage in public policy in this crucial area. Only time will tell, but
whatever happens in the future one thing is very clear from the past.

The achievement of road-builders in Lancashire over the past 2,000 years is remarkable. From the Romans to the road-builders of the late twentieth century, their imprint upon the county in all its manifold facets can never be understated.

RETROSPECTIVE:

THE LEGACY OF THE ROAD-BUILDERS

This book, like road-building in the 1990s, ends on a note of uncertainty. At the end of the twentieth century roads and road vehicles have become basic to the everyday life of all individuals in this country, just as they have become a fundamental element in the economy and society of the nation as a whole. A hundred years ago the motor car was invented – today it is ubiquitous. At the end of the nineteenth century roads and their maintenance were a minor element in the thinking and expenditure of most public authorities, and the construction of new roads – other than for access to housing or as town centre streets – the fanciful dream of a very few. By the 1990s, though, road-building (together with traffic and transportation policies) had become a crucial component of planning and development, involving the expenditure of very large sums of money and the creation of daring and spectacular works of civil engineering. Heated controversies arose during the second half of this century about roads and their traffic, and this – as part of the general 'environmental debate' – forms one of the great issues of our day.

Yet, as this book has made quite clear, roads are not new. Four thousand years ago our remote Neolithic ancestors were building trackways and creating the alignments of routes some of which are in use to this very day. The Romans, as we all know, were consummately skilful both in the planning of networks of roads and in the building of the roads themselves, with superb understanding of civil engineering and (though we cannot measure this) sparing little expense in ensuring that the routes they constructed were of excellent quality and durability. If we drive along the A49 from Ashton-in-Makerfield towards Wigan we are following the approximate line of a prehistoric trackway which eventually became a Roman road. The A6 from Manchester to Stockport follows the line of the Roman road to Buxton and Derby. Other examples of continuity over the centuries, indeed over the millennia, are numerous and impressive.

In the medieval period, contrary to widely-held belief, roads were in general use and although the engineering skills involved in building and maintenance were perhaps limited in comparison with those of the Roman period or of the turnpike builders who followed, the workmanship displayed in the construction of fine stone bridges was of a high order, as surviving examples testify. The sixteenth and seventeenth centuries saw the road network coming under increasing strain from such familiar-sounding causes as heavy goods vehicles and fast-growing volumes of commercial traffic. The uplands were criss-crossed with packhorse routes, some remaining in use until the last years of the nineteenth century and some surviving today as distinctive features of the Pennine landscape. But there was a growing need for more substantial investment in roads and for the improvement of the network to cope with the heavier traffic.

Existing administrative and financial structures were manifestly inadequate, and the eventual result was the development, in piecemeal fashion, of a turnpike network which continued to grow even into the railway age and which provided the framework for the twentieth century pattern of trunk roads and main roads. By the early seventeenth century issues such as pedestrian safety, damage to road surfaces, financial responsibility for the upkeep of roads, tolls and road-charging, and limitations on vehicle size and numbers were already being aired, and debates on these matters have continued, with increasing vigour, ever since.

The creation of the turnpike network, flawed though it was, represented a remarkable long-term achievement and one which provided an enduring legacy. The common view is that suddenly, 'when the railways came', the road network fell into disuse, but that was certainly not the case in Lancashire. The turnpike trusts may have been dissolved in the mid-nineteenth century but the roads themselves remained a key element in the transport system, ready to undergo a renaissance after 1900 as the impact of car, lorry and motorbus was felt.

When we drive along the roads of Lancashire, whether a country lane or a motorway, we are experiencing an essential element in the history of our county. Perhaps we should think of the immense contribution which roads have made, over the past two thousand years and more, to the economy, the society, the landscape, the character of Lancashire. The four centuries of Roman rule would not have been possible without them. The splendours of Furness Abbey and Whalley Abbey were paid for by goods such as wool, carried by road. The industrialisation of the county from the early seventeenth century relied very heavily upon the road network (which suffered accordingly). Urbanisation, that remarkable Lancashire phenomenon of the nineteenth century, was made possible by the laying-out of thousands of miles of streets and town roads. The motorway builders, those Romans of our day, tackled the problems of inadequate infrastructure head-on and with triumphant success.

These men changed the face of Lancashire, helping to mould and shape its economy, its society, its geography, its landscape. Their achievement was an outstanding and remarkable one, in which they led the rest of the country. Like the anonymous Roman designers and engineers with their consummate skill in engineering and technology, like the medieval bridge-builders who produced some of the most enduring monuments of their age, like the great turnpike builders of the late eighteenth century who saw the challenge of economic change and commercial development, like the builders of the trunk canals and the great railways, they have left their stamp, impressive and unmistakable, upon the county and their legacy will last for generations. This book records the outstanding achievement of the road-builders who helped to make Lancashire what it is today.

Notes on the text

CHAPTER ONE

FURTHER READING AND BIBLIOGRAPHY

It has been thought best not to burden the text with too many references, though there are a few. The enquiring reader will find some guidance in the next paragraphs and the bibliography which follows. Little has been published about prehistoric routes in the county. The stone axe trade was discussed by Manby (1965), but the Bronze Age routes have not been specifically discussed, though generally accepted. Descriptions of Kate's Pad were originally published by Thornber (1851) and some of the more recent researches by Sobee (1953). The most recent pollen analyses demonstrating its Neolithic date are mentioned briefly by Middleton (1992) and will be more fully published by the North West Wetlands Survey.

The first attempt to bring together work on Roman roads in Britain was by Codrington (1903). This work initiated the numbering system modified and continued by Margary (1955, 1957, 1967) whose book remains the standard work. For Lancashire in particular the then current state of affairs was summarised by Watkin (1883). His chapter and map included roads which we have not discussed because they and some of the alleged sites to which they led, have been disproved or are now considered unlikely. Other papers relating to Lancashire's Roman roads can be found listed amongst the Roman period section of Horrocks (1973) (items 927–1496), where about fifty entries refer. The *Ordnance Survey Map of Roman Britain* also shows the Roman road system as understood at the date of its publication (1978, 4th ed.).

T. Codrington, *Roman Roads in Britain* (1903).

F. Horrocks, *A Contribution towards a Lancashire Bibliography*, 6, Lancashire History and Topography: Historical Periods: Pre-Roman, Roman, pre-Norman (1973).

T. G. Manby, 'The distribution of rough-out, 'Cumbrian' and related stone axes of Lake District origin in Northern England', *T.C.W.A.A.S.*, second series, vol. 65 (1965) pp. 1–37.

I. D. Margary, *Roman Roads in Britain* (Baker, 2 vols, 1955, 1957; new ed., 1 vol. 1967).

R. Middleton, 'Excavations on the line of Kate's Pad at Brook Farm, Pilling, 1991', in *North West Wetlands Survey Ann. Rep.*, 1992, pp. 9–11.

F. Sobee, *A History of Pilling* (1953)

W. Thornber, 'An Account of the Roman and British Remains found north and east of the River Wyre', *T.H.S.L.C.*, vol. 3 (1851) pp. 116–26.

W. T. Watkin, *Roman Lancashire* (Liverpool, 1883).

NOTES, CHAPTER ONE

1. J. Porter, *The Making of the Central Pennines* (Moorland Publishing, 1980), p. 132.
2. W. B. Crump, 'Saltways from the Cheshire Wiches', *T.L.C.A.S.*, vol. 54 (1939) p. 111 and Pl, XXXIII. For an alternative view of this route, see Mary Higham's comments in chapter 2 of this book.
3. R. Rauthmell, *Antiquitates Bremetonacenses, or the Roman Remains of Overborough* (1746; reprint with additions 1824).
4. J. Just, 'On the Roman Roads in Lancashire, with a particular account of the Tenth Iter of Antoninus',

T.H.S.L.C., vol. 1 (1849), pp. 68–76.
5. J. Whitaker, *History of Manchester* (1773); E. B. Birley, 'The Roman Site at Burrow in Lonsdale', *T.C.W.A.A.S.*, 2nd series, vol. 46 (1946), pp. 126–156.
6. E. B. Birley, 'The Roman site at Burrow in Lonsdale' (1946), pp. 146–7.
7. P. Ross, 'The Roman Road from Ribchester to Low Borrow Bridge (near Tebay) through the Forest of Bolland, Lonsdale and Howgill Fells', *Bradford Antiquary*, new series, no. 6 (1916), pp. 243–266; I. D. Margary, *Roman Roads in Britain*, vol.

2 (Baker, 1st ed., 1957); P. Graystone, *Walking Roman Roads in Bowland* (C.N.W.R.S. Occasional Paper 22, 1992).
8. A discussion of the naming of Roman sites in the North West, including Lancaster, together with some new hypotheses, is given in D. Shotter, *Romans and Britons in North-West England* (C.N.W.R.S. Occasional Paper 27, 1992) Appendix 4, pp. 105–108.
9. E. B. Birley, 'The Roman site at Burrow in Lonsdale' (1946), p. 146.
10. J. L. Maxim, *A Lancashire Lion* (priv. pub. 1965).

NOTES, CHAPTER TWO

1. W. Farrer (ed.) 'Lancashire Inquests, Extents and Feudal Aids', pt 3 AD 1313–AD 1355, *R.S.L.C.*, vol. 70 (1915), pp. 36–7 and footnote
2. Although Lancashire was not officially described as 'the county of Lancaster' until 1182, the pre-1974 county is used as the basis for this chapter even for discussion of the earlier period
3. W. Farrer (ed.), The Chartulary of Cockersand Abbey of the Premonstratensian Order', *C.S.*, pt 1, new series, vol. 38 (1898); pt 2, new series, vol. 39 (1898); pt 3, new series, vol. 40 (1898); pt 4, new series, vol. 43 (1900); pt 5, new series, vol. 56 (1905); pt 6, new series, vol. 57 (1905); pt 7, new series, vol. 64 (1909). Hereafter all references to the cartulary of Cockersand Abbey are given as *Cockersand*.
4. M. C. Higham, 'Through a glass darkly – the Gough Map and Lancashire', in

A. G. Crosby (ed.), *Lancashire Local Studies* (Carnegie Publishing, 1993), pp. 29–41.
5. E. J. S. Parsons, *The Map of Great Britain c.1360 known as the Gough Map* (O.U.P., 1958), p. 1.
6. I. D. Margary, *Roman Roads in Britain* (Baker, 3rd ed., 1973); road refs. 70a–70d, 705, 7c (from Over Burrow), 806, 707, 7d, 7e.
7. This road is listed by Parsons as 'S3b'
8. J. J. Bagley and A. G. Hodgkiss, *Lancashire: A History of the County Palatine in Early Maps* (Neil Richardson, 1985), p. 8.
9. A. N. Webb (ed.), 'An edition of the Cartulary of Burscough Priory', *C.S.*, 3rd series, vol. 18 (1970), pp. 113–14.
10. B. P. Hindle, *Roads, Tracks and their Interpretation* (Batsford, 1993), p. 53.
11. *Cockersand*, pt 4 (1900), p. 534.

12. See the previous chapter, appendix 2
13. *Cockersand*, pt 3 (1898), p. 436.
14. The Guide House at Warton, lower down the estuary, was a famous landmark until the present century.
15. Grid reference SD 633707
16. The site is at grid reference SD 633707. W. Farrer (ed.), 'Lancashire Inquests, Extents and Feudal Aids', pt 2, AD 1310–AD 1333, *R.S.L.C.* vol. 54 (1907), p. 120.
17. W. Farrer (ed.), 'Lancashire Inquests, Extents and Feudal Aids', pt 1, *R.S.L.C.* vol. 48 (1903), p. 123.
18. W. Illingworth (ed.), *Placito de Quo Warranto*, Record Commission (1818), pp. 218–19.
19. The road is Margary 73 (1973), pp. 383–4.
20. *Cockersand*, pt 1 (1898), pp. 117–25.
21. L.R.O. DDPt 5/8, no date, but 13th-century. I am

grateful to Ben Edwards for drawing my attention to this reference. The road is Margary 72a.

22. For example, *Ravencros*, mentioned earlier, was on the boundary of Burton Chase; Cross o'Greet was on the boundary between Tatham and the Forest of Bowland. It should be noted that 'forest' here refers to the legal status of hunting areas and does not imply woodland or tree cover.

23. Holly was much favoured, by cattle themselves and by those who drove them, as a cattle fodder. An article by M. A. Atkin, 'Hollin names in North-West England', in *Nomina*, vol. 12 (1989), pp. 77–88, although concentrating mainly on Cumbria, offers useful material applicable to Lancashire.

24. The place-name is an OE dative plural, which indicates that it is a very early form – certainly pre-Conquest.

25. B. P. Hindle (1993), p. 48.

26. C. Taylor, *Roads and Tracks of Britain* (Dent, 1979), p. 95.

27. B. P. Hindle (1993), pp. 93–4.

28. *Cockersand*, pt 4 (1900), p. 731.

29. M. Morris, *Medieval Manchester* (Greater Manchester Archaeological Unit, 1983), p. 35.

30. P. Morgan (ed.), *Domesday Book – Cheshire* (Phillimore, 1978), p. 268b.

31. This reference is ambiguous – it may mean that salt packages were adulterated and 'padded out' by the addition of sand or dust.

32. J. McNulty, 'The Chartulary of the Cistercian Abbey of St Mary of Sallay in Craven', vol. 1, *Y.A.S.R.S.* vol. 87 (1933), p. 157.

33. E. Ekwall, 'The Place-Names of Lancashire', *C.S.*, new series, vol. 81 (1922), p. 204.

34. P. A. Lyons (ed.), 'Two 'Compoti' of the Lancashire and Cheshire Manors of Henry de Lacy, Earl of Lincoln', *C.S.*, old series, vol. 112 (1884), p. 185 (hereafter, *de Lacy 'Compoti'*).

35. I am grateful to John Wilson of Tatham for this information.

36. L.R.O. DRB 1/168.

37. L.R.O. DRB 1/8.

38. A. Cantle, 'The Pleas of Quo Warranto for the County of Lancaster', *C.S.*, new series, vol. 98 (1937), p. 139.

39. N. D. G. James, *A History of English Forestry* (Blackwell, 2nd ed., 1990), p. 6.

40. W. Brown (ed.), 'Yorkshire Inquisitions of the Reigns of Henry III and Edward I', *Y.A.S.R.S.* vol. 12 (1891), p. 48.

41. W. Farrer (ed.) 'Lancashire Inquests, Extents and Feudal Aids', pt 3, *R.S.L.C.*, vol. 70 (1915), p. 27.

42. G. E. Hadow, *Chaucer and his Times* (Thornton Butterworth, 1914), p. 27.

43. J. McNulty (ed.) 'The Chartulary of the Cistercian Abbey of St Mary of Sallay in Craven', vol. II, *Y.A.S.R.S.* vol. 90 (1934), p. 187.

44. T. D. Whitaker, *History of Whalley*, book 4 (Nichols, son and Bentley, 1818), pp. 98–9; quoted by M. Slack, *The Bridges of Lancashire and Yorkshire* (Hale, 1986), p. 75.

45. *Cockersand*, pt 1 (1898), p. 124.

46. Two feeder routes, both designated as 'king's highway', can be traced to Huncoat – one from the direction of

Whalley via Altham and one from Burnley.

47. *Cockersand*, pt 3 (1898), p. 502.

48. S. Penney, *Lancaster: the evolution of its townscape to 1800*, C.N.W.R.S. Occasional Paper no. 9 (1981), p. 18.

49. M. Morris, *Medieval Manchester* (1983), pp. 48–9.

50. Ibid., pp. 498–9.

51. M. C. Higham, 'The Mottes of North Lancashire, Lonsdale and South Cumbria', *T.C.W.A.A.S.* 2nd series, vol. 91 (1991), pp. 79–90.

52. A. G. Crosby, *Penwortham in the Past* (Carnegie Press, 1988), pp. 28–33.

53. P. A. Lyons (ed.), *de Lacy 'Compoti'* (1884), p. 175

54. *Cockersand*, pt 1 (1898), p. 182.

55. *Cockersand*, pt 4 (1900), p. 540.

56. Ibid., p. 713.

57. A. G. Crosby, 'The towns of medieval Lancashire: an overview' *C.N.W.R.S.*, Regional Bulletin, new series, no. 8 (1994), pp. 7–18: it should be noted that not all these boroughs and markets existed at any one time.

58. A. G. Crosby, 'Migration to Preston in the fourteenth century: the evidence of surnames', in *Lancashire Local Historian*, no. 8 (1993), pp. 6–16.

59. A. Cantle, 'The Pleas of Quo Warranto for the County of Lancaster', *C.S.*, new series, vol. 98 (1937), p. 141.

60. P. A. Lyons (ed.), *de Lacy 'Compoti'* (1884), p. 189.

61. Ibid., p. 126

62. J. C. Holt, *Robin Hood* (Thames & Hudson, 1988) and W. T. W. Potts, 'William Picard of Lee and the Legend of Robin Hood', *C.N.W.R.S.*, Regional Bulletin, new series, no. 6

(1992), pp. 35–9.

63. R. Cunliffe-Shaw, *The Royal Forest of Lancaster* (Preston Guardian, 1956), pp. 500–1.

64. M. Gelling, *Place-Names in the Landscape* (Phillimore, 1984), p. 81.

65. *Cockersand*, pt 2 (1898), p. 255.

66. *Cockersand*, pt 1 (1898), p. 88.

67. *Cockersand*, pt 3 (1898), p. 504.

68. *Cockersand*, pt 4 (1900), p. 705.

69. *Cockersand*, pt 1 (1898), p. 124.

70. Ibid., p. 102.

71. *Cockersand*, pt 2 (1898), p. 162.

72. A. G. Crosby, *Penwortham in the Past* (1988), p. 64.

73. *Cockersand*, pt 2 (1898), p. 255.

74. *Cockersand*, pt 2 (1898), p. 177 and pt 3 (1898) p. 432.

75. *Cockersand*, pt 4 (1900), p. 587.

76. A. N. Webb (ed.), *Cartulary of Burscough Priory* (1970),

77. R. A. Donkin, *The Cistercians: Studies in the Geography of Medieval England and Wales* (Toronto U.P., 1978), p. 196.

78. There is some evidence that Furness did, at times, export by sea from Piel Island – not always with permission. Donkin (1978), p. 146, notes that between 1418 and 1423 the abbey was suspected of loading wool at *Le Peele de Foddray* for transit to *Ememuthe en Zeeland*. In 1390 an enquiry had been held into the unauthorised export of wool from Cumberland, Westmorland and Furness.

79. R. A. Donkin (1978), p. 142.

80. *Cockersand*, pt 2 (1898), p. 303

81. Ibid., pp. 272–3.

82. *Cockersand*, pt 5 (1905), p. 787.

83. A. H. Smith, 'The Place-Names of the West Riding of Yorkshire' pt 6, *E.P.N.S.*, vol. 35 (1961),

p. 185; J. E. B. Gover et al., 'The Place-Names of Warwickshire', *E.P.N.S.*, vol. 13 (1936), p. 15.

84. *Cockersand*, pt 3 (1898), pp. 495–6.

85. A. G. Crosby, *Penwortham in the Past* (1988), pp. 13, 67–8.

86. *Cockersand*, pt 2 (1898), p. 155.

87. B. P. Hindle (1993), p. 90.

88. W. Farrer (ed.) 'Lancashire Inquests, Extents and Feudal Aids', pt 2, *R.S.L.C.*, vol. 54 (1907), p. 27.

89. J. Parker (ed.), 'Lancashire Assize Rolls 30–31 Henry III', *R.S.L.C.*, vol. 47 (1904), p. 102.

90. *Cockersand*, pt 2 (1898), p. 75.

91. M. C. Higham, 'A Thirteenth-Century Tide-Mill at Hackensall, Lancashire', *Archaeology North-West* no. 7 (vol. 2 pt I) 1994, pp. 26–7.

92. *Cockersand*, pt 2 (1898), pp. 80–1.

93. A. Goodman, *John of Gaunt: the exercise of princely power in fourteenth-century Europe* (Longman, 1992), p. 309.

NOTES, CHAPTER THREE

1. See, for example, J. Swain, 'Industry before the Industrial Revolution: North East Lancashire c.1500–1640', *C.S.*, 3rd series, vol. 32 (1986).

2. See J. K. Walton, *Lancashire: a social history 1558–1939* (Manchester U.P., 1987), chapter 2 and A. G. Crosby, 'The towns of medieval Lancashire: an overview', *C.N.W.R.S. Regional Bulletin*, new series, no. 8 (1994), pp. 7–18.

3. The classic source for the history of highway administration is S. and B. Webb, *The King's Highway* (Longman, 1908): like all of the Webbs' works it is a massive

and indigestible compendium. A useful summary, related to parish records, is given in W. E. Tate, *The Parish Chest* (3rd ed., Phillimore, 1984), pp. 242–50.

4. L.R.O., DDHo 542.

5. L.R.O., PR2993/3/1.

6. L.R.O., QSB 1/59/87.

7. L.R.O., QSB 1/17/30.

8. L.R.O., QSB 1/50/32.

9. L.R.O., QSB 1/114/74.

10. See also J. Porter, *The Making of the Central Pennines* (Moorland Publishing, 1980), chapter 10 and, for a very detailed account of such roads and their traffic elsewhere in Northern England, D. Hey, *Packmen, carriers and packhorse roads: trade*

and communications in North Derbyshire and South Yorkshire (Leicester U.P., 1980). W. Harrison, 'The pre-turnpike highways in Lancashire and Cheshire', *T.L.C.A.S.*, vol. 9 (1891), pp. 101–34, surveys a number of the early roads.

11. L.R.O., QSB 1/110/61.

12. L.R.O., QSB 1/123/57.

13. L.R.O., QSB 1/122/63.

14. L.R.O., QSB 1/122/70.

15. L.R.O., QSB 1/43/61.

16. L.R.O., QSB 1/43/60.

17. L.R.O., QSB 1/42/62.

18. L.R.O., QSB 1/18/38.

19. L.R.O., QSB 1/30/36.

20. L.R.O., QSB 1/106/85 and QSP 35/37.

21. L.R.O., QSB 1/112/26.

22. L.R.O., QSP 24/33.
23. L.R.O., QSP 10/11.
24. Anon. [A. G. Crosby], *The history of Haslingden Grane: a valley, its landscape and its people* (Lancashire County Council, 1991), pp. 26–7.
25. See A. G. Crosby, 'Fowl play? Keeping and stealing geese in Lancashire, 1550–1850', in A. G. Crosby (ed.), *Lancashire local studies in honour of Diana Winterbotham* (Carnegie Publishing, 1993), pp. 50–3.
26. L.R.O., QSB 1/18/39.
27. L.R.O., QSB 1/17/30.
28. L.R.O., QSB 1/70/52.
29. A. Hewitson, *Preston Court Leet Records* (George Toulmin, 1905), p. 101.
30. Ibid., pp. 100–3.
31. Ibid., pp. 32, 35, 111, 130, 158–9.
32. G. Chandler (ed.) *Liverpool under James I* (Liverpool Corporation, 1960) pp. 144, 245, 281.
33. J. Brownbill (ed.), 'The coucher book of Furness Abbey', vol. ii pt 3, *C.S.*, new series, vol. 78, 1919, pp. 669 and 676.
34. Hewitson, *Preston Court Leet*, pp. 133, 145
35. The background to the improvements of the 1770s is detailed in C. Sutton, 'Manchester Improvements, 1775–6', *T.L.C.A.S.*, vol. 21 (1913), pp. 63–8.
36. C.R.O., EDC 5 (1638) no. 86.
37. C.R.O., EDC 5 (1685) no. 14.
38. L.R.O., QSP 33/2.
39. L.R.O., DDCa 21/5, 21/6 and 21/27.
40. L.R.O., QSP 37/5.
41. A. Keenleyside, 'Old Skippool Bridge in the Seventeenth Century', *Poulton-le-Fylde Historical Society, 1981–1991* (Poulton le Fylde H.S., 1991), unpaginated.
42. R. Kuerden, *A Brief Description of the Burrough and Town of Preston* (written *c.*1682; ed. J. Taylor and pub. I. Wilcockson, Preston, 1818), p. 18.
43. I am indebted to John Greenhalgh for this information.
44. W. Harrison, 'Ancient fords, ferries and bridges in Lancashire', *T.L.C.A.S.* pt 1 (vol. 12 [1894], pp. 1–29) and pt 2 (vol. 13 [1895], pp. 74–102) describes many early crossings on Lancashire rivers, although the quality of the research is variable.
45. L.R.O., QSP 30/25(I).
46. L.R.O., QSB 4/18.
47. L.R.O., QSP 21/25 and 33/14.
48. L.R.O., DDX 760/1.
49. D. Winterbotham, 'The building of Barton bridge', *Lancashire Local Historian* no. 8 (1993), pp. 33–42.
50. L.R.O., QSB 1/109/46.
51. L.R.O., QSB 1/134/48.
52. L.R.O., QSP 22/19.
53. L.R.O., QSB 1/106/79.
54. L.R.O., QSB 1/31/55.
55. L.R.O., QSB 1/26/61.
56. L.R.O., QSB 1/22/48, apparently misfiled.
57. L.R.O., QSB 1/115/38.
58. L.R.O., QSP 44/11.
59. D. Winterbotham, 'The building of Barton Bridge' (1993), pp. 38–9.
60. L.R.O., QSB 1/50/27
61. L.R.O., QSB 1/130/51.
62. L.R.O., QSB 1/47/76.
63. L.R.O., QSB 1/55/35.
64. L.R.O., QSB 1/59/93.
65. R. Sharpe France, *The Lancashire Sessions Act, 1798* (Lancashire County Council, 1945).
66. A. Langshaw, 'The hundred bridges of the hundred of Blackburn in the 17th century', *T.H.S.L.C.*, vol. 98 (1946), pp. 28–9: this article gives detailed histories of many of the early bridges in Blackburn hundred.
67. I am very grateful to John Greenhalgh for providing the information in this and the following paragraph. For Ribchester Bridge, see also B. J. N. Edwards, 'How did Thomas Pennant cross the Ribble?', *Lancashire Local Historian*, no. 9 (1994), pp. 8–11.
68. A series of these books is now in the Lancashire Record Office (QAR): those for 1805 cover the whole of the county palatine.
69. L.R.O., 1/78/56 and 57.
70. L.R.O., QSB 1/62/60.
71. L.R.O., QSP 7/35.
72. L.R.O., QSP 24/33.
73. L.R.O., QSP 3/10.

NOTES, CHAPTER FOUR

1. T. S. Willan, *An Eighteenth-Century Shopkeeper: Abraham Dent of Kirkby Stephen* (Manchester U.P., 1969), especially pp. 29–31.
2. L. Toulmin Smith (ed.), *The Itinerary of John Leland in or about the Years 1535–1543* (Centaur Press, 1964). See vol. 4, pp. 4–11 and vol. 5, pp. 40–50 and 221–2 for Lancashire material. For an estimate of the dating see the introduction by John Chandler in *John Leland's Itinerary: Travels in Tudor England* (Alan Sutton, 1993).
3. Bridge chapels were a common feature of the medieval road system, but road widening and rebuilding mean that very few now survive. The Yorkshire examples at Rotherham and Wakefield

are among the handful which remain more or less intact.

4. W. Beamont (ed.), 'Discourse of the Warr in Lancashire' (anon., but known to be by Edward Robinson), *C.S.* old series, vol. 62 (1864), pp. 39, 52, 58.

5. L.R.O., QSP/118/7.

6. R. Cunliffe Shaw (ed.) *Clifton Papers: a Miscellaneous Set of Papers . . .* (Preston: Guardian Press, 1935).

7. P.R.O., DL41/12/11.

8. P.R.O., DL5/6, p.205.

9. C. Morris (ed.), *The Illustrated Journeys of Celia Fiennes, c.1682–c.1712* (1982, reprinted Michael Joseph, 1988). See pp. 160–6 for her Lancashire journey.

10. D. Defoe, *A Tour Through the Whole Island of Great Britain*, (with introductions by G. D. H. Cole and D. C. Browning), 2 combined volumes (Dent, 1974): see vol. 2, pp. 188–92 and 255–70.

11. G. H. Tupling, 'South Lancashire in the Reign of Edward II', *C.S.* 3rd series, vol. 1 (1944), p. 48. Dr Tupling provisionally identified the 'bridge of Loststock' as Bamber Bridge.

12. *L.P.R.S.*, vol. 59, Gressingham (1922).

13. W. Brockbank and F. Kenworthy (eds), 'The Diary of Richard Kay, 1716–51, of Baldingstone, near Bury', *C.S.* 3rd series, vol. 16 (1968), p. 103.

14. H. V. Hart-Davis, *History of Wardley Hall, Lancashire* (Sherratt & Hughes, 1908), pp. 157–8.

15. L.R.O., QSP 668/4.

16. J. P. Earwaker (ed.), *Constable's Accounts of the Manor of Manchester* [Manchester Constables' accounts] (Cornish, 3 vols, 1891–2), vol. 1 p. 5.

17. L.R.O., PR 2863/3/6.

18. *L.P.R.S.*, vol. 9, Didsbury (1901).

19. L.R.O., QSB/1/119/81.

20. Earwaker, *Constables' Accounts*, vol. 3, pp. 264, 269.

21. Ibid., vol. 1, p. 263.

22. L.R.O., QSB 1/57/33.

23. *L.P.R.S.*, vol. 4, Wigan (1899); vol. 32 Lancaster, part I (1908); vol. 5 Walton-on-the-Hill (1900); vol. 56 Manchester, part III (1919).

24. *L.P.R.S.*, vol. 121, Heaton Norris (1982).

25. *L.P.R.S.*, vol. 25, Eccles (1906).

26. Brockbank and Kenworthy, *Diary of Richard Kay*, p. 135.

27. J. Earwaker, *Constables' Accounts*, vol. 1, p. 262.

28. J. D. Marshall (ed.), *The Autobiography of William Stout of Lancaster* (Manchester U.P., 1967), pp. 236–7: quoted in J. J. Bagley, *Lancashire Diarists* (Phillimore, 1975), p. 74.

29. *L.P.R.S.*, vols 31, Manchester part I (1908) and 72, North Meols, part II (1934).

30. L.R.O., QSB 1/52/23.

31. *L.P.R.S.*, vols. 26, Ribchester (1906); 14, Chipping (1903); and 67, Thornton in Lonsdale (1930).

32. C.R.O., Runcorn parish register MS transcript.

33. *Lancaster Guardian*, 8 September 1894, p. 3.

34. *L.P.R.S.*, vol. 42, Bolton-le-Sands (1911).

35. G. Head, *A Home Tour Through the Manufacturing Districts of England . . . 1835* (2nd ed., with an introduction by W. H. Chaloner, reprinted Cass, 1968), pp. 432–5.

36. L.R.O., WCW Alexander Lowe of Flixton, 1623; WCW Leonard Platt of Flixton, 1637; WCW Margret Cheetome of Farnworth, 1598.

37. J. T. Swain, 'Industry

Before the Industrial Revolution', *C.S.*, 3rd series, vol. 32 (1986), p. 114.

38. B. C. Jones, 'Westmorland Pack-horse Men in Southampton', *T.C.W.A.A.S.*, new series, vol. 59 (1959), pp. 65–84.

39. S. Clarke, *Clitheroe in its Railway Days* (Clitheroe: Robinson, 1900), p. 57.

40. I am indebted to John Whiteley for the information in this paragraph.

41. L.R.O., WCW John Hanworth of Bury, 1570. I am greatly indebted to Janet Withersby for the information in this and the following paragraph.

42. L.R.O., WCW John Barrow of Culcheth, 1607; WCW Edmund Tasker of Walton-le-Dale, 1608.

43. J. Aikin, *A Description of the Country from Thirty to Forty Miles Around Manchester* (Stockdale, 1795), p. 261.

44. R. Watson, *A West Coast Marketing Chain* (unpublished paper deposited in Lancashire County Library Headquarters Local Studies Library, 1993).

45. J. Aikin, *Description*, p.261.

46. J. Holt, *General View of the Agriculture of the County of Lancaster* (London, printed for G. Nicol, 2nd ed., 1795), pp. 184–5.

47. L.R.O., WCW Ottes Sagar of Colne, 1595.

48. L.R.O., QSP 500/13.

49. L.R.O., DDX 927/1.

50. L.R.O., QSB 1/130/54.

51. J. Harland (ed.), 'The House and Farm Accounts of the Shuttleworth Family of Gawthorpe Hall', vol. 1, *C.S.*, old series, vol. 35 (1856): quoted in T. S. Willan, *The Inland Trade* (Manchester U.P., 1976), p. 5.

52. J. S. Fletcher (ed.), 'The Correspondence of Nathan

Walworth and Peter Seddon', *C.S.*, old series, vol. 109 (1853), pp. 28–9.

53. A. G. Crosby (ed.), 'The Family Records of Benjamin Shaw, Mechanic of Dent, Dolphinholme and Preston 1772–1841', *R.S.L.C.* vol. 130 (1991), p. 28.

54. A. W. Robertson, *Post Roads, Post Towns, Postal Rates 1635–1839* (privately published, 1961).

55. D. G. Haslam, 'Mail to Lancashire and Cheshire 1666–7', *Lancashire & Cheshire Mail* (formerly *Lancashire Mail*), vol. 7 no. 1 (1978).

56. J. W. Martin, 'A robbery of the Warrington post-boy in 1788', *Lancashire & Cheshire Mail*, vol. 5 no. 4 (1976), pp. 46–7.

57. D. G. Haslam, 'Difficulties

of early postmasters – part 1', *Lancashire & Cheshire Mail*, vol. 8 (1979), p. 37; quoting Calendars of Treasury Papers.

58. J. Simmons, *Transport* (A Visual History of Modern Britain series) (Vista Books, 1962). This is a very useful summary of the development of transport and this paragraph has drawn much information from it.

59. T. de Quincey, *The English Mail Coach and Other Essays* (Dent, 1961 ed.), pp. 29–39.

60. E. Baines, *History, Directory and Gazetteer of the County Palatine of Lancaster*, 2 vols (Liverpool: W. Wales, 1824–5).

61. *Lancaster Gazette*, 7 Oct. 1826, p. 3.

62. E. Weeton, *Journal of a Gov-*

erness, 2 vols (Oxford U.P., 1936–9, reprinted David & Charles, 1969), vol. 2, p. 233; quoted in J. J. Bagley, *Lancashire Diarists* (Phillimore, 1975).

63. G. Head, *Home Tour*, pp. 42–3.

64. Ibid., p. 427.

65. [S. Dyson], *Rural congregationalism: or, Farnworth as it was Fifty to Seventy Years Ago . . .* (Farnworth: Tubbs, Brook & Chrystal, 1881), p. 76.

66. Ibid., p. 73.

67. A. G. Crosby (ed.), *Family Records of Benjamin Shaw*, p. 34.

68. M. Brigg (ed.), 'The Journals of a Lancashire Weaver: John O'Neill', *R.S.L.C.*, vol. 122 (1982), p. 111.

NOTES, CHAPTER FIVE

1. Private Act 15 Car II.c.l, extensively quoted in many works on turnpikes.

2. E. Pawson, *Transport and economy: the turnpike roads of 18th century Britain* (Academic Press, 1977).

3. G.H. Tupling, 'The Turnpike Roads of Lancashire', *Trans. Manchester Literary & Philosophical Society*, vol. 94 (1953).

4. Private Act 12 Geo I c.xxi.

5. Petition quoted by Pawson, op. cit., chap.12.

6. L.R.O., TTG/1.

7. Private Act 19 Geo II c.xix.

8. Private Act 26 Geo II c.lxv.

9. The survival of records from turnpike trusts is particularly irregular and for many the documentary evidence is unfortunately minimal.

10. L.R.O., TTG/1.

11. Private Act 8 Geo II c.xiii.

12. C. Hadfield and G. Biddle, *The Canals of North West*

England vol.1 (David & Charles, 1970), chap.1.

13. Private Act 26 Geo II c.lxiii.

14. Private Act 28 Geo II clviii.

15. Private Act 28 Geo II c.lx.

16. E. Pawson, op.cit..

17. C. Hadfield and G. Biddle, op.cit.

18. Private Act 11 Geo III c.xciii.

19. Private Act 29 Geo III c.cvii.

20. L.R.O., TTG/1.

21. H. Skrine, *Three Successive Tours in the North of England and Parts of Scotland* (1795).

22. L.R.O., TTB/1.

23. Private Acts 45 Geo III c.vii; 7/8 Geo IV c.lv; 11 Geo IV c.xcii; 7 Wm IV c.xxxiv.

24. J. Stockdale, *Annales Caermolenses or Annals of Cartmel* (1801) quoted by B. P. Hindle, *Roads and Trackways of the Lake District* (Moorland Publishing, 1984).

25. See W. Rollinson, 'Schemes for the reclamation of land

from the sea in North Lancashire during the eighteenth and nineteenth centuries', *T.H.S.L.C.* vol.115 (1963), pp.133–145.

26. A. Hewitson, *A History of Preston* (Preston Guardian, 1883), pp.26–7.

27. Private Acts 5 Geo IV c.lv; 15–16 Vic c.cxix; 22–23 Vic c.xciii.

28. Private Act 5–6 Vic c.c.

29. G.H. Tupling, op.cit.; Private Act 4 Geo IV c.xxiii.

30. S.W. Partington, *The Toll Bars of Manchester* (1920, reprinted Neil Richardson 1983).

31. L.R.O., TTG/1.

32. R. Freethy, *Turnpikes and Toll Houses of Lancashire* (published by the author, 1986), includes several illustrations of toll houses.

33. L.R.O., TTB/1; TTA/4.

34. W. Bennett, *A History of Burnley, vol. III* (Burnley Corporation, 1949), p.148.

35. J. Holt, *General view of the Agriculture of the County of Lancaster* (1795), p.187.
36. This paragraph is based on an essay kindly provided by John Priestley, to whom acknowledgment is made with thanks.
37. Private Act 12 Geo I c.xxi.
38. Private Act 5 Geo IV c.lx.
39. Private Act 6 Geo IV c.ii.
40. Private Act 5/6 Vic c.c.
41. L.R.O., TTD/1.
42. L.R.O., TTH/2.
43. L.R.O., TTA/4.
44. L.R.O., TTB/1.
45. Private Act 6 Geo IV c.xxii.
46. L.R.O., TTD/1.
47. Private Act 6/7 Wm IV c.x.
48. L.R.O., TTG/1.
49. S.W. Partington, op.cit.
50. L.R.O., TTA/4.
51. L.R.O., TTE/2 and 3.
52. L.R.O., TTA/6.
53. L.R.O., TTC/1.
54. L.R.O., QTD 1/15.
55. G.H. Tupling, op.cit., J. Copeland, *Roads and their Traffic 1750–1850* (David & Charles, 1968).
56. Quoted in G.H. Tupling, op.cit.
57. J. Copeland op.cit.
58. Ibid.
59. P. Aughton, *Liverpool: A People's History* (Carnegie Publishing, 1990), p.71.
60. Ibid., pp.71–72.
61. *Ipswich Journal*, 15 Nov 1817; quoted by J. Copeland, op.cit.
62. The standard work on canals in the area is C. Hadfield and G. Biddle, *The Canals of North West England* (1969).
63. Accounts and papers no.1668 (1852) and no.2930 (1862), quoted by G.H. Tupling, op.cit.
64. Accounts and papers no.3627 (1866), quoted by G.H. Tupling, op.cit.
65. Report of the Select Committee on Turnpike Trusts (1839), quoted by G.H. Tupling, op.cit..
66. Accounts and papers no.2781 (1861), quoted by G. H.Tupling, op.cit.
67. L.R.O., TTC/1.
68. L.R.O., TTB/1.
69. J. Holt, op.cit., p.194–5.
70. R. Sharpe France, The Highway from Preston into the Fylde', *T.H.S.L.C.* vol.97 (1946), pp.27–58.
71. S.W. Partington, op. cit.

NOTES, CHAPTER SIX

1. For a discussion of the early years of cycling in Lancashire see Z. Lawson, 'Wheels within wheels – the Lancashire cycling clubs of the 1880s and '90s', in A. G. Crosby (ed.) *Lancashire Local Studies in honour of Diana Winterbotham* (Carnegie Publishing, 1993), pp.123–45.
2. The full list of Lancashire county boroughs is: Barrow-in-Furness, Blackburn, Blackpool, Bolton, Bootle, Burnley, Bury, Liverpool, Manchester, Oldham, Preston, Rochdale, St Helens, Salford, Southport, Stockport [mainly Cheshire], Warrington and Wigan. Blackpool, Southport and Warrington became C.B.s after 1889.
3. L.R.O., CC/MBM Jan. 1895 and Jan. 1896.
4. L.R.O., CC/MCM Feb 1889.
5. L.R.O., CC/CCM 20 and 21.
6. L.R.O., CC/CCM 11 and 12.
7. L.R.O., CC/CCM 15 and 16.
8. T. McTaggart, *The Big Box – England's Era of Steam Haulage* (Alloway Publishing [Ayr], 1986.
9. L.R.O., CC/CCM 20.
10. L.R.O., CC/CCM 17.
11. L.R.O., CC/CCM 18–24.
12. Aveling Barford Ltd, *A Hundred Years of Road Rollers* (Oakwood Press [Lingfield], 1965).
13. A.T. Davis, Presidential Address to the Institute of Municipal and County Engineers (1904).
14. L.R.O., CC/CCM 19, 20 and 21.
15. 'Racking' is the technical term for filling in spaces in a road surface.
16. L.R.O., CC/CCM 23.
17. L.R.O., CC/CCM 27.
18. L.R.O., CC/CCM 17.
19. I. Yearsley and P. Groves, *The Manchester Tramways* (Transport Publishing Co. [Glossop], 1988).
20. W.H. Bett and J.C. Gilham, *The Tramways of South East Lancashire* (Light Railway Transport League, 1976).
21. H.T. Chapman, *Reminiscences of a Highway Surveyor* (priv. pub., n.d.).
22. L.R.O., CC/CCM 48.
23. L.R.O., CC/CCM 49.
24. L.R.O., CC/CCM 47 and 49.
25. L.R.O., CC/CCM 56.
26. L.R.O., CC/CCM 48.
27. J.B. Horne and T.B. Maund, *Liverpool Transport, vol.2* (1982) and *vol.3* (1987), (Transport Publishing Co. [Glossop]).
28. L.R.O., CC/CCM 57.
29. L.R.O., CC/CCM 53.
30. L.R.O., CC/CCM 51.
31. L.R.O., CC/CCM 52.
32. L.R.O., CC/CCM 57.
33. L.R.O., CC/CCM 54.
34. T.B. Maund, *Mersey Ferries vol.1* (Transport Publishing

Co. [Glossop], 1991).

35. J.B. Horne and T.B. Maund, *Liverpool Transport,* vol.2 (1982) and vol.3 (1987) (Transport Publishing Co. [Glossop]; Anon., *The Mer-* *sey Tunnel: the story of an undertaking* (Mersey Tunnel Joint Committee, 1934).

36. Anon., *The Mersey Tunnel: the story of an undertaking* (Mersey Tunnel Joint Com- mittee, 1934).

37. L.R.O., CC/CCM 54, 58, 61 and 65.

38. L.R.O., CC/CCM 69.

39. L.R.O., CC/CCM 67 and 68.

REFERENCES, CHAPTER SEVEN

Much personal background knowledge and experience has been included in the compilation of this chapter. The author has also made use of the following docu- ments as well as brochures prepared for the opening ceremonies of various road schemes and other unpub- lished material.

Development plan (Lancashire County Council, 1951).
J. Drake, H. L. Yeadon and D. I. Evans, *Motorways* (Faber and Faber, 1969).
J. Drake, *M6 in Lancashire. An illustrated brochure* (Lanca- shire County Council,

1965?).
Eastern limb of the inner relief road and the connection to the Farnworth Kearsley by-pass: offi- cial opening on Tuesday 21st December 1971 by Sir Geoffrey Jackson, K.C.M.G. (County Borough of Bolton, Techni- cal Services Committee, 1971).
Mancunian Way. City of Man- chester Link Road 17/7 – stage 2 (City of Manchester, n.d.).
Motorways across the Pennines. The Lancashire–Yorkshire Mo- torway M62 and the Scammon- den Dam (Department of the Environment, Lancashire County Council, West Rid- ing County Council,

County Borough of Huddersfield, 1971).
Preston by-pass: official opening by the prime minister the Rt Hon. Harold Macmillan, M.P., 5th December 1958 (Lancashire County Council, 1958).
Runcorn–Widnes Bridge: offi- cial opening by H.R.H. Prin- cess Alexandra of Kent, 21st July 1961 (Runcorn–Widnes Bridge Joint Committee, 1961).
Great Britain. Ministry of Transport. *Traffic in towns.* Chairman, Colin Buchanan. (HMSO, 1963).

NOTES, EPILOGUE AND RETROSPECT

1. R. W. Daniels, 'Planning and Motorways 1929–74', in J. D. Marshall (ed.), *The His- tory of Lancashire County Council 1889–1974* (Martin Robertson, 1977 [in conjunc- tion with Lancashire County Council]), pp. 306–62, gives a detailed assessment of the changing circumstances of road-building in the county up to the mid-1970s.

2. Skelmersdale Development Corporation, *Skelmersdale New Town* [progress report] (1973), pp. 18–19.

3. Central Lancashire Develop- ment Corporation, *Outline Plan* (1974), pp. 109, 108.

4. City of Manchester, *Newton Heath Preliminary Planning Do- cument: time for a change* (1971) [based on proposals put forward in earlier city- wide plans], pp. 1–2.

5. F. J. C. Amos, 'Liverpool', chap. 5 in J. Holliday (ed.), *City Centre Redevelopment* (Charles Knight, 1973), pp. 186, 194.

6. North West County Plan- ning Officers Group, *The North West: Profile of an Eng- lish Region* (1985), p. 35.

7. James Drake, in J. Drake, H. L. Yeadon and D. I. Evans, *Motorways* (1969), p. 209.

Bibliography of Printed Sources

The documentary sources which have been used for this book are not listed here, but full record office and other references appear in the endnotes for each chapter.

J. Aikin, *A Description of the Country from Thirty to Forty Miles Around Manchester* (Stockdale, 1795; reprinted David & Charles, 1968).

Anon., *The History of Haslingden Grane: a valley, its landscape and its people* (Lancashire County Council, 1991).

Anon., *The Mersey Tunnel: the story of an undertaking* (Mersey Tunnel Joint Committee, 1934).

M. A. Atkin, 'Hollin names in North-West England', *Nomina*, vol. 12 (1989).

P. Aughton, *Liverpool: a People's History* (Carnegie Publishing, 1990).

Aveling-Barford Ltd., *A Hundred Years of Road Rollers* (Oakwood Press, 1965).

J. J. Bagley, *Lancashire Diarists* (Phillimore, 1975).

J. J. Bagley and A. G. Hodgkiss, *Lancashire: A History of the County Palatine in Early Maps* (Neil Richardson, 1985).

E. Baines, *History, Directory and Gazetteer of the County Palatine of Lancaster*, 2 vols (Liverpool: W. Wales, 1824–5).

W. Beamont (ed.), 'Discourse of the Warr in Lancashire' (by E. Robinson), *C.S.* OS vol. 62 (1864).

W. Bennett, *A History of Burnley, vol. 3* (Burnley Corporation, 1949).

W. H. Bett and J. C. Gilham, *The Tramways of South East Lancashire* (Light Railway Transport League, 1976).

E. B. Birley, 'The Roman Site at Burrow in Lonsdale', *T.C.W.A.A.S.* 2nd ser. vol. 46 (1946), pp. 126–56.

M. Brigg (ed.), 'The Journals of a Lancashire Weaver: John O'Neill 1856–60, 1860–64, 1872–75', *R.S.L.C.* vol. 122 (1982).

W. Brockbank and F. Kenworthy (eds), 'The Diary of Richard Kay, 1716–51, of Baldingstone, near Bury, a Lancashire doctor', *C.S.* 3rd ser. vol. 16 (1968).

W. Brown (ed.), 'Yorkshire Inquisitions of the Reigns of Henry III and Edward I', *Y.A.S.R.S.* vol. 12 (1891).

J. Brownbill (ed.), 'The Coucher Book of Furness Abbey vol. 2 pt 3', *C.S.* NS vol. 78 (1919).

A. Cantle, The Pleas of *Quo Warranto* for the County of Lancaster', *C.S.* NS vol. 98 (1937).

Central Lancashire Development Corporation Outline Plan (C.L.D.C., 1974).

G. Chandler (ed.), *Liverpool under James I* (Liverpool Corporation, 1960).

J. Chandler (ed.), *John Leland's Itinerary: Travels in Tudor England* (Alan Sutton, 1993).

H. T. Chapman, *Reminiscences of a Highway Surveyor* (pub. author, n.d.).

G. Charlesworth, *A history of British motorways* (Thomas Telford, 1984).

T. Codrington, *Roman Roads in Britain* (S.P.C.K. London, 1903).

J. Copeland, *Roads and their traffic 1750–1850* (David & Charles, 1968).

A. G. Crosby, *Penwortham in the Past* (Carnegie Press, 1988).

A. G. Crosby (ed.), *Lancashire Local Studies in honour of Diana Winterbotham* (Carnegie Publishing, 1993).

A. G. Crosby (ed.), The Family Records of Benjamin Shaw, Mechanic of Dent, Dolphinholme and Preston 1772–1841, *R.S.L.C.* vol. 130 (1991).

A. G. Crosby, 'Fowl play? Keeping and stealing geese in Lancashire, 1550–1850', in A. G. Crosby (ed.), *Lancashire Local Studies* (1993), pp. 43–62.

A. G. Crosby, 'Migration to Preston in the fourteenth century: the evidence of surnames', *Lancashire Local Historian*, no. 8 (1993), pp. 6–17.

A. G. Crosby, 'The towns of medieval Lancashire: an overview', *C.N.W.R.S. Regional Bulletin*, NS no. 8 (1994), pp. 7–18.

W. B. Crump, 'Saltways from the Cheshire Wiches', *T.L.C.A.S.*, vol. 54 (1939), pp. 84–142.

A. T. Davis, *1904 Presidential Address to the Institute of Municipal and County Engineers* (priv. pub., 1904).

D. Defoe, *A Tour Through the Whole Island of Great Britain* [with introduction by G. D. H. Cole and D. C. Browning] (Dent, 1974).

R. A. Donkin, *The Cistercians: Studies in the Geography of Medieval England and Wales* (Toronto U.P., 1978).

J. Drake, *Road Plan for Lancashire: a report on existing and proposed road communications within the administrative county* (Lancashire County Council, 1949).

J. Drake, *The M6 in Lancashire: an illustrated brochure with a general description* (Lancashire County Council, n.d. c.1965).

J. Drake, H. L. Yeadon and D. I. Evans, *Motorways* (Faber & Faber, 1969).

[S. Dyson], *Rural congregationalism: or, Farnworth as it was Fifty to Seventy Years Ago* (Farnworth: Tubbs, Brook & Chrystal, 1881).

J. P. Earwaker (ed.), *Constables' Accounts of the Manor of Manchester*, 3 vols (Cornish, 1891–2).

B. J. N. Edwards, 'How did Thomas Pennant cross the Ribble?', *Lancashire Local Historian* no. 9 (1994), pp. 8–11.

E. Ekwall, 'The Place-Names of Lancashire', *C.S.* NS vol. 81 (1922).

W. Farrer (ed.), 'The Chartulary of Cockersand Abbey of the Premonstratensian Order', *C.S.* pt 1, NS vol. 38 (1898); pt 2 NS vol. 39 (1898); pt 3 NS vol. 40 (1898); pt 4 NS vol. 43 (1900); pt 5 NS vol. 56 (1905); pt 6 NS vol. 57 (1905); pt 7 NS vol. 64 (1909).

W. Farrer (ed.), 'Lancashire Inquests, Extents and Feudal Aids, pt 1, AD 1205–1307', *R.S.L.C.* vol. 48 (1903).

W. Farrer (ed.), 'Lancashire Inquests, Extents and Feudal Aids, pt 2 AD 1310–AD 1333', *R.S.L.C.* vol. 54 (1907).

W. Farrer (ed.), 'Lancashire Inquests, Extents and Feudal Aids, pt 3 AD 1333–AD 1355', *R.S.L.C.* vol. 70 (1915).

J. S. Fletcher (ed.), 'The Correspondence of Nathan Walworth and Peter Seddon and other documents relating to Ringley chapel', *C.S.* OS vol. 109 (1880).

R. Sharpe France, *The Lancashire Sessions Act, 1798* (Lancashire County Council, 1945).

R. Sharpe France, 'The highway from Preston into the Fylde', *T.H.S.L.C.* vol. 97 (1946), pp. 27–58.

R. Freethy, *Turnpikes and Toll Houses of Lancashire* (author, c.1986).

M. Gelling, *Place-Names in the Landscape* (Phillimore, 1984).

R. Gill, 'Hanging Bridge, Manchester', in *T.L.C.A.S.* vol. 8 (1890).

A. Goodman, *John of Gaunt: the exercise of princely power in fourteenth-century Europe* (Longman, 1992).

J. E. B. Gover *et al*, 'The Place-Names of Warwickshire', *E.P.N.S.* vol. 13 (1936).

P. Graystone, 'Walking Roman Roads in Bowland' *C.N.W.R.S. Occasional Paper* no. 22, (1992).

C. Hadfield and G. Biddle, *The Canals of North West England* (2 vols, David & Charles, 1970).

G. E. Hadow, *Chaucer and his Times* (Thornton Butterworth, 1914).

J. Harland (ed.), 'The House and Farm Accounts of the Shuttleworth Family of Gawthorpe Hall vol. 1', *C.S.* OS vol. 35 (1856).

W. Harrison, 'Ancient fords, ferries and bridges in Lancashire', in *T.L.C.A.S.* pt 1 (vol. 12 [1894], pp. 1–29) and pt 2 (vol. 13 [1895], pp. 74–102).

W. Harrison, 'Pre-turnpike highways in Lancashire and Cheshire', *T.L.C.A.S.* vol. 9 (1891), pp. 101–34.

H. V. Hart-Davis, *History of Wardley Hall, Lancashire and its owners in bygone days* (Sherratt & Hughes, 1908).

D. G. Haslam, 'Mail to Lancashire and Cheshire, 1666–7', *Lancashire & Cheshire Mail*, vol. 7 no. 1 (1978).

D. G. Haslam, 'Difficulties of early postmasters – part 1', *Lancashire & Cheshire Mail*, vol. 8 (1979).

G. Head, *A Home Tour Through the Manufacturing Districts of England . . . 1835* (2nd ed., reprinted with introduction by W. H. Chaloner, Cass, 1968).

A. Hewitson, *A History of Preston* (Preston Chronicle, 1883).

A. Hewitson, *Preston Court Leet Records: extracts and notes* (George Toulmin, 1905).

D. Hey, *Packmen, carriers and packhorse roads: trade and communications in North Derbyshire and South Yorkshire* (Leicester U.P., 1980).

M. C. Higham, 'The Mottes of North Lancashire, Lonsdale and South Cumbria', *T.C.W.A.A.S.* 2nd ser. vol. 91 (1991).

M. C. Higham, 'A Thirteenth Century Tide-Mill at Hackensall, Lancashire', in *Archaeology North-West*, vol. 2 pt 1 (1994), pp. 26–7.

M. C. Higham, 'Through a glass darkly – the Gough Map and Lancashire', A. G. Crosby (ed.), *Lancashire Local Studies* (Carnegie Publishing, 1993), pp. 28–41.

B. P. Hindle, *Roads and trackways of the Lake District* (Moorland Publishing, 1984).

B. P. Hindle, *Roads, Tracks and their Interpretation* (Batsford, 1993).

J. Holt, *General View of the Agriculture of the County of Lancaster* (London, printed for G. Nicol, 2nd ed., 1795).

J. C. Holt, *Robin Hood* (Thames & Hudson, 1988).

J. B. Horne and T. B. Maund, *Liverpool Transport vol. 2* (1982) and *vol. 3* (1987) (Transport Publishing Co.).

S. Horrocks, *Lancashire history and topography: historical periods: pre-Roman, Roman, pre-Norman. Lancashire bibliography 6* (Joint Committee on the Lancashire Bibliography, 1973).

W. Illingworth (ed.), *Placito de Quo Warranto*, Record Commission (1918).

N. D. G. James, *A History of English Forestry* (2nd ed., Blackwell, 1990).

B. C. Jones, 'Westmorland Pack-horse Men in Southampton', *T.C.W.A.A.S.* 2nd ser. vol. 59 (1959).

J. Just, 'On the Roman Roads in Lancashire, with particular account of the Tenth Iter of Antoninus', *T.H.S.L.C.* vol. 1 (1849).

A. Keenleyside, 'Old Skippool Bridge in the Seventeenth Century', *Poulton-le-Fylde Historical Society 1981–1991* (Poulton-le-Fylde H.S., 1991).

R. Kuerden, *A Brief Description of the Burrough and Town of Preston and its Government and Guild* (written c.1682; ed. J. Taylor and pub. I. Wilcockson, Preston, 1818).

A. Langshaw, 'The hundred bridges of the hundred of Blackburn in the 17th century', *T.H.S.L.C.* vol. 98 (1946).

E. Z. Lawson, 'Wheels within wheels – the Lancashire cycling clubs of the 1880s and '90s', in A. G. Crosby (ed.), *Lancashire Local Studies* (Carnegie Publishing, 1993).

P. A. Lyons (ed.), Two 'Compoti' of the Lancashire and Cheshire Manors of Henry de Lacy, Earl of Lincoln, *C.S.* OS vol. 112 (1884).

T. G. Manby, 'The distribution of rough-out "Cumbrian" and related stone axes of Lake District origin in Northern England', *T.C.W.A.A.S.* 2nd ser. vol. 65 (1965).

H. C. March, 'The Road over Blackstone Edge', *T.L.C.A.S.* vol. 1 (1883).

I. D. Margary, *Roman Roads in Britain*, 3 vols (Baker, new ed. 1967–73).

J. D. Marshall (ed.), *The Autobiography of William Stout of Lancaster 1665–1752* (Manchester U.P., 1967).

J. W. Martin, 'A robbery of the Warrington post-boy in 1788', *Lancashire & Cheshire Mail*, vol. 5 no. 4 (1976), pp. 46–7.

T. B. Maund, *Mersey Ferries vol. 1: Woodside to Eastham* (Transport Publishing Co., 1991).

J. Maxim, *A Lancashire Lion* (priv. pub., 1965).

J. McNulty, 'The Chartulary of the Cistercian Abbey of St Mary of Sallay in Craven, vol. I', *Y.A.S.R.S.* vol. 87 (1933); vol. II, *Y.A.S.R.S.* vol. 90 (1934).

T. McTaggart, *The Big Box – England's Era of Steam Haulage* (Alloway Publishing, 1986).

R. Middleton, 'Excavations on the line of Kate's Pad at Brook Farm, Pilling, 1991', *North West Wetlands Survey Ann. Rep.* 1992.

P. Morgan (ed.), *Domesday Book 26 – Cheshire* (Phillimore, 1978).

C. Morris (ed.), *The Illustrated Journeys of Celia Fiennes c.1682–c.1712* (Macdonald, 1988).

M. Morris, *Medieval Manchester: a regional study* (Greater Manchester Archaeological Unit, 1983).

J. Parker (ed.), 'Lancashire Assize Rolls 30–31 Henry III', *R.S.L.C.* vol. 47 (1904).

E. J. S. Parsons, *The Map of Great Britain c.1360 known as the Gough Map: an introduction to the facsimile* (O.U.P., 1958).

S. W. Partington, *The Toll Bars of Manchester* (1920; reprinted Neil Richardson, 1983).

E. Pawson, *Transport and economy: the turnpike roads of eighteenth century Britain* (Academic Press, 1977).

S. Penney, 'Lancaster: the evolution of its townscape to 1800' *C.N.W.R.S. Occasional Paper no. 9,* (1981).

J. Porter, *The Making of the Central Pennines* (Moorland Publishing, 1980).

W. T. W. Potts, 'William Picard of Lee and the Legend of Robin Hood', *C.N.W.R.S. Regional Bulletin* NS no. 6 (1992), pp. 35–8.

T. de Quincey, *The English Mail Coach, and other essays* (Dent, 1961).

A. Raistrick, *Green Roads in the Mid-Peninnes* (Moorland Publishing, 1978).

R. Rauthmell, *Antiquitates Bremetonacenses, or the Roman Remains of Overborough* (Woodfall, Kirkby Lonsdale 1746; reprinted with additions 1824).

I. A. Richmond, 'The Roman Road across Blackstone Edge', *Trans. Rochdale Lit. & Sci. Soc.* vol. 15 (1925), pp. 41–70.

A. W. Robertson, *Post Roads, Post Towns, Postal Rates 1635–1839* (author, Pinner 1961).

W. Rollinson, 'Schemes for the reclamation of land from the sea in North Lancashire during the eighteenth and nineteenth centuries', *T.H.S.L.C.* vol. 115 (1963), pp. 133–45.

P. Ross, 'The Roman Road from Ribchester to Low Borrow Bridge (near Tebay) through the Forest of Bolland, Lonsdale and Howgill Fells', *Bradford Antiquary* NS vol. 6 (1916).

R. Cunliffe Shaw (ed.), *The Clifton Papers* (Preston Guardian Press, 1935).

R. Cunliffe Shaw, *The Royal Forest of Lancaster* (Preston Guardian Press, 1956).

J. Simmons, *Transport* (Vista Books, 1962).

H. Skrine, *Three Successive Tours in the North of England, to the Lakes and great part of Scotland* (London, 1795).

M. Slack, *The Bridges of Lancashire and Yorkshire* (Hale, 1986).

A. H. Smith, 'The Place-Names of the West Riding of Yorkshire pt 6', *E.P.N.S.* vol. 35 (1961).

F. Sobee, *A History of Pilling* (Exeter, 1953).

C. Sutton, 'Manchester Improvements, 1775–6', *T.L.C.A.S.* vol. 21 (1913), pp. 63–8.

J. Swain, 'Industry before the Industrial Revolution: North East Lancashire c.1500–1640', *C.S.* 3rd ser. vol. 32 (1986).

W. E. Tate, *The Parish Chest* (3rd edn, Phillimore, 1984).

C. Taylor, *Roads and Tracks of Britain* (Dent, 1979).

W. Thornber, 'An Account of the Roman and British Remains found north and east of the River Wyre', *T.H.S.L.C.* vol. 3 (1851), pp. 116–26.

L. Toulmin Smith (ed.), *The Itinerary of John Leland in or about the Years 1536–1543* (Centaur Press, 1964).

G. H. Tupling (ed.), 'South Lancashire in the Reign of Edward II', *C.S.* 3rd ser. vol. 1 (1949).

G.H. Tupling, 'The turnpike roads of Lancashire', *Memoirs of the Manchester Lit. and Phil. Soc.*, vol. 94 (1953), pp. 39–62.

J. K. Walton, *Lancashire: a social history 1558–1939* (Manchester U.P., 1987).

W. T. Watkin, *Roman Lancashire* (Liverpool, 1883).

A. N. Webb (ed.), 'An edition of the Cartulary of Burscough Priory', *C.S.* 3rd ser. vol. 18 (1970).

S. and B. Webb, *English Local Government vol. 5: the story of the King's Highway* (Longmans Green, 1913).

E. Weeton, *Journal of a Governess* (2 vols, Oxford U.P., 1936–9).

J. Whitaker, *A History of Manchester* (2 vols, J. Murray, 1773).

T. D. Whitaker, *An history of the original parish of Whalley and Honor of Clitheroe*, book 4 (3rd ed., Nichols, Son & Bentley, 1818).

T. S. Willan, *An Eighteenth Century Shopkeeper: Abraham Dent of Kirkby Stephen* (Manchester U.P., 1969).

T. S. Willan, *The Inland Trade* (Manchester U.P., 1976).

D. Winterbotham, 'The building of Barton Bridge', *Lancashire Local Historian* no. 8 (1993).

I. Yearsley and P. Groves, *The Manchester Tramways* (Transport Publishing Co., 1988).

Index

TT = Turnpike Trust
The appendices on pp. 174–182 have not been indexed